SWANSEA COLLEGE

ANSEA COLLEGE

D0415675

Nelson Advanced Science

Exchange and Transport, Energy and Ecosystems

John Adds • Erica Larkcom • Ruth Miller

Text © John Adds, Erica Larkcom and Ruth Miller 2000
Original illustrations © Nelson Thornes Ltd 2000

The right of John Adds, Erica Larkcom and Ruth Miller to be identified as authors of this work
has been asserted by them in accordance with the Copyright, Designs and Patents Act 1988.

All rights reserved. No part of this publication may be reproduced or transmitted in any form
or by any means, electronic or mechanical, including photocopy, recording or any information
storage and retrieval system, without permission in writing from the publisher or under licence
from the Copyright Licensing Agency Limited, of 90 Tottenham Court Road, London W1T 4LP.

Any person who commits any unauthorised act in relation to this publication may be liable to
criminal prosecution and civil claims for damages.

First published in 2000 by:
Nelson Thornes (Publishers) Ltd

Nelson Thornes Ltd
Delta Place
27 Bath Road
CHELTENHAM
GL53 7TH
United Kingdom

03 04 05 / 10 9 8 7 6 5

A catalogue record for this book is available from the British Library

ISBN 0 17 448294 9

Typeset by Hardlines, Charlbury Oxford
Picture Research by Zooid Pictures Limited

Printed in Croatia by Zrinski d.d. Cacovec

Acknowledgements

The authors and publishers are grateful for permission to
include the following copyright material:

Photographs

Telegraph Colour Library: cover.
John Bebbington: section cover, p.1; Queen carder bee, p.93.
Ruth Miller: figures 1.5b, 5.10, 7.14,
Science Photo Library: figures 1.13a Dept of Clinical Radiology,
Salisbury District Hospital/SPL; 1.13b Manfred Kage/SPL; 1.22b
Eric Grave/SPL; 2.14a Dr Jeremy Burgess/SPL; 2.14b J.C.
Revy/SPL; 2.18 SPL; 4.12, 6.6c Biophoto Associates/SPL; 5.1,
5.7a (top) Andrew Syred/SPL; 5.7a (bottom) David Scharf/SPL;
8.12 Simon Fraser/Northumbrian Environmental Management
Ltd/SPL.
John Adds: figures 2.21, 3.1, 3.2, section cover p.113, 7.1.
Bryan & Cherry Alexander: figure 4.1 (top).
Corbis UK Ltd: figures 4.1 (bottom) Bettmann/Corbis UK Ltd;
9.10 David Forman/Eye Ubiquitous/Corbis UK Ltd.
Gamma/Frank Spooner Pictures: figure 4.2.

Tony Stone Images: figures 4.8 Lorne Resnick/Tony Stone
Images; 4.11 James Balog/ Tony Stone Images; 4.14 Jess
Scott/Tony Stone Images; 4.15 (right) David Levy/ Tony Stone
Images.
Erica Larkcom: figures 4.9, 4.15 (left & centre), 4.16, 8.2, 8.3a,
8.3b, 8.5, 8.6, 8.7, 8.8, 8.14, 9.2a (left & right), 9.2b (left &
right), 9.3, 9.4 (left & right), 9.5, 9.7a–d, 9.25.
Biophoto Associates: figures 5.3a–e.
Heather Angel/Biofotos: figures 6.1(top, left & right).
Fibrowatt Ltd: figure 8.11.
Robin Crump: figures 9.26a–e.

Artwork

Figure 1.7 from Griffin & Redmore (1993), *Human Systems*,
3rd edn, p.35, fig 4.2d (ISBN 0534044824), Nelson.
Figure 2.16 from Salisbury & Ross, *Plant Physiology*, 3rd edn,
p.119, fig 6–8 (ISBN 0534044824), Wadsworth.
Figure 2.20 from Griffin & Redmore (1993), *Human Systems*,
3rd edition, p.35, fig 3.2b (ISBN 0534044824), Nelson.

Contents

CONTENTS

Introduction

This series has been written by Chief Examiners and others involved directly with the Edexcel Advanced Subsidiary (AS) and Advanced (A) GCE Biology and Biology (Human) specification and its assessment.

Exchange and Transport, Energy and Ecosystems is one of four books in the Nelson Advanced Science (NAS) series. These books have been developed by updating and reorganising the material from the Nelson Advanced Modular Science (NAMS) series so that they match the requirements of the Edexcel specifications from September 2000. The books will also be useful for other AS and A courses.

The other student books in the series are:
* *Molecules and Cells*
* *Respiration and Coordination*
* *Genetics, Evolution and Biodiversity*

Exchange and Transport, Energy and Ecosystems covers Units 2 and 3 of the Edexcel specification for AS and A GCE Biology and Biology (Human). Unit 2, for both Biology and Biology (Human), covers exchanges with the environment, the transport of materials, adaptations to the environment and reproduction.

In the Biology specification, consideration is given to both plants and animals, whereas in Biology (Human) specification the topics directly concern humans, and require a more detailed knowledge of gas exchange, the human circulatory system and human reproduction and development. The section on adaptations to the environment leads to an understanding that species are adapted to survive in particular environmental conditions. In the Biology specification, the emphasis is on the structural adaptations of organisms associated with the presence or absence of water and to the varying oxygen concentrations found in freshwater. In the Biology (Human) specification, the effects of extremes of environmental temperature and life at high altitudes are discussed.

The content of Unit 3, Energy and the Environment, is common to both specifications and the topics include modes of nutrition, ecosystems, energy, recycling of nutrients and human influences on the environment. Unit 3 also has a practical assessment component requiring candidates to present an individual investigation.

Other resources in this series

NAS *Tools, Techniques and Assessment in Biology* is a course guide for students and teachers. For use alongside the four student texts, it offers ideas and support for practical work, fieldwork and statistics. Key Skills opportunities are identified throughout. This course guide also provides advice on the preparation for assessment tests (examinations).

NAS *Make the Grade in AS and A2 Biology and Human Biology* are Revision Guides for students and can be used in conjunction with the other books in this series. They help students to develop strategies for learning and revision, to check their knowledge and understanding, and to practise the skills required for tackling assessment questions.

Features used in this book – notes to students

The NAS Biology student books are specifically written to help you understand and learn the information provided in the books, and to help you to apply the information to your coursework.

The following features will be found in the NAS Biology series.

The **text** offers complete and self-contained coverage of the topics in each Unit. Key words are indicated in **bold**.

4 Cellular organisation

Cells, tissues and organisms

Living organisms can be distinguished from non-living things by their ability to carry out the characteristic activities of respiration, nutrition, excretion, movement, sensitivity, growth and reproduction. All living organisms are composed of basic units called **cells**. Those organisms consisting of a single cell in which all the characteristic activities take place are often described as **unicellular**, whereas those composed of many cells are described as **multicellular**.

A good example of a unicellular organism is the fungus *Saccharomyces cerevisiae*, commonly known as brewer's yeast because its activities under certain conditions result in the production of alcohol. When seen under a light microscope (Figure 1.1a), each cell has a simple structure, consisting of a **nucleus** surrounded by **cytoplasm** enclosed by a **cell membrane**. In this organism, the living material is surrounded by a non-living **cell wall**. Within the cell, all the chemical reactions necessary to sustain life take place. New material can be added to enable growth and when the cell has reached a certain size, it will undergo reproduction, resulting in the formation of a new cell (Figure 1.1b).

Aggregations of cells

The multicellular organisms vary in their structural complexity, ranging from simple groups, or colonies, of similar cells performing the same activities to complex individuals containing thousands of specialised cells. In the simplest of the colonies, the component cells show little coordination, but as the complexity of organisms increases, so cells become specialised to carry out different functions, which contributes to the efficiency of the whole organism. Cells performing similar functions are organised into **tissues**, and the tissues contribute to the structure of the body **organs**. In mammals, for example, there are large numbers of highly specialised **liver** cells, which have the same structure and in which the same reactions take place. This liver tissue, together with other tissues, such as blood, forms the body organ we call the liver.

The leaf of a plant is also an organ, composed of several differe[nt]
of thes[e tissues]

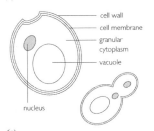

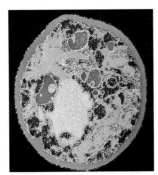

(a)

(b)

cell wall
cell membrane
granular
cytoplasm
vacuole
nucleus

(c)

Figure 4.1(a) Yeast cell as seen under an electron microscope; (b) yeast cells as seen under a light

The **definitions** in the margin reinforce and expand definitions of some key terms.

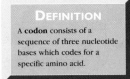

DEFINITION

A **codon** consists of a sequence of three nucleotide bases which codes for a specific amino acid.

As the nature of a protein is determined by the specific sequence of amino acids in the polypeptide chain, it seemed logical to suggest that the order of the nucleotides in the DNA determines the order in which the amino acids are arranged in a polypeptide. This relationship between the DNA nucleotide bases and amino acids is known as the **genetic code**. As there are 20 common amino acids and only four different nucleotide bases, it was obvious that more than one nucleotide base would have to be involved in coding for an amino acid. A code consisting of two bases for each amino acid would only cater for 16 amino acids, but if the code was three bases (**a triplet**), then there would be 64 possible combinations, more than enough for the 20 amino acids. This is known as the **base triplet hypothesis**, which is now accepted, and the triplets are called **codons**.

Boxes with **additional material** give further information to help you understand the topic you are studying. This information either gives more details or provides some more examples, extending your knowledge of the topic, but isn't strictly part of the Edexcel specification.

ADDITIONAL MATERIAL

Viruses

Viruses are much smaller than bacteria and cannot be seen using a light microscope (Figure 4.17). They range in size from about 20 nm to 400 nm and do not have a cellular structure, so they are described as **akaryotic**. They are intracellular parasites of plants, animals and bacteria, totally dependent on their host cells. The only characteristic they have in common with other living organisms is that they can reproduce once they are inside their host's cells. Viruses do not respire, feed, excrete, move, grow or respond to stimuli. They disrupt the normal activities of cells, often with harmful effects on the host organism, so they are associated with disease.

A virus consists of:

- a core of nucleic acid
- a protein coat, or capsid.

The nucleic acid may be:

- double-stranded DNA, as in *Herpes simplex*, which causes cold sores
- single-stranded DNA, as in *Parvovirus*, which causes gastroenteritis
- single-stranded RNA, as in the influenza virus and the human immuno- deficiency virus (HIV).

Most of the viruses causing diseases in plants, such as the tobacco mosaic virus, contain RNA.

The capsid surrounds the nucleic acid and consists of a number of subunits called **capsomeres**, arranged to form a geometrical structure. In addition, some viruses have an outer envelope of carbohydrate or lipoprotein and many bacteriophages (bacterial viruses) have tails that form part of the mechanism by which they gain entry to host cells (Figure 4.18a).

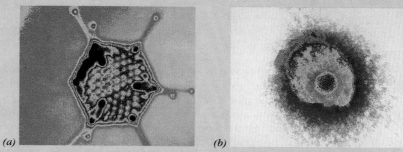

(a)   (b)

Figure 4.17 Electronmicrographs of (a) bacteriophage T₂, which parasitises the gut bacterium Escherichia. coli, *magnified; (b) tobacco mosaic virus, magnified*

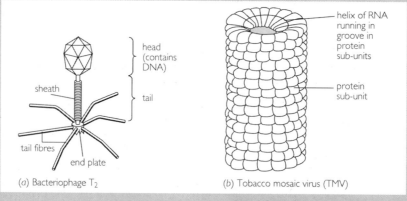

(a) Bacteriophage T₂   (b) Tobacco mosaic virus (TMV)

Figure 4.18 Structure of (a) bacteriophage T₂; (b) tobacco mosaic virus

Practical investigations offer opportunities to develop practical skills. Each practical gives guidance on carrying out and analysing your practical work.

| PRACTICAL | **The effect of temperature on the activity of trypsin** |

Introduction

Casein is a protein found in milk. When a suspension of casein is hydrolysed, the suspension starts cloudy but becomes clearer as the products dissolve. This hydrolysis is catalysed by proteolytic enzymes such as trypsin. The aim of this experiment is to investigate the effect of temperature on the activity of trypsin, using a suspension of casein as the substrate. Changes in the clarity of the casein suspension will be easier to see if the tubes are checked periodically by holding them against a piece of black card.

Materials

- Casein suspension, 4 per cent (use Marvel® milk powder, 4 per cent solution)
- Trypsin solution, 0.5 per cent
- Distilled water
- Test tubes and rack
- Graduated pipettes or syringes
- Glass beakers or water baths
- Thermometer
- Black card
- Stopwatch

Method

1 Set up a water bath at 30 °C.
2 Pipette 5 cm³ of casein suspension into one test tube and 5 cm³ of trypsin solution into another tube.
3 Stand both tubes in the water bath and leave them for several minutes to reach the temperature of the water bath.
4 Meanwhile, set up a control tube containing 5 cm³ of casein suspension plus 5 cm³ of distilled water. Stand this tube in the water bath.
5 Mix the enzyme and substrate together and replace the tube in the water bath. Start a stopwatch immediately.
6 Observe the contents of the tube carefully, checking against a piece of black card, and record the time taken for the suspension to become clear.
7 Repeat this procedure at a range of temperatures, for example between 25 °C and 65 °C. Use the same volumes of casein suspension and enzyme solution each time.

Results and discussion

1 Explain the function of the control tube.
2 Describe the relationship between temperature and the time taken for the case~

Review questions in the margin help to stimulate you to think about and understand the topics as you study them.

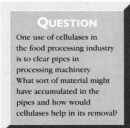

QUESTION

One use of cellulases in the food processing industry is to clear pipes in processing machinery. What sort of material might have accumulated in the pipes and how would cellulases help in its removal?

Cellulases

Cellulases break down cellulose to shorter chains, then to the disaccharide **cellobiose** and to β-glucose (Figure 3.8). Fungal sources include species of *Aspergillus*, *Trichoderma* and *Penicillium*. These cellulases currently have limited use in the food industry, but can be used to produce more fermentable sugars in brewers' mashes, to clarify orange and lemon juices, to improve the release of colours from fruit skins, to clear the haze from beer and to tenderise green beans. When used with lignases, cellulases may have great potential in the processing of waste materials such as straw, sugarcane bagasse, sawdust and newspaper, to produce sugars (**saccharification**) from the cellulose contained in these materials. First the wood must be treated to remove lignin. Sugars from wood can then be fermented to alcohol (ethanol). A yeast (*Candida* spp.) has been grown on wood pulp hydrolysed by cellulases to

Chapter 1 Molecules

1 Phospholipid structure:

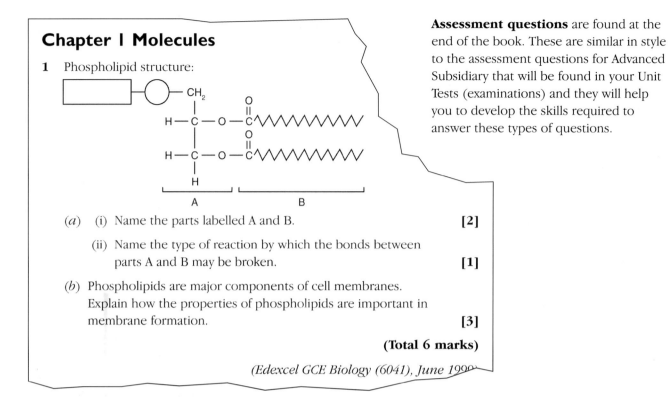

(a) (i) Name the parts labelled A and B. **[2]**

(ii) Name the type of reaction by which the bonds between parts A and B may be broken. **[1]**

(b) Phospholipids are major components of cell membranes. Explain how the properties of phospholipids are important in membrane formation. **[3]**

(Total 6 marks)

(Edexcel GCE Biology (6041), June 1990)

Assessment questions are found at the end of the book. These are similar in style to the assessment questions for Advanced Subsidiary that will be found in your Unit Tests (examinations) and they will help you to develop the skills required to answer these types of questions.

Mark schemes for these questions are also provided. These will enable you to self-check your knowledge and understanding.

Chapter 1 Molecules

1 (a) (i) A = glycerol ; B = fatty acid (residue); **[2]**

(ii) hydrolysis; **[1]**

(b) polar molecule / has hydrophilic heads and hydrophobic tails ; forms a bilayer / bimolecular double layer ; polar / hydrophilic heads outside / non-polar / hydrophobic tails outside; **[3]**

(Total 6 marks)

2

Note to teachers on safety

When practical instructions have been given we have attempted to indicate hazardous substances and operations by using standard symbols and recommending appropriate precautions. Nevertheless teachers should be aware of their obligations under the Health and Safety at Work Act, Control of Substances Hazardous to Health (COSHH) Regulations, and the Management of Health and Safety at Work Regulations. In this respect they should follow the requirements of their employers at all times. In particular, they should consult their employer's risk assessments (usually model risk assessments in a standard safety publication) before carrying out any hazardous procedure or using hazardous substances or microorganisms.

In carrying out practical work, students should be encouraged to carry out their own risk assessments, that is, they should identify hazards and suitable ways of reducing the risks from them. However they must be checked by the teacher or lecturer. Students must also know what to do in an emergency, such as a fire.

Teachers and lecturers should be familiar and up to date with current advice on safety, which is available from professional bodies.

Acknowledgements

The authors would like to thank Sue Howarth and David Hartley for their help and support during the production of this book, as well as Robin Crump, Christopher Pater, English Nature, the Field Studies Council and the WorldWide Fund for Nature. Thanks also to Sally Morgan for contributing to the Assessment Questions.

About the authors

John Adds is Chief Examiner for AS and A GCE Biology and Biology (Human) for Edexcel and Head of Biology at Abbey College, London.

Erica Larkcom is Deputy Director of Science and Plants for Schools at Homerton College, Cambridge, and a former Subject Officer for A level Biology.

Ruth Miller is Chief Examiner for AS and A GCE Biology and Biology (Human) for Edexcel and former Head of Biology at Sir William Perkins's School, Chertsey.

Unit 2 – What do I need to study?

*2B = Biology Unit 2; 2H = Biology (Human) Unit 2

Exchange, Transport, Adaptation and Reproduction

Large skipper (Ochlodes venata) *feeding on a flower of the fragrant orchid* (Gymnadenia conopsea). *"Pollinia" (pollen) of the orchid can be seen on the "elbow" of the proboscis. (Photograph taken near Dorking, Surrey, UK.)*

Exchanges with the environment

Exchange processes

All living organisms constantly need to exchange materials with the environment in order to survive and grow. All organisms need to respire to release energy from their food. Most take up oxygen from the environment and, as a consequence of the catabolic reactions involved, release carbon dioxide as a waste product. **Heterotrophic** organisms require a ready-made source of food, which they obtain from their environment. This food consists of complex organic compounds, which need to be digested into simple, soluble molecules. Any undigested material is egested and thus returned to the environment.

Autotrophic organisms make their own organic nutrients from simple, inorganic molecules. In order to achieve this, they need to obtain the raw materials from their environment. Green plants are photoautotrophs, which means they use light energy in the process of photosynthesis. Carbon dioxide from the atmosphere, together with water and mineral ions from the soil, are used in the synthesis of all the organic molecules needed for growth and reproduction. In this process, the waste product is oxygen, which is returned to the atmosphere.

In heterotrophic organisms, where the rate of metabolism is faster, carbon dioxide is also produced, together with nitrogenous waste substances, which can become toxic if allowed to accumulate. These nitrogenous substances, together with any other compounds in excess of requirements, are excreted.

All organisms produce waste products as a result of their metabolic processes. In autotrophic organisms, the main excretory products are carbon dioxide from respiration and oxygen from photosynthesis. Any other waste substances are usually converted to insoluble, harmless compounds, which are stored in places such as the heartwood and bark of trees. The rate of metabolism of autotrophic organisms is much slower, so these waste substances are not produced in large quantities.

The physical processes involved with such exchanges are:
- **passive** – such as diffusion involved in the exchange of gases in the leaves of flowering plants
- **active** – as in the uptake of mineral ions against concentration gradients in the roots of flowering plants and the ventilation movements involved with respiratory mechanisms in insects and mammals.

The nature of exchange surfaces

Exchange surfaces are the sites where materials are exchanged between the organism and the environment. In simple organisms, this process occurs over the entire surface but in more complex, multicellular organisms there are specialised regions adapted for a particular function. Most of the exchanges

DEFINITIONS
- **Heterotrophic organisms** obtain their carbon in the form of ready-made, complex organic substances, such as glucose.
- **Catabolism** is the process of breakdown of complex substances into simpler ones, such as the breakdown of glucose to carbon dioxide and water, in the process of cell respiration.
- **Autotrophic organisms** can make complex organic compounds from simple inorganic substances, such as carbon dioxide and water.

QUESTION
Use the information given here to construct a diagram showing the circulation of carbon and oxygen compounds in an ecosystem.

between flowering plants and their environment occur through the roots or through the aerial parts, particularly the leaves. In mammals, most exchanges occur internally and involve **epithelial tissues**.

Epithelial tissues are found on the internal and external surfaces of organs and may have several roles, depending on their location. Many epithelia protect underlying tissues against water loss, abrasion, pressure or infection. In addition, epithelial tissues may be involved in processes such as respiratory gas exchange, the uptake or release of nutrients and excretion.

A **simple epithelium** consists of cells arranged in a single layer, whereas **compound** or **stratified epithelia** are composed of several layers of cells. The compound epithelia, being thicker, often form impervious barriers on the external surface, but the simple epithelia form efficient exchange surfaces.

The main features of simple epithelial tissues are that:
- they form continuous layers on internal and external surfaces
- the cells are held together by a thin layer of intercellular substance containing hyaluronic acid
- the cells rest on a basement membrane made up largely of collagen fibres
- there are no blood cells present
- the free surfaces of the cells may be highly specialised
- damaged cells are rapidly replaced by cell division.

Types of simple epithelia

Cuboidal epithelium (Figure 1.1.) is the simplest type of epithelium and consists of cube-shaped cells, each with a centrally-situated spherical nucleus. The cells are closely packed together and appear pentagonal or hexagonal in outline when viewed from above. This type of epithelium occurs in the nephrons of the kidney and lines the salivary and pancreatic ducts. It is also present in many glands (mucus, salivary, sweat and thyroid), where it has a secretory function.

Squamous epithelium (Figure 1.2) consists of thin, flattened cells with little cytoplasm. The nucleus of each cell is disc-shaped and centrally situated. Cytoplasmic connections exist between adjacent cells. The cells fit closely together and, when viewed from above, the margins of the cells are seen to be irregular (tesselated). This type of epithelium is found in the Bowman's capsule of the

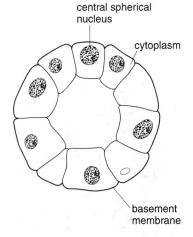

Figure 1.1 Cuboidal epithelium – found in nephrons, salivary and pancreatic ducts and secretory glands

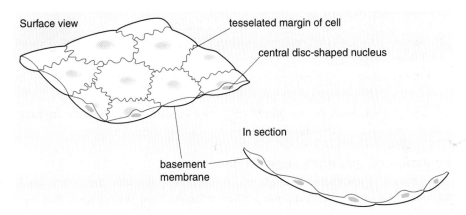

Figure 1.2 Squamous epithelium – found in the Bowman's capsule, alveoli, and in the lining of blood vessels and heart chambers

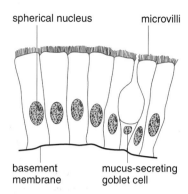

Figure 1.3 Columnar epithelium – found in the lining of the stomach and intestine, and in some ducts of the kidney

DEFINITION

Microvilli (singular microvillus) are minute, finger-like projections of the surface membrane of many epithelia. Microvilli are about 0.5 to 1.0 µm in length and are too small to be seen individually with a light microscope. Microvilli increase the surface area of cells for absorption.

kidney, the alveoli of the lungs and lining the blood vessels and the chambers of the heart.

Columnar epithelium (Figure 1.3) is made up of tall, narrow cells. A large spherical nucleus is situated near the base of each cell and the free surface often possesses **microvilli**. Mucus-secreting goblet cells are often found amongst the columnar cells. This tissue lines the stomach and intestine, and is also present in some ducts of the kidney.

Respiratory gas exchange

As has already been mentioned, aerobic respiration is common to most living organisms and necessitates the uptake of oxygen and the release of carbon dioxide. Respiring cells are constantly using up oxygen and releasing carbon dioxide, so concentration gradients exist between the organism and its environment with respect to these gases. Usually within the organism there will be a lower concentration of oxygen and a higher concentration of carbon dioxide than in the environment, so oxygen tends to diffuse in and carbon dioxide diffuses out.

It must be remembered that the situation is slightly different in green plants (Table 1.1). Respiration takes place all the time, so oxygen is continually taken up by respiring cells and carbon dioxide is released. During the hours of daylight, photosynthesis will occur in the palisade and spongy cells in the mesophyll of the leaves, involving the uptake of carbon dioxide and the release of oxygen. As this process takes place at a more rapid rate than respiration, during the day the concentration gradients of oxygen and carbon dioxide are reversed: carbon dioxide diffuses in and oxygen diffuses out.

Table 1.1 *Gas exchange in flowering plants*

Feature	Day	Night
respiration occurring	✓	✓
photosynthesis occurring	✓	✗
state of stomata	open	closed
concentration of CO_2 in leaf	low	high
concentration of CO_2 in atmosphere	higher	lower
concentration of O_2 in leaf	high	low
concentration of O_2 in atmosphere	lower	higher
net gas exchange	O_2 diffuses out CO_2 diffuses in	CO_2 diffuses out O_2 diffuses in

The site of respiratory gas exchange is referred to as the **respiratory surface** and, in order for gas exchange to be efficient, it has special features.

Features of gas exchange surfaces

The features of gas exchange surfaces, or respiratory surfaces, are determined by the factors which affect the rate of diffusion. We have already seen that the

rate of diffusion will depend on the existence of concentration gradients, but other factors that need to be considered are:
- the area over which diffusion occurs
- the distance over which diffusion occurs
- the nature of any barrier through which the molecules must pass
- the nature of the diffusing molecules.

The area of the respiratory surface must be large enough to provide sufficient oxygen for the organism's requirements. In very small organisms, such as the unicellular *Amoeba*, where the surface area : volume ratio is large, the general body surface is the respiratory surface. In such organisms, gas exchange takes place through the cell surface membrane, oxygen diffusing in and carbon dioxide diffusing out. With larger, multicellular organisms, an increase in volume results in a decrease in the surface area : volume ratio; in other words there is less surface area per unit volume of organism and exchange of gases through the body surface may not be enough to satisfy the organism's needs. In such cases, specialised respiratory surfaces exist in the form of lungs or gills, providing a large area over which the exchange can occur.

In small organisms, the distances over which the diffusion of the gases occurs are small, but with increase in size there is a corresponding increase in bulk. This results in an increase in the distance of the respiring cells from the respiratory surface, slowing the rate of diffusion. In some larger organisms such as the flatworms, where there is no special respiratory surface, the body is flattened. This increases the efficiency of diffusion as no respiring cells are far from the respiratory surface. In other organisms where specialised respiratory surfaces are present, other mechanisms have evolved which improve the efficiency of gas exchange. A ventilation mechanism often exists, bringing fresh supplies of air or water in contact with the respiratory surface and maintaining a high concentration of oxygen. In addition, the concentration gradients are maintained by an internal transport system, such as the blood circulatory system, which brings deoxygenated blood to the respiratory surface and removes the oxygenated blood. In such cases, the oxygen-carrying capacity of the blood is increased by the presence of a respiratory pigment. In mammals, this pigment is **haemoglobin** and is present in specialised blood cells: erythrocytes.

The respiratory surface needs to be permeable to the respiratory gases. All cell surface membranes are permeable to oxygen, carbon dioxide and water.

Gas exchange in flowering plants

Gas exchange in flowering plants involves the aerial parts, mainly the leaves and stems. Leaves have a large surface area : volume ratio, which is favourable for the exchange of gases. Access to the respiring cells is by means of **stomata**, which are pores in the epidermis of the leaves (Figure 1.4). Inside the leaf, the large intercellular air spaces in the spongy mesophyll facilitate the diffusion of gases and the cells bordering these air spaces increase the total area available for gas exchange still further. During the day, when photosynthesis is occurring, the fixation of carbon dioxide maintains a concentration gradient of carbon dioxide between the interior of the leaf and the external atmosphere. The rate of diffusion of carbon dioxide is directly proportional to the concentration gradient, but it is also affected by factors such

> **QUESTION**
>
> Work out how the surface area to volume ratio alters in cubes with sides of 1, 2, 3, 4, etc. units.

as the number and size of the stomata, the cuticle of the leaf and the layer of air surrounding the leaf. As these are factors which also affect the movement of water in the plant, they will be described in more detail in Chapter 2.

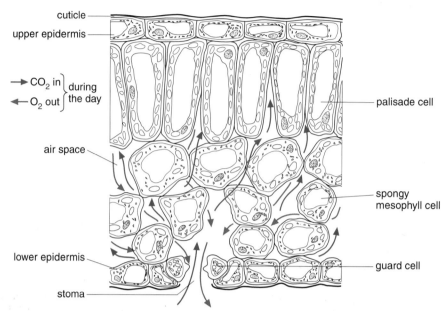

cuticle
upper epidermis

→ CO_2 in ⎱ during
← O_2 out ⎰ the day

palisade cell

air space

spongy
mesophyll cell

lower epidermis

guard cell

stoma

Figure 1.4 Vertical section through leaf lamina to show gas exchange surfaces and gas exchange during the day

ADDITIONAL MATERIAL

(a)

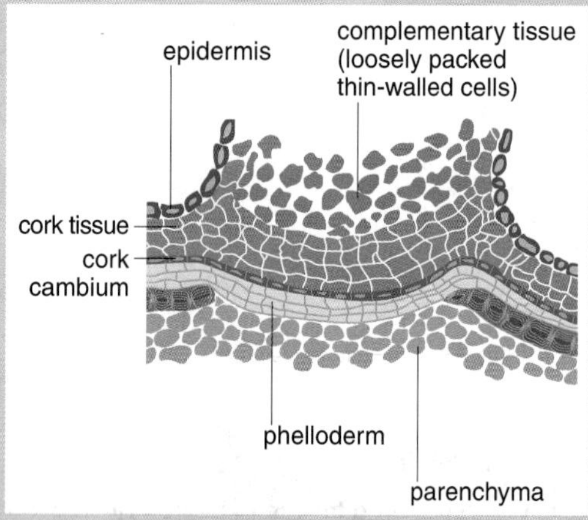

epidermis

complementary tissue
(loosely packed
thin-walled cells)

cork tissue
cork
cambium

phelloderm

parenchyma

(b)

In addition to the stomata on the leaves, gas exchange in woody plants takes place through structures called **lenticels** (Figure 1.5). As a result of the growth of the secondary xylem in a woody stem, the epidermis ruptures and is replaced by a layer of cork (phellem), produced by the activities of cork cambium (phellogen). The cells of this cork cambium produce a layer of cork to the outside and a layer of secondary cortex (phelloderm) to the inside. The walls of the cork cells become impregnated with a fatty material called **suberin**, which makes them impermeable to gases and water and causes the living contents to disappear. The suberised cells form a protective layer, preventing desiccation, mechanical injury and the entry of pathogenic organisms. At intervals, the cork cambium produces groups of loosely packed, thin-walled cells with no deposits of suberin. These groups of cells, which have large air spaces between them, form the lenticels and allow gaseous exchange to occur between the living cells of the stem and the environment. They appear as tiny slits or bumps on the bark of stems and twigs, easily visible with a hand lens.

Figure 1.5 (a) Vertical section through surface layers of woody twig showing lenticel structure; (b) photograph of a sycamore twig with lenticels

Gas exchange in simple animals

Many groups of invertebrate animals, such as cnidarians (eg, jellyfish) and annelids (segmented worms), rely on simple diffusion of gases across their outer surface as a means of respiratory gas exchange. Their outer surface is moist and permeable to gases, and functions as a gas exchange structure. In addition, their requirement for oxygen is relatively small. As organisms become larger and more complex, and their outer surface impermeable to gases, an efficient gas exchange system is necessary to supply the body tissues with oxygen and to remove carbon dioxide.

ADDITIONAL MATERIAL

Gas exchange in insects

The exoskeleton of an insect is covered with a thin waxy layer, the epicuticle, which helps to prevent desiccation. The surface area of an insect is large in relation to its volume and these animals would readily dry out if not efficiently waterproofed. As a consequence of this waterproofing, the exoskeleton is impermeable to gases, so how do insects obtain the oxygen they need for respiration? Close examination of a large insect, such as a locust, reveals the presence of paired **spiracles**, or pores, in the exoskeleton (Figure 1.6). Spiracles may have valves, which are able to open and close. At rest, the spiracles are opened only occasionally, which helps to minimise water loss by evaporation and diffusion of water vapour through the spiracles. Each spiracle leads to a complex system of air-filled tubes, known as **tracheae** (singular trachea). Tracheae are strengthened by the taenidia, long spirals of chitin (a polysaccharide), which prevent them from collapsing. As they divide and ramify through the tissues of the insect's body, the tracheae become progressively smaller in diameter, ending in blind-ended minute tracheoles. The end of each tracheole is enclosed in a long, invaginated cell about 0.1 μm in diameter and up to about 400 μm in length. The tip of each tracheole is branched and filled with fluid; exchange of oxygen and carbon dioxide occurs in solution between the tracheoles and body cells.

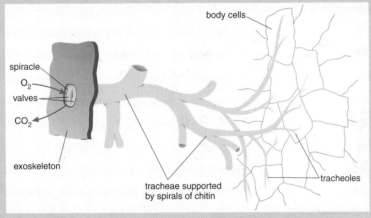

Figure 1.6 Spiracle and part of the tracheal system of an insect

At rest, small insects rely on simple diffusion of oxygen into their tracheal system and diffusion of carbon dioxide out. Closure of the spiracles both reduces water loss and helps to maintain a steep diffusion gradient for respiratory gases. When the spiracles are closed, the concentration of oxygen within the tracheal system decreases, resulting in a rapid influx of oxygen when the spiracles open. Conversely, carbon dioxide accumulates in the tracheae and rapidly diffuses out when the spiracles are opened.

When insects are more active, ventilation of the tracheal system is increased by muscular movement of the abdomen. Contraction of abdominal muscles results in the alternate compression and expansion of the tracheae, which increases the flow of air into and out of the tracheal system. In locusts, the thoracic and abdominal spiracles open and close alternately, resulting in a flow of air from front to back. This improves the efficiency of gas exchange as air is drawn into the thorax, where there is a high demand for oxygen by the flight muscles.

During periods of increased metabolic activity, lactate may begin to accumulate in the tissues. This decreases the tissue solute potential and water is drawn out of the tracheoles by osmosis. This brings air into closer contact with the respiring tissues and further increases the efficiency of gas exchange.

Gas exchange in humans and other mammals

The gas exchange system in humans and other mammals consists essentially of two major parts, a **conducting system**, for the conduction of inspired and expired gases, and an **interface** for the exchange of gases between air and blood. The conducting system begins with the nasal passages and continues as the **trachea**. The trachea divides to form the left and right primary or main **bronchi** which supply the lungs. Each primary bronchus divides repeatedly to form airways of progressively smaller diameter, the secondary bronchi supply air to the lobes of the lungs and the tertiary bronchi supply segments of each lobe. The tertiary bronchi divide into numerous smaller **bronchioles** which ultimately lead into the **alveoli**, where gas exchange occurs.

The structure of the airways conforms to a common basic plan. They consist essentially of a tube, lined with epithelium, containing variable amounts of cartilage and/or smooth muscle in the wall. The type of epithelium changes progressively from one type of airway to the next. In the trachea, the epithelium is described as pseudostratified columnar ciliated epithelium. This undergoes a progressive change to a simple cuboidal, non-ciliated type in the smallest airways. **Goblet cells**, which secrete mucus, are frequent in the epithelium of the trachea but they decrease in number and are absent in the terminal bronchioles.

Alveoli are the major sites of gas exchange. Each alveolus consists of a pocket-shaped structure 100 to 300 μm in diameter, open on one side, and lined with extremely flattened epithelial cells (Figure 1.7). It has been estimated that there are about 300 million alveoli in the human lungs, giving a considerable total surface area (40 to 60 m^2) for gas exchange. Each alveolus consists of three tissue components: epithelium, connective tissue and blood vessels. The epithelium consists of two cell types, referred to as **Type I** and **Type II pneumocytes**. Type I pneumocytes are large, extremely flattened cells and make up most of the alveolar wall. Type II pneumocytes secrete **surfactant**, a mixture of lipids and proteins, which helps to reduce the surface tension within each alveolus. Without this surfactant, the alveoli collapse and lung tissue loses its elastic recoil. The connective tissue forms a supporting layer beneath the epithelium and consists of fine fibres, such as collagen and elastin, together with cells known as fibroblasts. The blood vessels surrounding the alveoli are mainly capillaries, referred to as pulmonary capillaries, 7 to 10 μm in diameter, which form a dense network around each alveolus.

The structure of each alveolus, with its surrounding capillaries, is well adapted for the process of gas exchange. Each alveolus is very thin-walled and there are millions of alveoli in each lung. The barrier for exchange of gases between alveolar air and the blood, known as the respiratory membrane, is of minimal thickness, less than 0.5 μm, which increases the efficiency of diffusion of gases.

The lungs have a number of defence mechanisms against inhaled microorganisms and small particles such as carbon in smoke (see page 14). These defence mechanisms include filtration of inhaled air by the nose, the cough reflex and cilia and mucus within the larger airways. Cilia and mucus help to trap small particles in inspired air. Some particles, such as carbon, may reach

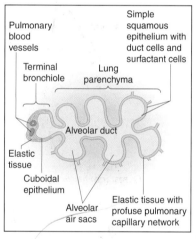

Figure 1.7 *Transverse section of the alveolar air sac.*

Labels (from figure):
- Pulmonary blood vessels
- Simple squamous epithelium with duct cells and surfactant cells
- Terminal bronchiole
- Lung parenchyma
- Alveolar duct
- Elastic tissue
- Cuboidal epithelium
- Alveolar air sacs
- Elastic tissue with profuse pulmonary capillary network

the alveoli and are engulfed by wandering phagocytic cells known as **alveolar macrophages** or dust cells. These are derived from **monocytes** in blood, which migrate through blood vessel walls into various organs to become macrophages.

Ventilation in humans and other mammals

Pulmonary ventilation is the term given to the process of breathing, that is, the movement of air into and out of the respiratory system. Movement of air into the lungs is referred to as inspiration, while the movement of air out of the lungs is expiration.

Air moves into or out of the lungs as a result of differences in pressure between the atmosphere and alveolar air. When the atmospheric pressure (normally about 101 kPa, or 760 mm Hg) is greater than the pressure within the lungs, air will tend to flow down this pressure gradient and inspiration occurs. When the pressure in the lungs is greater than atmospheric pressure, air moves out of the lungs and into the atmosphere. The mechanism of pulmonary ventilation therefore depends on two gas pressure gradients, one in which the **intrapulmonary pressure** (pressure within the lungs) is lower than atmospheric pressure for inspiration to occur, and one in which the intrapulmonary pressure is higher than atmospheric pressure for expiration to occur. These pressure gradients are brought about by changes in the volume of the thorax which, in turn, are produced by contraction or relaxation of the respiratory muscles. The lungs follow these changes passively.

Inspiration

During inspiration (Figure 1.8), the volume of the thorax is increased by movements of the ribs upwards and outwards, and by contraction of the **diaphragm**. The diaphragm consists of striated muscle and a central tendinous area. It separates the thoracic and abdominal cavities. As the diaphragm contracts (when stimulated by the phrenic nerve), it flattens and descends, which increases the length of the thoracic cavity. Contraction of the **external intercostal muscles** pulls the anterior end of each rib upwards and outwards, increasing the diameter of the thorax. As the overall volume of the thorax increases, the intrapulmonary pressure decreases and inspiration occurs.

Expiration

Quiet expiration is brought about mainly by relaxation of the inspiratory muscles (the diaphragm and external intercostals), contraction of the **internal intercostal muscles**, and elastic recoil of lung tissue. The changes which occur are essentially the reverse of those described for inspiration, that is, the volume of the thorax decreases and, as a result, the intrapulmonary pressure increases, establishing a gradient to the atmosphere. Expiration then follows passively.

The intrapulmonary pressure therefore varies during inspiration and expiration. At the end of expiration during quiet breathing, the intrapulmonary pressure is the same as atmospheric pressure. As inspiration starts, the intrapulmonary pressure drops to about 0.4 kPa below atmospheric. During quiet expiration, the intrapulmonary pressure initially increases to about 0.4 kPa above atmospheric but returns to the atmospheric value by the time quiet expiration is completed.

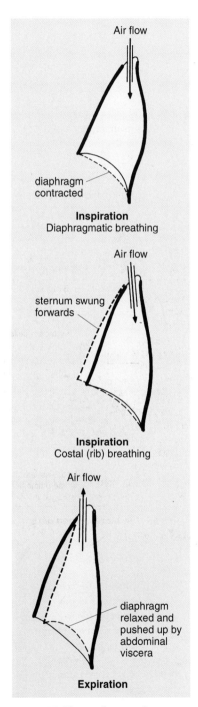

Figure 1.8 The mechanics of inspiration and expiration (see also Figures 1.9 and 1.10)

It should be noted that the diaphragm and intercostal muscles are not the only muscles of ventilation. During quiet breathing, movement of the diaphragm accounts for about 75 per cent of the volume of air breathed. However, during forced inspiratory and expiratory efforts, many other muscles are used, including the abdominal muscles which contract during forced expiration. Forced expiratory efforts can greatly increase the intrapulmonary pressure. For example, forced expiration against a closed glottis (known as the Valsalva manœuvre) or when attempting to blow up a balloon, may raise the intrapulmonary pressure by 13 kPa or more.

The mechanisms of inspiration and expiration are summarised in Figures 1.9 and 1.10.

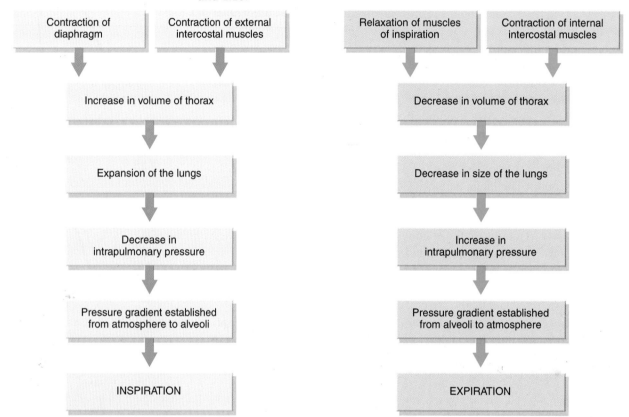

Figure 1.9 Mechanism of inspiration   *Figure 1.10 Mechanism of expiration*

DEFINITIONS

- **Tidal volume** is the volume of air breathed in or out during quiet breathing.
- **Expiratory reserve volume (ERV)** is the maximum volume of air which can be forcibly expired after a tidal expiration.
- **Inspiratory reserve volume (IRV)** is the volume of air which can be inspired over and above a tidal respiration.

Lung capacities

A **spirometer** (Figure 1.11) is a device which is used to measure and record the volumes of air inspired and expired. These volumes are of great importance as they can indicate whether or not adequate ventilation of the lungs is occurring so that there is normal exchange of oxygen and carbon dioxide between alveolar air and the pulmonary capillary blood.

The recording of the volumes of air inspired and expired, usually as a function of time, is referred to as a **spirogram** (Figure 1.12). The volume of air breathed in or out by an adult human during quiet breathing is about 500 cm^3. This is referred to as the resting **tidal volume** (TV). After a person has expired tidal air, it is possible to force more air out of the lungs. The maximum volume of air which can be forcibly expired after a tidal expiration is known as the **expiratory reserve volume** (ERV). The **inspiratory reserve volume** (IRV) is the volume of air which can be inspired over and above a tidal inspiration. Even after breathing out as far as possible, air remains in the

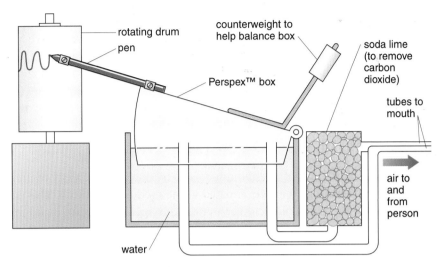

Figure 1.11 A spirometer

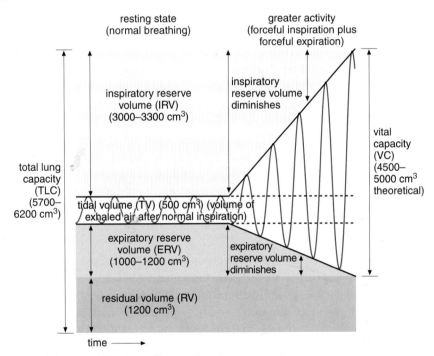

Figure 1.12 Major subdivisions of lung volumes

alveoli. This air, which keeps the alveoli partly inflated and enables gas exchange to continue between breaths, is known as the **residual volume** (RV).

The total of IRV + TV + ERV is known as the **vital capacity** (VC). The term 'capacity' is used for the sum of two or more separate lung volumes. Vital capacity is related to the body size of a person and is usually about 2.6 dm^3 m^{-2} body surface area in males and 2.1 dm^3 m^{-2} in females. It is higher in swimmers and divers, and lower in older people and in people who have diseases of the lungs,

---

QUESTION

Use Figure 1.12 to explain what is meant by the term **total lung capacity**.

---

such as emphysema. Vital capacity is also affected by posture, being greater when the person is standing upright than when lying down.

Control of breathing

Breathing occurs due to the rhythmic activity of motor nerves which send impulses to the muscles of respiration. This rhythmic activity is entirely dependent on nerve impulses from the brain, as the muscles do not have any inherent rhythmic activity. Breathing is controlled by two interacting mechanisms, a voluntary system, situated in the cerebral cortex, and an automatic system, situated in the pons and the medulla oblongata. The voluntary system is used to regulate breathing in activities such as speaking or playing a wind instrument, and the automatic system is used to regulate breathing to match the metabolic needs of the body.

The basic regular rhythm of breathing seems to be due to the activity of the **medullary rhythmicity centre**, situated in the medulla oblongata. This is turn consists of two interconnected centres: the **inspiratory centre** and the **expiratory centre**. Although the term 'centre' is used, it is recognised that these actually consist of scattered groups of nerve cells within the brain stem. Nerve impulses from the inspiratory centre stimulate inspiration and impulses from the expiratory centre stimulate expiration. The medullary rhythmicity centre is similar to the pacemaker region of the heart (described in Chapter 2) as it has an inherent rhythm which can be modified by external influences.

The activity of the medullary rhythmicity centre is influenced by feedback information that comes from many sensors throughout the nervous system. Stimuli affecting the medullary rhythmicity centre can be divided into two groups: chemical and non-chemical. Chemical stimuli include the respiratory gases, oxygen and carbon dioxide, and changes in the pH of arterial blood. Non-chemical stimuli include feedback from, for example, stretch receptors located in the lungs. The effects of these types of stimuli are summarised below.

- **Oxygen** The precise role of oxygen in controlling breathing is not clear, but a decrease in arterial oxygen below about 9.3 kPa causes reflex stimulation of the inspiratory centre. An increase in arterial oxygen has little effect on breathing.
- **Carbon dioxide** Chemoreceptors in the medulla oblongata are sensitive to changes in the carbon dioxide content of arterial blood. A slight increase in carbon dioxide has a stimulating effect, resulting in faster breathing with a greater volume of air moving in and out of the lungs each minute. This increases the removal of carbon dioxide via the lungs and brings the arterial blood carbon dioxide level back towards the normal range. Decreased carbon dioxide has the opposite effect, resulting in inhibition of the medullary rhythmicity centre and slower breathing. Breathing may stop entirely for a few seconds if arterial carbon dioxide drops to about 4.6 kPa (the normal range for arterial carbon dioxide is about 5.1 to 5.3 kPa).
- **pH of blood** A decrease in arterial blood pH (increase in acidity) has a stimulating effect on breathing and pulmonary ventilation increases.
- **Non-chemical stimuli** These include feedback from stretch receptors in the lungs which, as the lungs inflate, send inhibitory impulses to the inspiratory centre, and impulses from sensory nerve endings in joints and tendons which help to control breathing during exercise.

Effects of exercise on pulmonary ventilation

Exercise can be considered to be of two types, moderate and very severe. These types of exercise have different effects on pulmonary ventilation. Moderate exercise is a type of exercise which can be maintained for long periods of time, such as walking briskly at 8 km per hour, or steady running. During moderate exercise, pulmonary ventilation increases steadily in proportion to the extent of the exercise, in order to supply sufficient oxygen to the active muscles. The exact reasons for this increase in ventilation are not clear, but probably are due to a number of factors including:

- nervous stimuli from higher centres in the brain and from sensory nerve endings in joints and muscles
- increased production of carbon dioxide
- production of lactate and consequent decrease in pH.

Table 1.2 shows the pulmonary ventilation of a man walking at different speeds.

Table 1.2 *Pulmonary ventilation of a man walking at different speeds*

Walking speed / km h^{-1}	Pulmonary ventilation / dm^3 min^{-1}
rest	10.0
3.2	19.0
4.8	25.0
6.4	37.0
8.0	60.0

Very severe exercise, such as running 100 m at top speed, can be maintained only for a relatively short period of time. At the end of this exercise the runner is completely exhausted. Breathing remains much above the resting value for a prolonged period after the exercise is over. As an example, in a man who ran 200 m in 23.4 seconds, it took 27 minutes for his pulmonary ventilation to return to normal. After a 400 m race, followed by vigorous gymnastics, the pulmonary ventilation returned to normal in 44 minutes. In the case of a 100 m sprint, the runner may scarcely draw breath during the race, but will breathe heavily for some time afterwards.

Effects of training

The adaptations which are seen in the respiratory and cardiovascular systems and the muscles as a result of training depend on the nature of the training programme being followed. As an example, endurance training for prolonged exercise results in the following adaptations:

- an increase in the maximal blood supply to muscles and an increase in the maximal cardiac output (the volume of blood pumped out by the heart during one minute) (see *Respiration and Coordination*, Adds, Larkcom and Miller, Nelson, 2000)
- an increase in the ability of the muscles to use oxygen
- more energy is derived from fat and less from carbohydrates
- less fatigue.

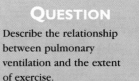

QUESTION

Describe the relationship between pulmonary ventilation and the extent of exercise.

QUESTION

Apart from an increase in pulmonary ventilation, what other physiological changes will occur in a person during and after very severe exercise?

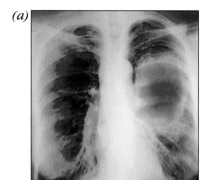

(a)

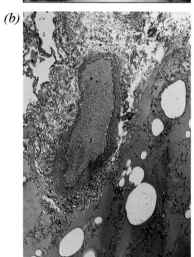

(b)

Figure 1.13 (a) X-ray of lung cancer caused by smoking cigarettes; (b) part of an emphysematous lung, showing destruction of alveolar walls

Effects of smoking on ventilation and gas exchange

Cigarette smoke contains a complex mixture of substances, including nicotine, carbon monoxide, aromatic hydrocarbons, phenols and fatty acids. The hydrocarbons include tumour initiators, that is, substances which are able to start a malignant process – there is a linear relationship between the number of cigarettes smoked and the mortality risk from lung cancer (Figure 1.13a). In addition to this increased risk of lung cancer, cigarette smoke has a number of other harmful effects, including increasing the risk of **chronic bronchitis** and **emphysema**.

Cigarette smoke increases mucus production in the airways and makes the mucus more viscous. The smoke also paralyses the cilia which normally move mucus up the airways towards the pharynx. As a result, mucus tends to accumulate in the airways (chronic bronchitis), making infection almost inevitable. Bronchitis obstructs air flow and, as a result, there is inefficient gas exchange.

Emphysema is a destructive disease of the lungs due to damage to the connective tissue. The alveoli enlarge, their walls rupture and they fuse into large, dilated, irregular air spaces. Destruction of lung tissue in this way is believed to be caused by the release of elastase, a proteolytic enzyme, by the alveolar macrophages and by neutrophils. Emphysema produces distended lungs with an appearance which has been described as similar to that of wire wool saucepan cleaners (Figure 1.13b).

This destruction of lung tissue greatly decreases the surface area for gas exchange and as a result the blood may be poorly oxygenated, a condition referred to as **hypoxia**. This can cause serious distress and death from respiratory failure, heart failure or chest infection. There is no cure for emphysema, which is responsible for about 20 000 deaths per year in Great Britain.

Digestion and absorption

Digestion

Digestion is the process in which complex food molecules are broken down into simpler molecules. It can be divided into:

- **mechanical** digestion
- **chemical** digestion.

The structure of the alimentary canal is specialised to facilitate digestion and absorption in heterotrophic organisms.

Structure of the alimentary canal in relation to digestion and absorption

The alimentary canal, or gut, has a basic common structure along its length, although it is specialised in certain regions to carry out its various roles (Figure 1.14). It extends as a tube from the **mouth** to the **anus** and along its length the wall is composed of four layers. These are:

- the **mucosa**, the innermost layer surrounding the **lumen** (Figure 1.15), made up of glandular epithelium and connective tissue containing blood vessels and lymph vessels

> **DEFINITION**
>
> The **lumen** is the cavity of the gut, through which food passes.

- a layer of connective tissue, the **submucosa**, containing nerves, blood vessels and lymph vessels, together with elastic fibres and collagen
- the **muscularis externa**, composed of circular and longitudinal layers of smooth muscle fibres
- the outermost layer, the **serosa**, made up of loose connective tissue.

Along the whole length of the gut, the glandular epithelium of the mucosa contains **goblet cells** which secrete **mucus**. The mucus lubricates the passage of food along the gut and also protects it from the digestive action of enzymes. In the mucosa of the stomach, there are simple, tubular **gastric glands** which secrete **gastric juice**. In the mucosa of the duodenum and ileum, the **intestinal glands** in the **crypts of Lieberkühn** secrete **intestinal juice** which contains mucus and enterokinase.

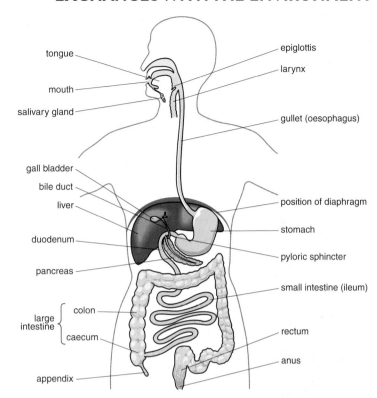

Figure 1.14 Human alimentary canal and associated organs

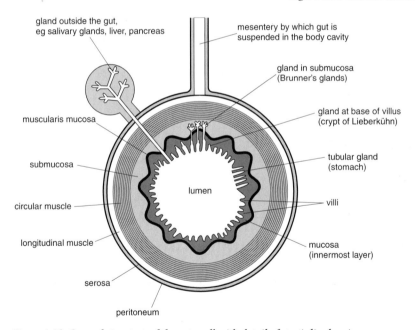

Figure 1.15 General structure of the gut wall with detail of specialised regions

QUESTION

Explain why salivary amylase does not break down much starch.

The mucosa is separated from the submucosa by a thin layer of smooth muscle, the **muscularis mucosa**. In the submucosa of the duodenum, **Brunner's glands** produce an alkaline solution containing mucus, but no enzymes. External to the serosa is the **peritoneum**, which is a double-layered membrane surrounding the gut and lining the abdominal cavity. The **mesenteries**, which are extensions of the peritoneum, hold the gut canal in place by anchoring it to the abdominal wall. The surfaces of the cells of the peritoneum are moist, preventing frictional damage as the gut moves against other organs in the abdominal cavity.

EXCHANGES WITH THE ENVIRONMENT

At certain regions along the gut are ducts from external glands, such as the salivary glands, the liver and the pancreas. Figure 6.3 gives a general plan of the gut wall with detail of specialised areas.

Mechanical digestion

In mechanical digestion, the large particles of ingested food may be sliced, crushed or otherwise broken up by the teeth. This reduces the food to smaller lumps which are easier to swallow and have a larger surface area, so that subsequent enzyme action during chemical digestion is more effective.

Mechanical digestion of ingested food is referred to as **mastication** and is achieved by means of teeth in the mouth, or buccal cavity. Teeth are present in the upper and lower jaws and in an adult human there are 32 permanent teeth. These consist, in each jaw, of: four **incisors**, two **canines**, four **premolars** and six **molars**, arranged as shown in Figure 1.16.

The exposed part of each tooth, the **crown**, projects above the gum and is covered with **enamel**, which is very hard and resistant to decay. The **root** is embedded in the jawbone and is held in place by **periodontal fibres**, connected to the jawbone at one end and to the **cement** surrounding the outside of the root at the other. The **neck** is the part which is surrounded by the gum, but not embedded in the jawbone.

Most of the tooth consists of **dentine**, a hard, bone-like substance, which has many tiny channels extending through it. These channels, known as **canaliculi**, contain strands of cytoplasm from the dentine-producing cells in the pulp cavity, which is located in the central part of the tooth. In addition to the dentine-producing cells, the pulp cavity contains nerve endings and blood vessels (Figure 1.17).

The incisors have flattened crowns with sharp, chisel-like edges, which are used to bite off lumps of food. The canines have conical, pointed crowns and assist in the biting process. In carnivorous animals, the canines are much bigger and more pointed and are used to pierce and hold live prey. Both the incisors and the canines have single roots. The cheek teeth (the premolars and molars) have rounded projections, called **cusps**, on their crowns. These assist in crushing and grinding food during the process of chewing. Typically the cheek teeth each have more than one root, the molars on the upper jaw possessing three or four, so giving greater anchorage in the jawbone.

Crushing and grinding of the food not only breaks up larger lumps into smaller pieces, but also mixes them with saliva, which moistens and lubricates them. The tongue and cheek muscles also help to form the moistened food into a mass called a **bolus**, which is manipulated to the back of the buccal cavity before being swallowed.

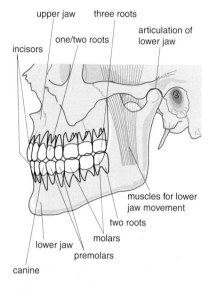
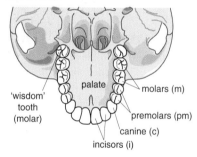

Figure 1.16 Arrangement of adult human teeth

> ### DEFINITION
> The dental formula summarises the number and different types of teeth on the upper and lower jaws for one side of the skull.
> For a human, the formula is:
> i (incisors) 2/2
> c (canines) 1/1
> pm (premolars) 2/2
> m (molars) 3/3
> making a total of 32 teeth in the adult dentition.

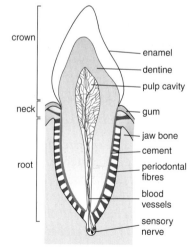

Figure 1.17 LS human canine tooth

Movement of food along the alimentary canal

Associated with the muscularis externa are networks of nerves, one of which controls the contraction and relaxation of the muscles which bring about the movement of food along the alimentary canal. This movement, known as **peristalsis**, is initiated by the act of swallowing (Figure 1.18). The bolus stretches the wall and the circular muscle behind the bolus contracts, pushing the food forward. The circular muscle in the region surrounding the bolus is relaxed, increasing the diameter of the lumen and enabling the food to be pushed forward. Peristaltic movements occur all the way along the gut. In the small intestine, the alternate contraction and relaxation of the muscles brings about **segmentation movements** which help bring the contents of the lumen of the gut in contact with the epithelium of the wall where absorption occurs.

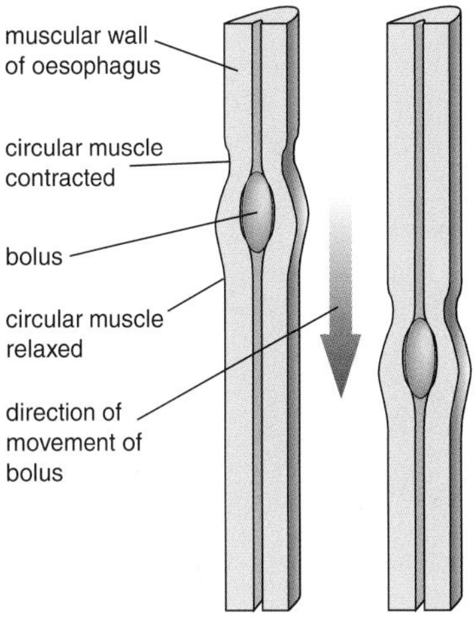

At certain points along the alimentary canal, the circular muscle is thicker and forms rings of muscle called **sphincters**, which control the passage of food from one region to another. The **cardiac sphincter**, found between the oesophagus and the stomach, controls the entry of food into the stomach. At the other end of the stomach, the **pyloric sphincter** relaxes to allow the passage of food from the stomach into the duodenum when it has reached the right consistency. There are additional sphincters at the junction of the ileum and the caecum, and at the anus.

Chemical digestion

Chemical digestion involves the action of **hydrolases** (hydrolytic enzymes) on the food constituents. The chemical breakdown of the complex organic molecules takes place progressively in stages until simple, smaller, soluble molecules are formed, which can then be absorbed. There are three major groups of digestive enzymes involved:

- **carbohydrases** hydrolyse the glycosidic bonds in carbohydrates
- **proteases** hydrolyse the peptide bonds in proteins and polypeptides
- **lipases** hydrolyse the ester bonds in triglycerides.

The processes which take place are the reverse of the condensation reactions which occur when carbohydrates, proteins and lipids are formed.

Figure 1.18 Diagram to illustrate peristalsis

> ### DEFINITION
> **Peristalsis** is the term used to describe the muscular movements which control the passage of food along the gut. It is achieved by alternate relaxation and contraction of the circular muscles as illustrated in Figure 1.18.

Carbohydrases

Some monosaccharide sugars, such as glucose and fructose, may be ingested, but the bulk of carbohydrate in the human diet is in the form of polysaccharides and, as such, requires digestion. Starch from plants and glycogen from animal sources are split into smaller units, usually disaccharides, by **amylases**. The disaccharides are then hydrolysed to monosaccharides which are small enough to be absorbed (Figure 1.19).

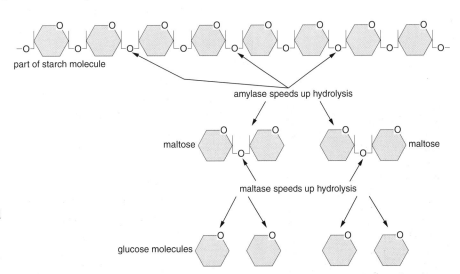

Figure 1.19 Hydrolysis of starch to maltose and glucose, catalysed by amylase and maltase

EXCHANGES WITH THE ENVIRONMENT

Carbohydrate digestion occurs in the mouth, duodenum and ileum under alkaline conditions. Carbohydrate digestion in humans is summarised in Table 1.3.

Table 1.3 *Carbohydrate digestion in humans*

Location in alimentary canal	Optimum pH	Enzymes involved	Products of digestion
mouth and buccal cavity	7.0	salivary amylase	dextrins (short chains of glucose residues), some maltose; food does not remain here long enough for much digestion
duodenum	7.0	pancreatic amylase from pancreatic juice	starch broken down to maltose
ileum (bound to membranes of microvilli on the epithelial mucosa)	8.5	maltase lactase sucrase	maltose to glucose; lactose to glucose and galactose; sucrose to glucose and fructose

In the mouth, saliva is produced from three pairs of salivary glands (humans normally secrete about 1.5 dm^3 each day). Saliva consists mostly of water, together with enzymes, mineral ions and mucus. The constituents of saliva and their roles are summarised in Table 1.4.

Table 1.4 *Constituents of saliva and their roles*

Constituent	Role
salivary amylase	initiates the digestion of cooked starch to maltose
lysozyme	catalyses the breakdown of cell walls of some pathogenic bacteria
mucus	helps to stick the food together to form a bolus
chloride ions	activate salivary amylase
other mineral ions (phosphates, hydrogencarbonate)	help to maintain the correct pH (about pH 7)

Very little starch digestion takes place in the mouth, because the food does not remain there long enough. When a bolus of food is swallowed, it is transported down the oesophagus to the stomach, where the extremely acid conditions inhibit the action of salivary amylase. No carbohydrases are present in the gastric juice from the gastric glands in the mucosa of the stomach wall.

When the food reaches the duodenum, pancreatic juice containing amylase enters through the pancreatic duct. In addition to proteases and lipases, pancreatic juice also contains alkaline salts which help to neutralise the acid from the stomach. Bile from the liver is also added via the bile duct. It contains hydrogencarbonate ions which contribute to the creation of alkaline conditions in which the enzymes from the pancreas and from the intestinal juice work most effectively. Pancreatic amylase hydrolyses any remaining starch to maltose.

The enzymes involved in the hydrolysis of disaccharides, such as maltose, lactose and sucrose, are located on the membranes of the microvilli of the epithelial mucosa. When hydrolysis is completed, the monosaccharides can then be absorbed.

ADDITIONAL MATERIAL

Proteases

There are two groups of proteases:
- endopeptidases speed up the hydrolysis of peptide bonds within the protein molecules
- exopeptidases act on terminal peptide bonds (those at the ends of the polypeptide chains).

Hydrolysis involving endopeptidases results in proteins being broken down into short polypeptide chains (Figure 1.20). Pepsin, trypsin and chymotrypsin are endopeptidases, each only capable of hydrolysing specific peptide bonds. For example, trypsin catalyses the hydrolysis of peptide bonds which involve the amino acids lysine or arginine. Pepsin, trypsin and chymotrypsin are secreted into the alimentary canal in their inactive forms: pepsin as pepsinogen, trypsin as trypsinogen and chymotrypsin as chymotrypsinogen. This ensures that these enzymes are activated only when there is food requiring digestion in the alimentary canal and prevents the enzymes damaging the cells in which they are produced.

Pepsinogen is converted to pepsin by the action of hydrochloric acid in the stomach. Once some pepsin has been formed, it will bring about the conversion of more pepsinogen to pepsin. Trypsinogen is converted to trypsin by the action of the enzyme enterokinase, which is secreted in the ileum, and chymotrypsinogen is activated by trypsin.

It is also worth noting that some young mammals produce the enzyme rennin, secreted as pro-rennin, in the stomach. It is activated by hydrochloric acid and its function is to coagulate the soluble milk protein, caseinogen, to the insoluble calcium salt of casein, which is then hydrolysed by pepsin.

The action of exopeptidases results in the breakdown of the short polypeptide chains by the removal of amino acids. There are two kinds of exopeptidases:
- aminopeptidases hydrolyse peptide bonds at the amino end of a polypeptide chain
- carboxypeptidases hydrolyse peptide bonds at the carboxyl end of a polypeptide chain.

Protein digestion begins in the stomach, where the optimum pH for hydrolysis by pepsin is 1.5 to 2.0. Here the proteins and long polypeptide chains are broken down to shorter polypeptides. In the duodenum and ileum, where the pH is alkaline, trypsin and chymotrypsin from the pancreatic juice hydrolyse the proteins to shorter polypeptides. Carboxypeptidases are present in the pancreatic juice and their action results in the production of amino acids. Aminopeptidases are present on the microvilli of the epithelial mucosa.

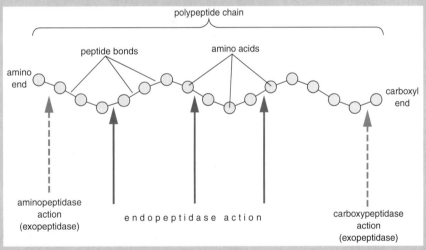

Figure 1.20 Digestion of protein involving endo- and exopeptidases

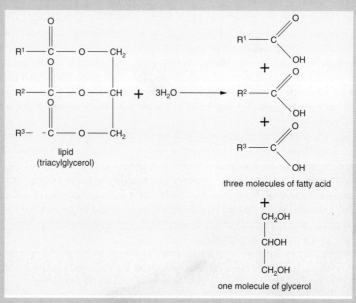

ADDITIONAL MATERIAL

Lipases

Most of the lipids in a human diet are triglycerides and, before they can be digested, they need to undergo emulsification into droplets. Bile salts from the liver, mostly sodium glycocholate and sodium taurocholate, are released into the duodenum via the bile duct from the gall bladder, where they have been stored. These salts lower the surface tension between the oil globules and water, bringing about emulsification and providing a larger surface area for the action of lipases (Figure 1.21).

Figure 1.21 Hydrolysis of lipids catalysed by lipase

Lipases are secreted by the pancreas and released into the duodenum in the pancreatic juice. They catalyse the hydrolysis of triglycerides into monoglycerides, fatty acids and glycerol.

Absorption

Most absorption occurs in the small and large intestines, although it has been shown that water and alcohol can be absorbed from the stomach. The digested food is absorbed in the small intestine and water is mostly taken up from the large intestine.

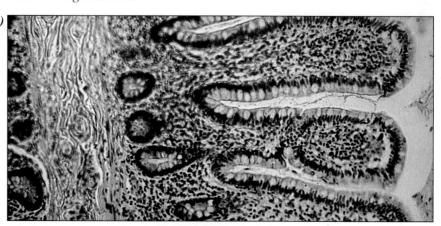

(a) microvilli

goblet cell (secretes mucus)

blood capillary

columnar epithelium

lacteal

lymph system

(b)

Figure 1.22 (a) Diagram to illustrate VS through a villus; (b) photomicrograph of a section through the ileum showing villi

The first 20 cm of the small intestine is known as the **duodenum** and it is here that the secretions from the liver and the pancreas are added. The rest of the small intestine is called the **ileum** and is about 5 m long. As has already been described, the final stages of digestion of carbohydrates, lipids and proteins take place in the duodenum and ileum, whilst at the same time the process of absorption is occurring. There are several features of this region of the gut which contribute to the efficiency of absorption.

- It is long, providing a large surface area over which absorption can occur.
- There are large numbers of finger-like projections, the **villi** (Figure 1.22), in the mucosa, increasing the surface area for absorption.
- The villi possess smooth muscle fibres, which contract and relax, mixing up the contents and bringing the columnar epithelial cells of the absorptive surface into greater contact with the digested food.
- The columnar epithelial cells possess **microvilli**, which further increase the surface area available for absorption.
- Each villus has an extensive capillary network so that the absorbed food is transported away quickly, maintaining concentration gradients.
- There is a lacteal in each villus into which absorbed fats pass.

Carbohydrates, in the form of monosaccharides, and amino acids are absorbed partly by diffusion and partly by active transport. Soon after a meal, there will be a higher concentration of monosaccharides and amino acids in the ileum, so a concentration gradient will exist and diffusion of these molecules will occur across the mucosal epithelium into the blood capillaries. This process is rather slow and will not take up all the digested food, so it is supplemented by active transport involving a sodium–potassium pump (Figure 1.23).

In the membrane of the epithelial cells is a **glucose transporter protein**, which has binding sites for both glucose molecules and sodium ions. The sodium–potassium pump actively transports sodium ions out of the cells against the electrochemical gradient. Glucose molecules and sodium ions bind to the transporter proteins and the sodium ions diffuse into the cells along their electrochemical gradient, carrying the glucose molecules with them. Inside the cells, the glucose molecules and sodium ions dissociate from the transporter protein, the glucose concentration of the cell increases and glucose moves into the blood by facilitated diffusion. Similar mechanisms exist for the active uptake of dipeptides and amino acids.

DEFINITION

A **lacteal** is a lymph capillary which is present in a villus. The products of lipid digestion, fatty acids and glycerol, pass into the lacteals and from there into the rest of the lymphatic system, eventually entering the bloodstream via a duct in the neck region.

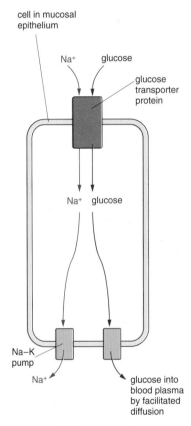

Figure 1.23 Diagram to illustrate glucose transporter protein and sodium–potassium pump in operation in a mucosal epithelial cell

> ## ADDITIONAL MATERIAL
>
> ### Digestion and absorption of fats
>
> The absorption of the products of fat digestion, namely fatty acids and glycerol, involves a different mechanism. If the fatty acids are short, they can diffuse directly into the blood from the epithelial cells. The longer chain fatty acids, monoglycerides and glycerol diffuse into the epithelial cells of the mucosa, where they recombine to form fats. The fatty acids and monoglycerides have polar heads and non-polar tails, so they tend to clump together to form spherical structures, called **micelles**, in the lumen of the gut. Within a micelle, the non-polar tails point towards the middle and the polar heads are on the outside. Micelles can diffuse into the mucosal epithelial cells, but do so more slowly than single fatty acids. The molecules of fat diffuse into the lacteals, where they become coated with proteins present in the lymph to form droplets of lipoprotein called **chylomicrons**. These droplets are passed into the bloodstream from the lymph, where they are hydrolysed back into fatty acids and glycerol by an enzyme present in the blood plasma. They are then transported in the blood, from where they may be taken up and used as respiratory substrates by cells or stored as fat.
>
> Mineral ions, vitamins and water are also absorbed from the contents of the duodenum and the ileum. Any remaining mineral ions and large amounts of water are absorbed from the food residues as they pass through the large intestine. Present also in this region are large numbers of bacteria which synthesise amino acids and vitamins, some of which are of use to humans and can be taken up and absorbed into the bloodstream.

Histology of the ileum wall

The structure of the ileum wall is similar to the general structure of the alimentary canal shown in Figure 1.15 on page 15. More detail, including the structure of a villus, is shown in Figure 1.22 on page 20. In the ileum region, the surface layer of the mucosa consists of columnar epithelial cells with large numbers of mucus-secreting goblet cells and the submucosa contains large amounts of lymphoid tissue.

It is relevant to note that the constant passage of food through the ileum damages the tips of the villi and cells are lost from the mucosa. These cells are replaced by cells from the bottom of the crypts of Lieberkühn situated at the base of the villi. These cells migrate to the surface and gradually move up the villus, eventually being shed from the tip. New cells are produced by mitotic divisions of the crypt cells. It has been estimated that between 50 and 200 g of the intestinal mucosa are renewed every day in an adult human. It takes from 5 to 7 days for a cell from the bottom of the crypt to move up to the tip of a villus.

PRACTICAL

Ventilation movements in an insect

Introduction

The aim of this practical is to measure and record the ventilation rate in an insect, and to investigate some of the factors which influence this rate. Locusts are suitable insects to use for this investigation and will be unharmed by the procedure.

Materials

- Adult (or 5th stage hopper) locust
- Transparent plastic 20 cm³ syringe. If syringes are not available, a boiling tube fitted with a cotton wool plug and a drinking straw makes a suitable alternative
- Cotton wool
- Rubber or PVC tubing
- Stop clock
- Access to a refrigerator

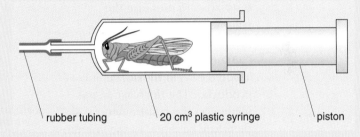

Figure 1.24 Apparatus for investigating ventilation in a locust

rubber tubing   20 cm³ plastic syringe   piston

Method

1 Place a locust in a plastic syringe as shown in Figure 1.24. Carefully insert the piston and push this in gently so that the locust cannot move.
2 Observe the locust and count the number of ventilation movements of the abdomen which occur during 30 seconds. Record the results of three successive counts.
3 Attach a length of tubing to the syringe, remove the piston and replace with a plug of cotton wool so that the locust cannot escape. Breathe gently out through the tube for 10 to 15 seconds, then count ventilation movements as in step 2.
4 Remove the cotton wool plug and replace with the piston. Carefully move the piston in and out to replace the air in the syringe with fresh air.
5 Count and record the ventilation movements as before, then place the syringe in a refrigerator at about 5°C for 15 minutes. Finally, count and record the ventilation movements.

Results and discussion

1 Record all your results in a table.
2 Formulate a hypothesis about the composition of the air and the ventilation rate of the locust.
3 Which factors changed when you breathed onto the locust?
4 How could you reduce these variables?
5 Explain the effect of reducing the temperature on the ventilation rate.

Using a simple respirometer

Introduction

A respirometer is used to measure either the volume of carbon dioxide produced or the volume of oxygen consumed by living organisms. There are many different types of respirometer, which vary in complexity from a simple respirometer to elaborate and sensitive types which can be used to measure minute volumes of gas.

One of the problems in respirometry is that gas volumes are influenced by changes in temperature and pressure. Therefore, it is important to control and make allowances for these variables if meaningful results are to be obtained. The respirometer shown in Figure 1.25 consists of two tubes; one contains the respiring material or organisms, the other acts as a thermobarometer and compensates for small changes in temperature or pressure. If the air in this tube expands or contracts it will oppose similar changes in the respiration tube. Differences in the level of the manometer fluid are therefore due only to respiratory activity.

If we wish to measure the volume of oxygen used in respiration, the respirometer contains a substance which absorbs carbon dioxide as it is produced. The decrease in gas volume in the respirometer will therefore be equal to the volume of oxygen used. Substances which absorb carbon dioxide include potassium hydroxide and soda lime.

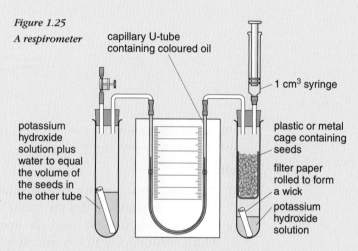

Figure 1.25
A respirometer

capillary U-tube containing coloured oil

1 cm³ syringe

potassium hydroxide solution plus water to equal the volume of the seeds in the other tube

plastic or metal cage containing seeds

filter paper rolled to form a wick

potassium hydroxide solution

CORROSIVE
Potassium
hydroxide

CAUTION:

Great care should be exercised when using these substances – potassium hydroxide in particular is corrosive – gloves and safety glasses should be worn when handling it.

Materials

- Respirometer
- Germinating barley grains or pea seeds
- Potassium hydroxide solution, 15 per cent w/v
- Filter paper
- Manometer fluid (Brodie's fluid)
- Water bath and thermometer

Method

1 Carefully pour about 5 cm³ of potassium hydroxide solution into each tube of the respirometer, or add about 5 g of soda lime granules. If you use potassium hydroxide solution, be careful not to allow it to touch the sides of the tubes. If you spill potassium hydroxide solution onto your skin or clothes, wash it off immediately with cold water.

2 Fill the wire or plastic basket with germinating seeds and place in one vessel, ensuring that the seeds do not come into contact with the potassium hydroxide solution.

PRACTICAL

3 Fill another basket with an equivalent volume of glass beads and place in the other tube.

4 Carefully draw Brodie's fluid into the manometer tube so that it comes about half-way up the scale on either side. It is very important that there are no air bubbles in the manometer fluid.

5 Remove the syringe and screw clip, then connect the manometer to both tubes.

6 Stand the respirometer in a water bath at 20 °C with the manometer outside the water bath.

7 Leave the respirometer for at least 5 minutes to equilibrate. Adjust the piston of the syringe so that it is at about the 0.5 cm^3 mark, then connect to the respirometer as shown in the diagram. Close the screw clip.

8 Use the syringe to adjust the manometer fluid so that the levels are equal on both sides.

9 Record the positions of the syringe piston, the level of the manometer fluid and the time.

10 Record the level of the manometer fluid at suitable time intervals. How frequently you need to take readings will depend on the respiration rate of the organisms you are using.

11 When the manometer fluid reaches the end of the scale, the syringe can be used to return the fluid to its original level.

12 Repeat the experiment at 30 °C and 40 °C, recording your results carefully each time.

13 When you have completed the experiment, record the mass of living material.

Results and discussion

1 Plot a graph of manometer readings against time for each set of results at a particular temperature.

2 If the graph is a straight line, what does it indicate about the rate of respiration at a particular temperature?

3 You can use the syringe to calibrate the respirometer and then calculate the respiration rate. This should be expressed as mm^3 of oxygen used per milligram of living material per hour (mm^3 oxygen mg^{-1} hr^{-1}).

4 What effect did increasing the temperature have on the respiration rate? How could this effect be expressed quantitatively?

PRACTICAL

Measuring vital capacity

Introduction

The vital capacity (maximum volume of air which can be expired following maximal inspiration) of a person can be measured simply by using a suitably calibrated glass bell jar, supported in a sink of water (Figure 1.26).

Materials

- Large (5 dm^3) calibrated bell jar
- Wide diameter rubber or PVC tubing
- Suitable supports for the bell jar

> **Estimated vital capacities**
>
> For males: 2.6 dm^3 m^{-2} body surface area
>
> For females: 2.1 dm^3 m^{-2} body surface area

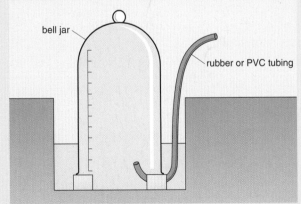

Figure 1.26 *Method for determining the vital capacity*

EXCHANGES WITH THE ENVIRONMENT

Method

1 First calibrate the bell jar by inverting it and pouring in known volumes of water. Use a marker pen to graduate the jar.
2 Fill the jar and invert into a large sink filled with water. Support the jar on suitable blocks.
3 If available, use a standing waste so that the sink is about two-thirds full.
4 Each student then uses the tubing and, following maximal inspiration, exhales as far as possible into the jar.
5 The vital capacity can then be recorded.

Results and discussion

NB: When investigating physiological parameters, it should be noted that there is always variation from person to person. The data should therefore be interpreted with care as there are many factors which can influence the results obtained.

1 Record class results in a suitable table.
2 Is there a consistent difference between the vital capacity of males and females ? If so, can this be quantified?
3 Investigate the effect of posture on vital capacity and suggest reasons for the results.
4 If available, use a surface area nomogram to determine your body surface area and, using the relationship in the margin above, calculate your estimated vital capacity. Suggest reasons for any differences there may be.

Transport systems

The need for transport systems

In addition to the exchange of materials between an organism and its environment, which was discussed at the beginning of Chapter 1, there is the need for materials to be transported within the organism. Oxygen and nutrients need to be transported from their place of uptake to the respiring cells; carbon dioxide and other waste products must be removed. In green plants, water and mineral ions needed for photosynthesis are taken up by the roots and need to be transported to the leaves, where light and carbon dioxide are absorbed. The resulting organic compounds must be transported away from their site of synthesis to other regions for use in metabolic activities or for storage. The transport system in flowering plants consists of the vascular tissue, composed of xylem and phloem.

In mammals, absorption of the digested food takes place in the small intestine, from where it is transported to the liver and then to the respiring cells. Absorption of oxygen and removal of carbon dioxide occurs in the lungs, so a transport system is needed to deliver oxygen to the respiring cells and to remove carbon dioxide.

In many small organisms, efficient internal transport of all materials can be achieved through diffusion or active transport, because the distances involved are small and, where diffusion is concerned, the concentration gradients are favourable. In larger organisms, the distances between the different parts are too large and these processes are too slow. In addition, larger animals tend to be more active than smaller animals, leading to greater metabolic activity and a consequent need for a faster supply of oxygen and nutrients to the respiring cells.

In the Kingdom Animalia, Phylum Cnidaria, an adequate supply of oxygen can be supplied to respiring cells by diffusion alone. For example, in *Hydra* (Figure 2.1), a cnidarian frequently found clinging to water plants in freshwater habitats, the body wall consists of two layers of cells: the ectoderm and the endoderm. Water enters the body cavity and circulates so both the layers of cells are in contact with the water, from which oxygen is obtained by diffusion.

In the Phylum Platyhelminthes (flatworms), the body consists of three layers of cells: the ectoderm on the outside, the mesoderm in the middle and the endoderm surrounding the gut cavity. These animals, though much more complex than *Hydra*, do not have a special transport system as their bodies are flattened and the gut, when present, is much branched. In *Planaria* (Figure 2.2), a free-living flatworm of the Class Turbellaria, gaseous exchange occurs by diffusion over the external surface of the organism and the products of digestion can diffuse from the much branched gut to all the respiring cells. Other members of this phylum, such as the flukes (Class Trematoda) and the tapeworms (Class Cestoda) are internal parasites of vertebrates and do not possess a gut. They absorb their nutrients by diffusion over their body surface.

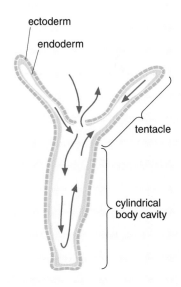

Figure 2.1 Hydra *showing two-layered body wall (the arrows indicate the circulation of water)*

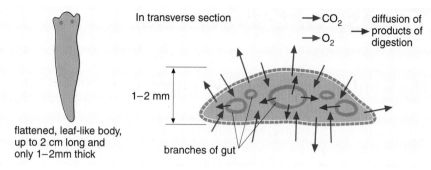

Figure 2.2 Planaria *showing flattened body and diffusion paths of oxygen and nutrients*

In all the other animal phyla, internal transport systems are present. These usually consist of a fluid, blood, which is pumped around the body by one or more muscular structures called hearts. The blood is either pumped through a system of internal spaces, as in the open circulation of arthropods and molluscs, or through a continuous system of closed tubes, the blood vessels, in the closed circulation of vertebrates.

In the open circulatory system of an insect (Figure 2.3), the blood leaves the head region and enters spaces called **sinuses**, where it bathes the body organs. The blood is under relatively low pressure and there are valves which, together with waves of contraction of the muscular heart, maintain the movement of the blood back towards the head region, where the circulation starts again.

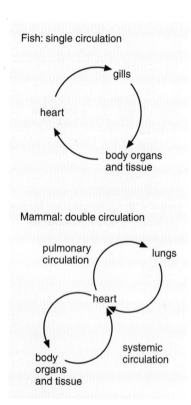

Figure 2.4 *Fish and mammal circulations – to show differences between single and double circulatory systems*

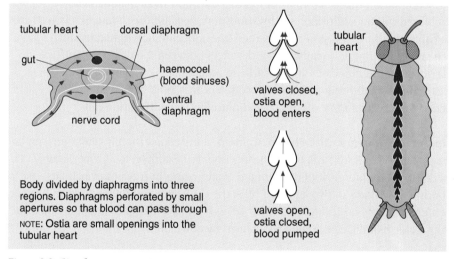

Figure 2.3 *Circulatory system in an insect*

Types of circulatory system

There are two types of closed circulatory system (Figure 2.4):

- **single circulations** – present in fish, in which blood is pumped from the heart to the gills, then to the rest of the body before being returned to the heart
- **double circulations** – typical of mammals, where blood is pumped from the heart to the lungs and back to the heart in a pulmonary circulation, followed by the systemic circulation in which the blood is pumped from the heart to the body organs and back to the heart.

The concept of mass flow

Mass flow, alternatively known as bulk flow, is thought to account for the long-distance transport of fluids in living organisms. The fluid, together with any substances dissolved or suspended in it, moves in bulk, in response to a pressure gradient. This can be illustrated by considering the flow of liquid up a drinking straw. The person sucking the drinking straw lowers the pressure at the top end, which causes the liquid to move from a high pressure to a lower pressure area. In plants, movement of water and mineral ions up the xylem from the roots to the leaves is largely brought about by the evaporation of water from the leaves. This causes a lowering of the pressure at the top of the plant and does not involve metabolic energy.

Transport in flowering plants

In flowering plants, water, mineral ions and organic solutes are transported from their sites of uptake or synthesis to where they are used or, in the case of water, removed. This transport can occur over short distances from cell to cell, or over greater distances involving the vascular tissue, which is specialised for conducting water and solutes. Movement of substances from cell to cell may involve diffusion or active transport.

The structure of the vascular tissues

The vascular tissues are the **xylem** and **phloem**, both of which are composed of several distinct types of cells.

Water and mineral ions are transported from the roots to the aerial parts of the plant in the xylem tissue. This tissue may contain:
- vessels
- tracheids
- fibres
- xylem parenchyma.

Tracheids, fibres and vessels become lignified during their development, losing their living contents.

Tracheids are characteristic of conifer wood and vessels are found only in flowering plants. Both the tracheids and the vessels provide conducting tissue for the water and mineral ions, in addition to contributing support. The fibres found in xylem tissue are very similar to those found in sclerenchyma tissue in leaves and other non-woody structures. They have no conducting function, but contribute significantly to the strength of the tissue.

Tracheids (Figure 2.5) are elongated single cells with lignified walls and tapered ends. As they develop, they lose their living contents, so the lumen of each cell is empty when mature. The thickening of lignin may take the form of rings, spirals, scalariform (consisting of interconnecting bars of lignin) or reticulate (more connections than scalariform), similar to those found in vessels. Typically, tracheids have bordered pits, allowing the rapid transport of water from cell to cell.

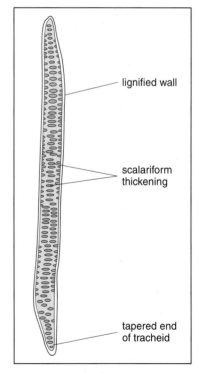

lignified wall

scalariform thickening

tapered end of tracheid

Figure 2.5 Tracheid structure

Vessels (Figure 2.6) are found abundantly in the xylem of flowering plants and are long tubular structures with lignified walls. The vessels are formed by the joining of vessel segments, or vessel elements, end to end, the end walls of each vessel segment breaking down and leaving a perforation plate. The lignification can occur as rings, spirals, scalariform or reticulate, as described for tracheids. The rings and spirals occur more frequently in the first-formed xylem, thus allowing for the limited amount of stretching which might occur in young structures.

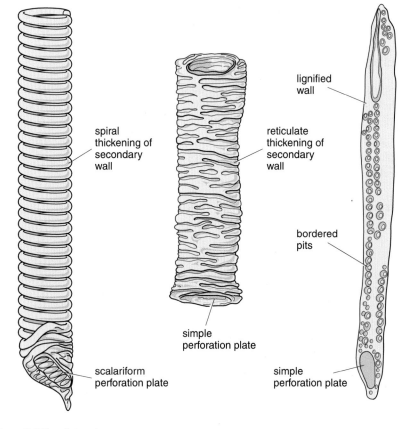

Figure 2.6 Vessel structure

Organic solutes, which are the products of photosynthesis, are transported from their sites of synthesis in the leaves to other regions of the plants through the phloem. This tissue also contains four types of cells:

* sieve tube elements
* companion cells
* phloem fibres
* phloem parenchyma.

The sieve tube elements and companion cells (Figure 2.7) are involved in the long-distance transport of the organic solutes. The phloem parenchyma may serve as packing tissue, but some cells become modified to form **transfer cells**, which are responsible for the loading of the sieve tube cells and thus achieve the transport of the organic molecules over short distances.

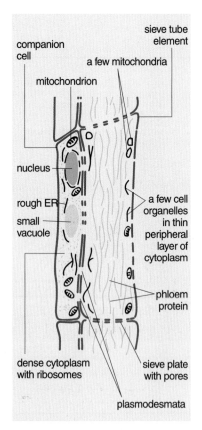

Figure 2.7 Sieve tube element and companion cell

Sieve tube elements are highly specialised living cells, linked end to end to form sieve tubes. The end walls of each of the sieve tube elements are perforated by sieve plates, so that long conducting tubes are formed. During development, each sieve tube element loses its nucleus and ribosomes, the vacuolar membrane breaks down and the remaining organelles, consisting of a few mitochondria and plastids, are distributed around the periphery of the cell. The cell surface membrane remains intact and large amounts of a special phloem protein, referred to as as **P-protein**, are formed. This protein may be organised into fibrils and it occupies most of the interior of the cell. It is not known precisely how the fibrils are arranged.

The contents of the sieve tubes are under high hydrostatic pressure, so that when specimens of tissue are observed, it is difficult to know whether the organelles have been disturbed by the sudden release of this pressure during preparation. In some preparations, the P-protein is seen to be blocking the pores in the sieve plates, whilst in others it does not. Another material, called **callose**, an insoluble polysaccharide, is often found deposited around the sieve plates. Again, it is difficult to know whether this material is found naturally in such situations or whether it is an artefact, formed during the procedures undergone in the preparation of the specimens. Callose is known to be formed when tissue is damaged.

Companion cells are closely associated with the sieve tube elements. Each companion cell is derived from the same parent cell as its neighbouring sieve tube element. In contrast with the sieve tube elements, companion cells retain their nuclei, ribosomes and other organelles. The cytoplasm is dense and there are large numbers of mitochondria, indicating the potential for high levels of metabolic activity. There are numerous plasmodesmata connecting the cytoplasm of the companion cell with its neighbouring sieve tube element. It is suggested that the companion cells may provide replacement P-protein, enzymes and energy for activators of the sieve tube elements. Some companion cells appear to act as transfer cells and are involved in the movement of solutes into and out of the sieve tubes.

The general function of the transfer cells (Figure 2.8) appears to be the collection and transfer of organic solutes and inorganic ions into the sieve tubes. The inner walls of these cells are much folded and there are large numbers of mitochondria close to the folds. The folding increases the surface area available for the uptake of ions and solutes and the large numbers of mitochondria are able to supply the adenosine triphosphate (ATP) necessary for the active transport which is involved.

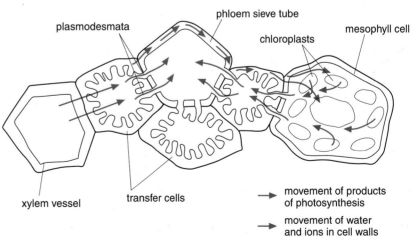

Figure 2.8 Transfer cells

Movement of water
Water relations of plant cells

Plant cells, such as those in the epidermis and cortex regions of the roots, have living contents surrounded by a plasma membrane and a thick, relatively inelastic cellulose cell wall. The cell wall confers special properties on these cells as it resists the osmotic uptake of water. A plant cell placed in distilled water will not swell up and burst, but will take up water until the pressure exerted by the cell wall prevents any further expansion. A plant cell in this condition is said to be **fully turgid**. Turgor is important for maintaining mechanical support in plants and, if plant cells lose water, the plant may wilt.

We use the term **water potential** to describe the force acting on water molecules in a solution, when separated from pure water by a membrane which is impermeable to water only. Water potential is given the symbol ψ (Greek psi) and is measured in units of pressure, kilopascals (kPa). By definition, the water potential of pure water is zero. Adding a solute, such as sucrose, to pure water will decrease the water potential: it becomes negative. The more solute molecules present in a solution, the lower (or more negative) the water potential becomes. This change in water potential due to the presence of a solute is referred to as the **solute potential** and is given the symbol ψ_s.

Plant cells contain various solutes, such as sugars, which will exert a solute potential, so plant cells placed in distilled water will tend to take up water. This uptake is opposed by the pressure exerted by the cell wall. This pressure is known as the **pressure potential**, given the symbol ψ_p, and because it opposes the solute potential, it usually has a positive value. The overall water relationships of a plant can be summarised in the following equation:

$$\psi = \psi_s + \psi_p$$

water potential = solute potential + pressure potential

In plant tissues, water always tends to move, by osmosis, from a region of high water potential to a region of low water potential, down a water potential gradient.

In a fully turgid cell, the overall water potential of the cell is zero because the values of ψ_s and ψ_p are equal and opposite, so they cancel each other out. If a turgid cell is placed in a concentrated sugar solution, water will leave the cell because the solute potential of the sugar solution is much lower (more negative) than the water potential of the cell. As the cell loses water, the volume of the cell decreases and eventually the plasma membrane may lose contact with the cellulose cell wall. In this condition, the cell is said to be **plasmolysed**. The point at which the plasma membrane is just about to lose contact with the cell wall is known as the point of incipient plasmolysis. At this point, the potential pressure is zero, so the water potential of the cell is equal to its solute potential. Plasmolysis can be induced experimentally by placing suitable cells, such as small pieces of epidermis from a rhubarb petiole, into concentrated sugar solutions, but it does not occur under natural conditions.

The structure of a dicotyledonous root

Before describing the process of water uptake, it is important to understand the structure of the root and the pathways involved in water transport. A transverse section of a young dicotyledonous root is shown in Figure 2.9.

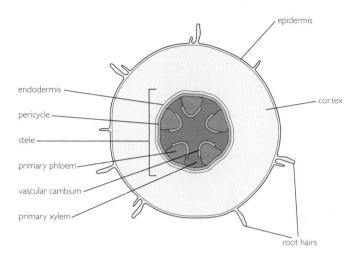

Figure 2.9 Transverse section of young Ranunculus *root*

The layer of cells around the outside of the root is the **epidermis**. Some epidermal cells develop projections called **root hairs**. The central part of the root contains the conduction tissues of the plant: the **xylem** and **phloem**. The xylem tissue provides a continuous system for the transport of water and dissolved mineral salts from the root, through the stem to the leaves. The function of the phloem is the transport of organic solutes, including sucrose which is formed in photosynthesis. The xylem and phloem are surrounded by a layer of cells known as the **pericycle**. The vascular tissues and their surrounding pericycle form a cylinder of conducting cells called the stele. Just around the outside of the **stele** is a layer of cells called the **endodermis**, which, as described later, has an important role in water movement in the plant.

Between the endodermis and the epidermis, there are several layers of relatively large, thin-walled cells forming the **cortex**. The cell walls of the cortical cells are highly permeable to water and dissolved solutes. There are also air spaces in the cortex which are important to allow oxygen to diffuse into the root for cell respiration.

Uptake of water

Water is taken up mainly by the younger parts of the roots (Figure 2.10), in the region of the root hairs. These are long projections (up to 15 mm) from the epidermal cells which extend among soil particles and serve to increase greatly the surface area for water uptake. The concentration of solutes, such as ions, is very low in the soil water of most soils, so the water potential of this water is close to zero. The solute potentials of plant cells are usually between about −500 and −3000 kPa, so there is a water potential gradient between root hair cells and soil water, and therefore water will be taken up by osmosis.

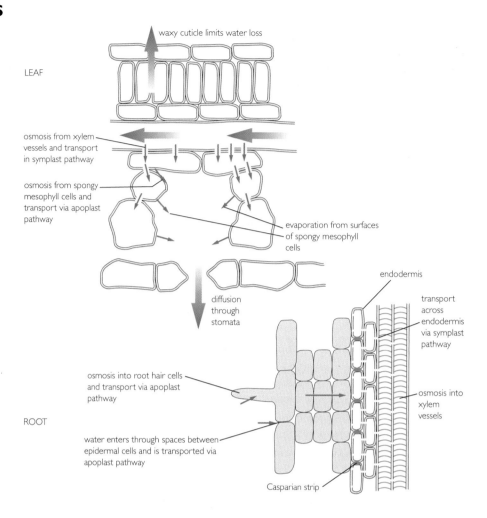

Figure 2.10 The transpiration stream showing uptake of water in a root and loss by evaporation from the leaf

There are three ways in which water moves across the cortex of the root from the epidermis to the central tissues (Figure 2.11). These are:

- the **apoplast** pathway, in which water passes through the continuous system of adjacent cell walls
- the **symplast** pathway, in which water moves through the cytoplasm from cell to cell (the cytoplasm of adjacent cells in the cortex is in contact via the plasmodesmata, which are fine channels through the cell walls)
- the **vacuolar** pathway, in which water moves from vacuole to vacuole.

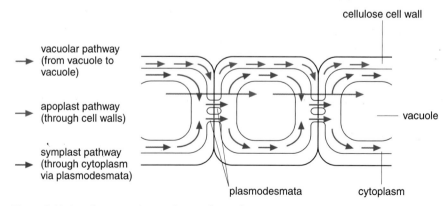

Figure 2.11 Apoplast, symplast and vacuolar pathways

However, when water reaches the endodermal cells its movement is stopped by a waterproof layer in the cell walls, called the **Casparian strip**. This is impregnated with suberin, a waxy compound, which is impermeable to water. Water is therefore prevented from passing around the endodermal cells through the cell walls, but instead it must pass through the plasma membrane and cell contents. It is believed that, in this way, endodermal cells are able to regulate the movement of water and dissolved mineral salts from the soil into the xylem.

Water moves through a plant from the root hairs, where uptake occurs, through the root to the stem and leaves, where most of it is lost as water vapour in the process of **transpiration**. The continual evaporation of water from the aerial parts of the flowering plant into the atmosphere is due to a water potential gradient which exists between the soil and the atmosphere (Figure 2.12). The root hairs are in contact with the soil water, which has a high water potential, and the leaves and stems are exposed to the atmosphere, which has a much lower water potential. Consequently, there is a tendency for water to be drawn through and lost from the plant. This movement of water is a passive process. As water evaporates from the aerial parts of the plant, it changes from a liquid to a vapour. This change of state requires heat energy, referred to as the **latent heat of vaporisation**.

Water vapour may be lost from three sites on the aerial parts of the plant:
- leaves (cuticle, stomata)
- flowers
- stems (herbaceous, lenticels on woody stems).

Most of the water vapour loss occurs through the stomata, which are open during the day, allowing for the exchange of gases in photosynthesis. Evaporation through the cuticle, which accounts for about 10 per cent of the total water loss, will vary with its thickness. The amount of evaporation through the lenticels is very small, but this is the main way in which water is lost from the stems of deciduous trees after leaf fall.

The transpiration stream
Most of the water lost by a plant is in the form of water vapour. Evaporation occurs from the cellulose cell walls of the mesophyll cells into the intercellular spaces, from where it diffuses out through the stomata, from a high water potential inside the leaf to a lower water potential outside. In dicotyledonous plants, there are usually larger numbers of stomata on the lower surfaces of leaves than on the upper, but in monocotyledonous plants like the grasses, with long, narrow leaves, the stomata are evenly distributed on both leaf surfaces.

Water reaches the mesophyll cells from the xylem of the vascular bundles in the leaf veins. At their extreme ends, these veins consist of little more than one or two vessels with little lignification, so water can easily pass to the adjacent mesophyll via the apoplast, symplast or vacuolar pathways.

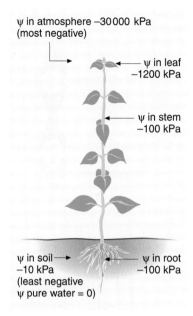

ψ in atmosphere $-30\,000$ kPa (most negative)

ψ in leaf -1200 kPa

ψ in stem -100 kPa

ψ in soil -10 kPa (least negative ψ pure water = 0)

ψ in root -100 kPa

Figure 2.12 Water potential differences between soil and atmosphere

TRANSPORT SYSTEMS

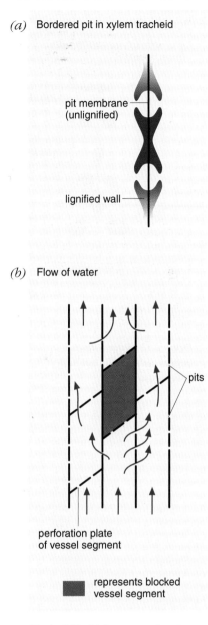

(a) Bordered pit in xylem tracheid

pit membrane
(unlignified)

lignified wall

(b) Flow of water

pits

perforation plate
of vessel segment

represents blocked
vessel segment

*Figure 2.13 (a) Structure of a pit;
(b) sideways flow of water through
the xylem*

The cohesion–tension theory

Removal of water from the xylem in the veins of the leaf creates a pulling force which draws water through the vascular tissue from the roots to the stem in continuous columns. The maintenance of these continuous columns is due to the structure of the xylem tissue and the properties of water. The **cohesion–tension theory** was put forward to account for the movement of water through the plant, bearing in mind the nature of the xylem tissue, the large quantities of water involved and the distances over which the transport was required.

In the xylem tissue, **tracheids** and **vessels** are the main conducting cells. Tracheids are dead, elongated cells with lignified walls and tapered ends. Their walls are pitted, that is, they possess unlignified areas consisting of just the middle lamella and the remains of the primary cell wall. Vessels consist of columns of cells, called vessel segments, joined end to end, each with a lignified, pitted wall and no cell contents. The end walls of these segments break down during development, forming a long tube. Both tracheids and vessels have strong, rigid walls, which are able to withstand tension, and are small in diameter. There is an attraction between the water molecules and the walls of these cells (**adhesion**) and the water molecules stick to the walls. There are also strong forces between the water molecules (**cohesion**), which play a major role in maintaining the continuity of the water columns in the tissue.

Water columns under such tension are sometimes broken through wounding, entry of air, or pressure decreasing. Water will vaporise and the affected vessel will develop an air bubble, which blocks water movement. Due to the presence of pits, enabling the sideways movement of water, the affected vessel may be bypassed (Figure 2.13). The pit membrane gets pushed against the pit aperture and prevents the air bubble passing from one vessel to another.

Water movement in the xylem can be affected to some extent by **root pressure**. If the shoot of a plant is cut off close to the ground, sap will exude from the xylem tissue of the stump. This process occurs because ions are still being taken up actively by the roots and there is also osmotic uptake of water into the xylem. It can be demonstrated that a positive hydrostatic pressure of about 150 kPa may be generated by root pressure, so although it could not account for all the water movement in the xylem, it may have a contributory role. It has been suggested that air bubbles in the xylem of herbaceous plants may be removed by root pressure occurring when transpiration ceases at night.

Stomata and their role in transport

Stomata are pores in the epidermis of leaves, flowers and herbaceous stems through which exchange of gases occurs. They are found most frequently on leaves and may occur on both surfaces, but are more common on the lower (abaxial) surface. Surrounding each pore are two **guard cells** (Figure 2.14), which control the size of the opening by changes in their turgidity. The guard cells are usually kidney-shaped, but in grasses they are dumb-bell-shaped. The adjacent epidermal cells are often arranged in a characteristic pattern and are referred to as **subsidiary cells**. The guard cells are different from the rest of the epidermal cells in that they contain chloroplasts, they are not linked to adjacent cells by plasmodesmata and their walls are unevenly thickened. The part of the cellulose cell wall which borders the pore is thicker, and also less elastic, than the opposite wall. As water is taken into the guard cells, increasing their turgidity, they become more curved and the pore between them opens wider. When the guard cells lose turgidity, they become less curved and the pore closes.

(a)

(b)

(c)

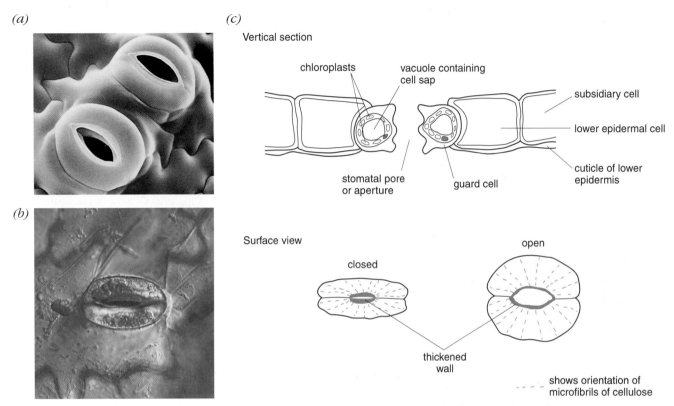

Vertical section

chloroplasts

vacuole containing cell sap

subsidiary cell

lower epidermal cell

stomatal pore or aperture

guard cell

cuticle of lower epidermis

Surface view

closed

open

thickened wall

- - - - shows orientation of microfibrils of cellulose

*Figure 2.14 Stomatal structure – (a) scanning electronmicrograph of open stomata on the leaf of a tobacco plant (*Nicotiana tabacum*); (b) light micrograph of closed stomata on the leaf of a broad bean (*Vica faba*); (c) vertical section and surface view.*

The chemiosmotic mechanism of stomatal opening and closing

Concurrent with the opening of a stoma, there is a considerable increase in the concentration of solutes in the guard cells, causing the water potential to become more negative (lower) (Figure 2.15). This causes water to move into the cells and the **turgor pressure** increases. Investigations of the concentrations of different ions in the guard cells of open and closed stomata have shown that, as the stoma opens, there is a steep rise in the concentration of potassium ions and chloride ions. The first stage in this process is thought to involve the removal of hydrogen ions from the guard cells due to the action of a **proton pump**. An electrochemical gradient builds up across the guard cell membrane and the potassium ions diffuse in passively. Due to the active removal of hydrogen ions, the pH inside the guard cell increases, whilst that outside decreases.

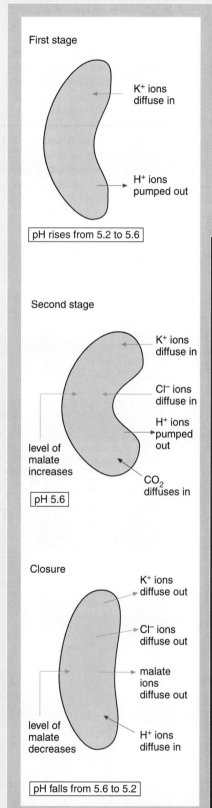

First stage

K+ ions diffuse in

H+ ions pumped out

pH rises from 5.2 to 5.6

Second stage

K+ ions diffuse in

Cl− ions diffuse in

H+ ions pumped out

CO₂ diffuses in

level of malate increases

pH 5.6

Closure

K+ ions diffuse out

Cl− ions diffuse out

malate ions diffuse out

level of malate decreases

H+ ions diffuse in

pH falls from 5.6 to 5.2

ADDITIONAL MATERIAL

To control the intracellular pH, there is a second stage to the process, which involves the inward diffusion of chloride ions, either as a result of the change in pH or linked with hydrogen ion uptake. In addition, there is an increase in the amount of malate in the guard cell. It is thought that the increase in pH activates the enzyme phosphoenolpyruvate carboxylase (PEP carboxylase), which catalyses the fixation of carbon dioxide to produce oxaloacetic acid. The oxaloacetic acid can be reduced to malic acid, which dissociates, providing malate ions to balance the potassium ions and hydrogen ions for the proton pump. Starch stored in the guard cells provides the pyruvate, which is first converted to phosphoenolpyruvate before carbon dioxide fixation occurs.

Figure 2.15 The chemiosmotic mechanism of stomatal opening and closing

A number of factors influence the opening and closing of the stomata. These include the prevailing light conditions, the supply of water to the plant and the supply of respiratory substrates. In plants that are well supplied with water, the stomata open at dawn and close at dusk and this pattern appears to be controlled by light and the amount of carbon dioxide in the intercellular spaces of the leaves. Photosynthesis is initiated by light and, as soon as the process begins, there will be a decrease in the amount of carbon dioxide in the leaf. It has been observed that low concentrations of carbon dioxide in the leaves promote stomatal opening and high concentrations bring about stomatal closure. Although it has been possible to show that the guard cells are sensitive to different levels of carbon dioxide, the precise mechanism of how this might cause stomatal opening is not known.

It is quite common for stomatal closure to occur around midday in leafy trees. When air temperatures are high and the humidity is low, transpiration is high and water loss may exceed water uptake, so this pattern of closure could avoid air locks in the xylem vessels impeding the transpiration stream. This pattern of closure appears to be controlled by external factors, but if wilting is imminent, the stomata close rapidly. Under these circumstances, the decrease in turgor of the leaf cells triggers the synthesis of a plant growth inhibitor, **abscisic acid** (ABA), in the chloroplasts. If the level of ABA is sufficiently high, it affects the cell surface membrane of the guard cells, preventing the proton pump from operating and bringing about closure of the stomata. As soon as more water is available to the plant, the ABA is broken down.

Factors affecting the rate of transpiration

The rate of transpiration can be affected by environmental factors and also by a number of structural or internal features of the plants. The environmental factors include:

- light
- temperature
- humidity
- air movements.

Light affects the rate of transpiration because the size of the stomatal aperture is controlled by light. As stomata open in the morning, the rate of transpiration increases, decreasing at dusk when the stomata close. Some transpiration may occur through the cuticle, referred to as **cuticular transpiration**, when stomata are closed.

The rate of transpiration increases with an increase in **temperature**, because higher temperatures cause water to evaporate more rapidly from the cell walls of the mesophyll tissue. This increases the concentration of water vapour molecules in the air spaces in the leaf. Warmer temperatures also lower the humidity of the air outside the leaf, thus increasing the difference in water potential between the leaf and the atmosphere, so water will diffuse out more rapidly.

The water vapour pressure, or **humidity**, of the atmosphere has an effect on the rate of transpiration. If the humidity is low, the air is relatively dry and there is a steeper diffusion gradient between the external atmosphere and the atmosphere inside the leaf, so the rate of transpiration is higher. If the humidity is high, the air is more saturated with water vapour molecules and the converse applies.

In still air, 'shells' of air saturated with water vapour molecules are built up around the leaves, with the effect of reducing the rate of transpiration as the diffusion gradients are less steep. Any air movement can disturb these shells, moving the water vapour molecules away from the surface of the leaves and thus creating steeper diffusion gradients.

Internal factors which affect the transpiration rate include:
- the surface area of the leaf – the greater the surface area, the higher the rate of transpiration
- the thickness of the cuticle – a thick cuticle reduces the rate of cuticular transpiration
- stomatal density – the greater the number of stomata per unit area of leaf, the greater the rate of transpiration.

Many plants living in dry conditions show adaptations which have the effect of reducing the rate of transpiration and thus conserving water. Such plants are referred to as **xerophytes** and their adaptations as **xeromorphic**. The adaptations shown by some xerophytic plants are described in Chapter 3.

Movement of nutrients
Uptake of mineral ions, their transport and circulation
Mineral ion uptake in flowering plants takes place at the roots, the ions being absorbed along with water from the soil solution. Small amounts of ions can be also absorbed by the leaves from rainwater. Most of the uptake occurs in the root hair region of young roots (Figure 2.16), where there is a large surface area available for efficient uptake. The uptake of most ions is an active process,

> **QUESTION**
> What combination of environmental factors causes the highest rate of transpiration?

> **QUESTION**
> What additional features are typical of the leaves of xerophytes?

against a concentration gradient, as the majority of ions needed are present in higher concentrations in the root cells than they are in the soil solution. Ions may diffuse in passively by mass flow through the apoplast, if their concentration outside the roots is higher than their concentration within the cells. This situation occurs in the case of calcium ions, which are nearly always in higher concentrations in the soil solution than in the root cells.

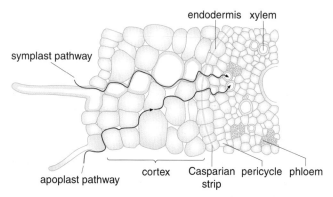

Figure 2.16 Anatomical aspects of symplastic and apoplastic pathways of ion absorption in the root hair region. The symplastic pathway involves transport through the cytosol (stippled) of each cell all the way to the non-living xylem. The apoplastic pathway involves movement through the cell wall network as far as the Casparian strip, then movement through the symplasm. Casparian strip of endodermis is shown only as it would appear in end walls.

Active transport requires a supply of energy to drive proton pumps in the cell surface membrane. Hydrogen ions are pumped out of the cells across the cell surface membrane, creating electrochemical gradients for selective ion uptake by specific transport proteins or carriers. Once inside the root cells, the ions are transported across the cortex to the endodermis via the symplast pathway.

Many of the cells of the endodermis have bands of impermeable suberin on their cell walls. These bands are referred to as **Casparian strips** (Figure 2.17) and prevent the passage of water and ions into the xylem via the apoplast pathway. Water and mineral ions must pass through the cell surface membrane and cytoplasm of these cells before entering the xylem. This has prompted suggestions that the endodermis can regulate the uptake of ions by the plant. Observations of transverse sections of roots indicate the presence of certain endodermal cells, referred to as 'passage cells', that lack Casparian strips and would allow water and mineral ions to move freely into the xylem.

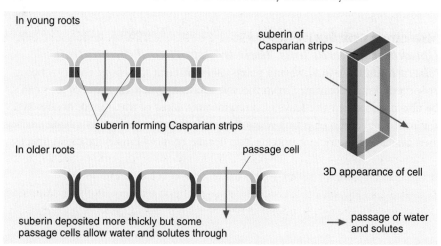

Figure 2.17 Casparian strips in endodermal cells and passage cells

Once the ions reach the xylem, transport is by mass flow, and by water. Most ions reach the leaves, where those that are not required in synthesis may be redistributed by the phloem tissue to sites of metabolic activity, such as developing buds, growing leaves, storage organs or fruits and seeds. Lateral transport from the xylem to the phloem is aided by specialised parenchyma cells called **transfer cells**.

ADDITIONAL MATERIAL

Evidence for translocation in the phloem

Early investigations of phloem transport involved the removal of a ring of bark from the trunk of a tree to see what would happen. Such an experiment was carried out by Marcello Malpighi in 1679. He removed the bark and underlying soft tissues of the stem, leaving the xylem intact. After a few weeks, the tissue on the upper side of the ring was swollen while that below was not. Malpighi found that the swelling only occurred if there were green leaves present on the tree and if the tree was kept in the light, so he deduced that substances were being made in the light and transported down the stem. At the time, this was quite a novel idea, and was some indication that a special tissue was involved, independent from that in which water transport occurred.

Figure 2.18 Aphid feeding on phloem

In the 1950s, more sophisticated techniques were developed involving the use of radioactive tracers. It was possible to supply a leaf with radioactively-labelled carbon dioxide ($^{14}CO_2$) in the light. After a period of time, stem tissue from the plant could be taken, frozen, dehydrated and cut into thin sections. If the sections were placed on photographic film, the position of any radioactively-labelled substances would show up when the film was developed. In this way, not only the tissue but also the cells involved in the transport of the organic substances could be identified.

Analysis of phloem exudates enables the contents of the phloem sap to be identified. It is possible to collect sap directly from some monocotyledonous species, such as palms, when they are cut, due to the high hydrostatic pressure forcing the sap out, but the use of aphids eliminates the possibility of contamination. Aphids are allowed to feed on a plant by inserting their stylets into the phloem tissue (Figure 2.18). Once penetration of the tissue has occurred, the aphids are anaesthetised to prevent them withdrawing their stylets and then their bodies are cut off, leaving the stylets still inserted into the phloem. Each stylet acts like a tiny pipette and sap can be collected over a number of days. This technique has its drawbacks as it is difficult to carry out and the amounts of sap collected are small. However, it can be combined with the use of radioactive tracers to provide useful information on the rate of translocation. If radioactively-labelled material is introduced, it is possible to measure the time taken for this material to be transported over a measured distance.

Using some of the techniques described above, it has been shown that phloem sap is an alkaline solution, consisting mostly of sucrose, together with organic nitrogen compounds and potassium ions. The concentration of sugars in the sap varies from 15 to 30 per cent, compared with 0.5 per cent in the leaf cells, indicating that the loading of the sieve tube elements is an active process, requiring energy. Any process or compound, such as a metabolic poison, which slows or inhibits respiration, will slow down or stop translocation in the phloem.

The mechanism of phloem transport

It has proved extremely difficult to establish the precise mechanism of phloem transport. It is known that large quantities of material are moved at rapid rates and that the conducting tissue is composed of fine tubes, but the tissue is delicate and easily damaged. It is also difficult to see how the roles of P-protein and the sieve plates can be accounted for in most of the theories put forward. The most acceptable model of phloem transport is the **pressure flow hypothesis** (Figure 2.19), based on an hypothesis put forward by E. Münch in 1930. He suggested that the movement of substances depended on a gradient of hydrostatic pressure. The sieve tubes in the leaves, at the **source** end of the system, have a higher hydrostatic pressure than the sieve tubes in places such as the roots, apical meristems or seeds, known as the **sink** end of the system.

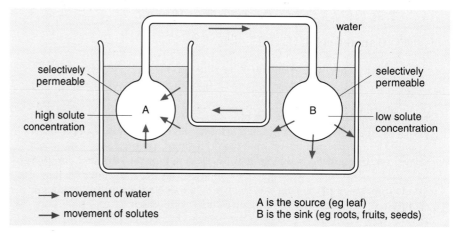

Figure 2.19 A model illustrating the pressure flow hypothesis

In the model (Figure 2.19), A represents the source and B the sink. The solute concentration at A will be higher than at B and water will enter A by osmosis. As water enters, a high hydrostatic pressure builds up, forcing water out of B. Mass flow of the contents of A along to B results, due to the hydrostatic pressure gradient. If this model is applied to the situation in living plants, it can be appreciated that there would be high concentrations of sugars at A due to photosynthesis in the leaves. Water enters the leaf cells by osmosis, increasing their turgor pressure. It is known that sugars will be used for respiration and synthesis in other regions of the plant, represented by B, so solutes and water will move out, resulting in a lower hydrostatic pressure at B. Mass flow occurs along the phloem from the source to the sink.

The pressure flow hypothesis predicts that a pressure gradient exists along sieve tubes and, although difficult to measure, such a pressure gradient has been demonstrated. It is not known whether the gradient would account for the rapid transport of materials in phloem tissue, but it is possible to work out a theoretical value based on the diameter of the sieve tubes and the nature of any obstacles, such as sieve plates, P-protein or callose. The hypothesis also suggests that the water and solutes move together at the same rate in the same direction. In some of the experiments carried out with radioactively-labelled sugars and water, the sugars moved at a more rapid rate, but it was suggested that, as the sieve tubes were permeable to water, some moved out into the surrounding tissues.

Münch's original hypothesis was a purely physical one and did not include any reference to living tissues or the possibility of active transport. It would seem necessary to modify the original hypothesis to account for the active transport of solutes into the sieve tubes in the leaf and the unloading of solutes at the sinks, but mass flow seems to account for the movement once the solutes have reached the phloem tissue.

Transport in humans and other mammals

The circulatory system

The function of the circulatory system is the transport of nutrients and other substances, including gases, hormones and excretory products, to and from various parts of the body. The blood must therefore be kept in a state of continuous circulation, the energy for which is provided by the heart. The force of contraction of the heart propels blood to the tissues through thick-walled **arteries** and back to the heart through the thinner-walled **veins**. In the tissues, blood passes through a network of **capillaries** in which exchange of materials occurs between blood and the tissue fluid.

Mammals have a double circulatory system, which consists of the **systemic circulation**, in which blood is pumped from the left side of the heart to the various tissues and organs of the body, and the **pulmonary circulation**, in which blood is pumped from the right side of the heart to the pulmonary capillaries of the lungs.

QUESTION

Animals such as fish have a single circulatory system, in which blood is pumped from the heart to the gills and then directly round the body. What are the advantages of a double circulatory system?

Structure and function of the heart

The human heart weighs about 300 g and is situated in the middle region of the thorax. The lower border of the heart, known as the apex, points towards the left of the thorax. The structure of the heart and major blood vessels is shown in Figure 2.20.

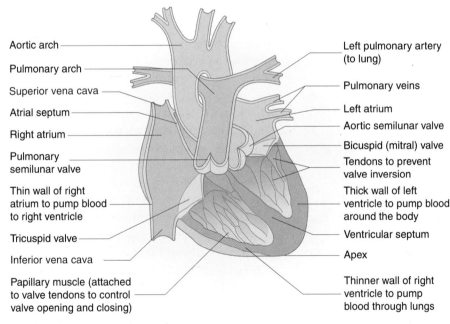

Aortic arch
Pulmonary arch
Superior vena cava
Atrial septum
Right atrium
Pulmonary semilunar valve
Thin wall of right atrium to pump blood to right ventricle
Tricuspid valve
Inferior vena cava
Papillary muscle (attached to valve tendons to control valve opening and closing)

Left pulmonary artery (to lung)
Pulmonary veins
Left atrium
Aortic semilunar valve
Bicuspid (mitral) valve
Tendons to prevent valve inversion
Thick wall of left ventricle to pump blood around the body
Ventricular septum
Apex
Thinner wall of right ventricle to pump blood through lungs

Figure 2.20 Internal structure of the heart

The wall of the heart is made up of three distinct layers:
- an outer **epicardium**, consisting of a layer of flattened epithelial cells and supporting connective tissue
- a very thick, muscular **myocardium**, consisting of **cardiac muscle**
- an inner **endocardium**, consisting of flattened epithelial cells supported by a delicate layer of connective tissue.

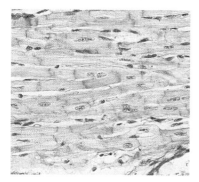

Figure 2.21 Histology of cardiac muscle, as seen using a light microscope

Cardiac muscle consists of many branching cells, each of which may contain one or two nuclei. Cardiac muscle cells are joined by structures known as **intercalated discs**, specialised junctions between cells which both transmit the force of contraction and allow the rapid spread of electrical excitation throughout the myocardium. In histological preparations, intercalated discs appear as dark, transverse lines, as seen in Figure 2.21. Notice too that cardiac muscle has cross-striations, similar to those of skeletal muscle.

Cardiac muscle is said to be **myogenic**. This means that, unlike striated muscle, cardiac muscle is self-exciting. Cardiac muscle cells show a continuous, inherent rhythm of electrical excitation and contraction on their own, although this can be changed by nervous or hormonal influences. Cardiac muscle has a very dense capillary network which receives blood by means of the left and right **coronary arteries**. These are the first branches from the aorta and, at rest, receive about 5 per cent of the total **cardiac output**.

After passing through the capillaries, blood returns mainly via a series of cardiac veins which drain into the right atrium via a channel known as the coronary sinus. Some smaller veins from the right ventricle do not enter the coronary sinus but drain directly into the right atrium.

The interior of the heart is divided into four chambers: two upper **atria** and two lower **ventricles**. The atria receive blood from veins which return it to the heart. The atria contract and push blood into the ventricles, which then contract with considerable force and pump blood into the arteries. The myocardium of the ventricles is thicker than that of the atria and the myocardium of the left ventricle is much thicker than that of the right ventricle. The left ventricle pumps blood into the aorta and around the entire body at a higher pressure than the right ventricle, which pumps blood into the pulmonary arteries and through the pulmonary capillaries.

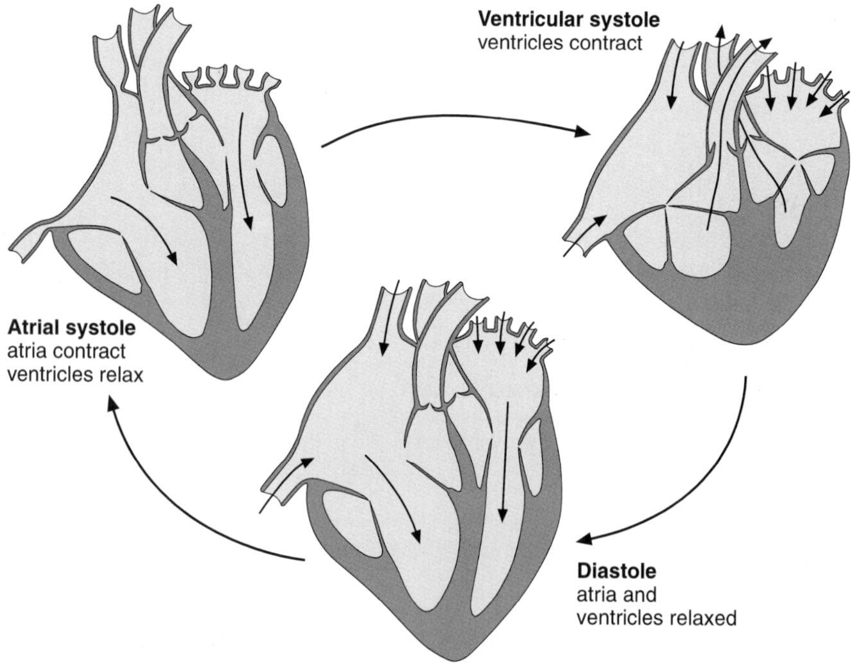

> **DEFINITION**
>
> **Cardiac output** is the volume of blood pumped out of either the left or right ventricle per minute.

The rhythmic sequence of events which occurs each time the heart beats is known as the **cardiac cycle** (Figure 2.22). At rest, the heart beats about 72 times per minute, so each cycle lasts about 0.83 seconds. The cardiac cycle consists of:

- **atrial systole** – contraction of the atria
- **ventricular systole** – contraction of the ventricles
- **complete cardiac diastole** – relaxation of the atria and ventricles.

Ventricular systole
ventricles contract

Atrial systole
atria contract
ventricles relax

Diastole
atria and
ventricles relaxed

Figure 2.22 Chambers and valves of the heart showing the action of the heart chambers during atrial systole and ventricular systole

The heart valves

The heart valves ensure that blood flows in one direction only and are essential for the normal function of the heart. The **atrioventricular (AV) valves** are situated between the two atria and the ventricles, at the atrioventricular orifices. The right atrioventricular valve has three flaps and is also known as the **tricuspid valve**. The left atrioventricular valve is similar in structure but has two, rather than three flaps, and is therefore called the **bicuspid**, or **mitral valve**. These valves prevent blood from flowing back into the atria when the ventricles contract and ensure that blood moves into the aorta and pulmonary arteries. The free edges of these valves are attached to papillary muscles, small projections of the inner walls of the ventricles, by chordae tendinae, which prevent the valves from opening upwards. The opening of the pulmonary trunk is guarded by the **pulmonary semilunar valve** and the opening of the aorta is guarded by the **aortic semilunar valve**. When the semilunar valves close during diastole, blood is prevented from flowing back into the ventricles from the aorta and pulmonary arteries.

It is the closure of these valves which is responsible for the heart sounds. During the cardiac cycle, the atrioventricular valves close simultaneously at the start of ventricular systole. This produces the first heart sound, followed shortly afterwards by the second sound, produced by the closure of the semilunar valves indicating the start of diastole. The first and second heart sounds are frequently described as 'lubb' and 'dup' respectively and may be heard using a stethoscope.

The conducting system of the heart

The rhythmic sequence of events during the cardiac cycle is coordinated by tissues within the heart itself. These tissues consist of modified cardiac muscle cells which, in humans, are not easy to distinguish from other cardiac muscle cells. The conducting system (Figure 2.23) comprises:

- the sinuatrial, or sinoatrial, (SA) node
- the atrioventricular (AV) node
- the bundle of His and its branches.

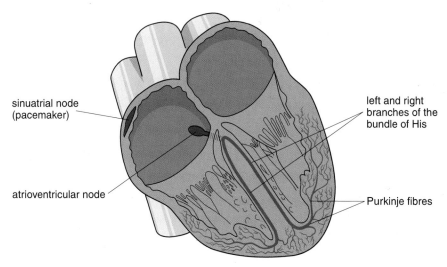

Figure 2.23 The conducting system of the human heart

The sinuatrial node (SA node) consists of a small group of specialised cells situated in the wall of the right atrium, near the opening of the superior, or anterior, vena cava (see Figure 2.20 on page 43). The SA node is often referred to as the **pacemaker** because it initiates the heart beat by sending out a wave of electrical excitation that spreads over the right and left atria. This stimulates the myocardium to contract. The atrioventricular node (AV node) is situated in the wall of the right atrium, near the opening of the coronary sinus. The wave of excitation reaches the AV node and is conducted, via the bundle of His and branches, to the ventricular myocardium. The bundle of His and its branches consist of Purkinje (or Purkyne) tissue – modified cardiac muscle. This arrangement of the conducting tissues ensures that there is a delay between contraction of the atria and contraction of the ventricles and that the electrical excitation reaches most of the ventricular cells simultaneously, which ensures a single, coordinated contraction.

The electrical impulses which accompany contraction of the heart are conducted through body fluids and can be recorded by placing electrodes on the surface of the skin, either on the chest wall, or on the wrists and ankles. The pattern of electrical activity can then be displayed on an oscilloscope screen, or printed out onto paper. This recording is known as an **electrocardiogram**, or **ECG**, and shows changes in voltage against time. A normal ECG shows five waves, which are conventionally referred to as the P wave, the QRS complex and the T wave (Figure 2.24)

The P wave is caused by electrical excitation of the atria, the QRS complex indicates excitation of the ventricles and the T wave is due to recovery (repolarisation) of the ventricles. The ECG has considerable clinical importance as it indicates abnormalities in the pattern of excitation of the heart. Part of an ECG from a healthy patient is shown in Figure 2.24.

QUESTION

Identify the P, Q, R, S and T waves in Figure 2.20. How many complete cardiac cycles are shown?

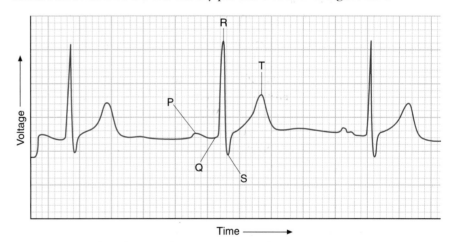

Figure 2.24 Part of an electrocardiogram (ECG) recording

Pressure changes in the heart

Figure 2.25 shows the pressure changes in the heart during a cardiac cycle, starting with the beginning of atrial systole at time 0. Notice that, although the pressure in the ventricles drops to zero during diastole, the pressure within the aorta and pulmonary artery remains relatively high. This pressure is maintained by the closure of the semilunar valves and by the elastic recoil of the arterial walls.

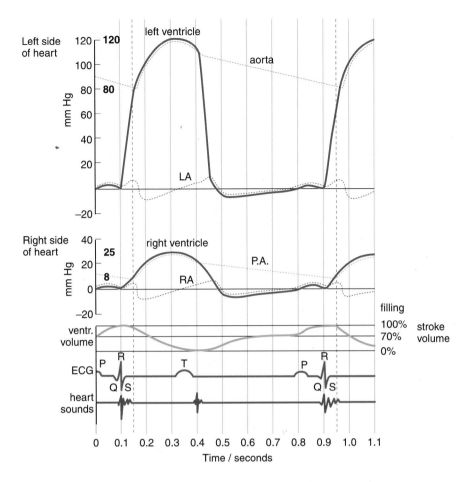

Figure 2.25 The sequence of events in the cardiac cycle. PA = blood pressure in the pulmonary artery; RA = pressure in the right atrium; LA = pressure in the left atrium. Blood pressure is usually expressed in mm Hg, but may be converted to kilopascals by dividing by 7.5.

Nervous and hormonal control of the rate of heart beat

The heart is supplied by nerves of the autonomic nervous system. Sympathetic and parasympathetic (vagus nerve) fibres combine to form cardiac plexuses, situated near the aortic arch. From here, nerve fibres enter the heart and most end in the SA node, but some end in the AV node and the atrial myocardium. Although the SA node normally initiates the heart beat, the rate can be changed by a number of factors, including the ratio of impulses in the sympathetic and parasympathetic nerves to the SA node. Increased sympathetic activity will increase the heart rate, whereas increased parasympathetic activity will decrease heart rate.

Reflexes involving factors such as exercise, hormones, blood temperature and pain can also affect heart rate. In exercise, for example, the heart rate normally increases. The precise mechanism for this is not known, but it involves impulses from the cerebrum, through the hypothalamus to the cardiac centre in the medulla oblongata. Adrenaline, released from the adrenal medulla, acts directly on the heart and increases both the heart rate and the cardiac output (see Human Health and Fitness in *Respiration and Coordination*, Adds, Larkcom and Miller, Nelson, 2000).

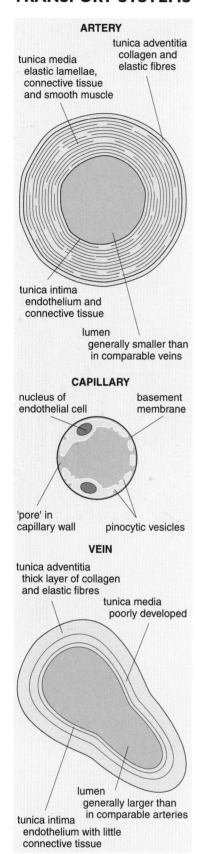

ARTERY

tunica adventitia
collagen and
elastic fibres

tunica media
elastic lamellae,
connective tissue
and smooth muscle

tunica intima
endothelium and
connective tissue

lumen
generally smaller than
in comparable veins

CAPILLARY

nucleus of
endothelial cell

basement
membrane

'pore' in
capillary wall

pinocytic vesicles

VEIN

tunica adventitia
thick layer of collagen
and elastic fibres

tunica media
poorly developed

lumen
generally larger than
in comparable arteries

tunica intima
endothelium with little
connective tissue

*Figure 2.26 Structure of blood vessels
(not to same scale)*

Artificial pacemakers

On occasions, myocardial infarction results in damage to the conducting system of the heart. As a result, the atria may continue to beat normally but the ventricles, which no longer receive impulses via the bundles of His, start to contract, but much more slowly than is required to maintain adequate cardiac output. Patients may become very short of breath, or suffer from dizziness or blackouts. This condition can be treated by the insertion of an **artificial pacemaker**, a device which delivers an electrical stimulus to the heart muscle. There are several different types of artificial pacemakers, including permanent pacemakers, which are inserted into the patient's chest and connected to the apex of the heart via a pacing wire. The pacemaker is powered by lithium batteries and generates an electrical stimulus which ensures that the ventricles contract at a steady rate of 60 to 70 beats per minute. Some advanced types of pacemakers, known as rate-responsive pacemakers, can alter the rate of stimulation to match physiological demand. For example, the rate will increase during physical exercise.

ADDITIONAL MATERIAL

Heart transplants are surgical procedures in which healthy hearts are removed from donors and used to replace the hearts of patients who are otherwise likely to die because of heart disease. A healthy heart is removed from a donor after brain stem death and packed in a sterile plastic bag surrounded by crushed ice. A heart may be stored in this way prior to transplantation and will remain viable for up to 4 hours.

Arteries, capillaries and veins

Arteries are blood vessels which transport blood away from the heart. Although arteries vary in diameter, they all have a similar structure, consisting of three layers of tissue:

- an inner tunica intima, consisting of flattened epithelial cells (endothelium) and their supporting connective tissue
- a middle tunica media, containing smooth muscle cells and elastic fibres
- an outer tunica adventitia, consisting of connective tissue.

Arterioles are defined as vessels of the arterial system with a diameter of less than 0.3 mm. Their tunica media consists almost entirely of smooth muscle cells. Arterioles divide repeatedly and become progressively smaller in diameter, eventually leading into **capillaries**. The wall of a capillary consists of a single layer of flattened epithelial cells, which allow efficient exchange of materials between blood and the surrounding tissue fluid. The diameter of capillaries varies, but is typically about 7 μm, approximately the same as that of a red blood cell. Capillary networks drain into venules, then **veins**, which return blood to the heart. The wall of a vein has the same three layers as the wall of an artery, but the wall is very much thinner in relation to the diameter of the lumen. Some veins contain valves: delicate projections of the tunica intima. These valves are present mainly in the veins of the limbs and prevent backflow of blood. The structures of an artery, capillary and vein are shown in Figure 2.26.

Blood pressure

The term **blood pressure** usually refers to the pressure within the aorta and main arteries. The pressure is not constant, but varies between a minimum (or diastolic) value and a maximum (or systolic) value. Blood pressure is usually measured in mm Hg, although this is not an SI unit. Typical blood pressures for an adult at rest are about 120 mm Hg (systolic) and about 80 mm Hg (diastolic), usually written as 120/80 mm Hg. However, it must be noted that these figures will vary according to the time of day (there is a circadian rhythm of changes in blood pressure), posture, sex and age of the person.

Blood pressure depends on a number of factors including:
• cardiac output
• blood volume
• peripheral resistance (resistance to blood flow mainly due to the diameter of arterioles)
• elasticity of artery walls
• volume of blood returning to the heart.

As an example, cardiac output depends on the volume of blood pumped out of the ventricles with each beat and the heart rate. Any factor which makes the heart beat faster, or makes it beat more strongly and increases the stroke volume, will increase cardiac output and will therefore tend to increase blood pressure. High blood pressure, or **hypertension**, occurs when the diastolic pressure exceeds 95 mm Hg and the systolic pressure exceeds 160 mm Hg (World Health Organisation classification). Many risk factors have been identified in the development of hypertension and include:
• genetic factors
• gender – men experience higher rates of hypertension at an earlier age than women
• age
• high stress levels
• obesity
• smoking.

There are numerous complications of untreated hypertension, including heart failure, kidney failure, atherosclerosis and stroke.

> **DEFINITION**
>
> **Hypotension** is a relatively rare condition in which the systolic blood pressure is typically below 105 mm Hg (14 kPa) and the diastolic pressure less than 60 mm Hg (8 kPa).

Blood and body fluids

Blood is a tissue consisting of a variety of cells suspended in a fluid medium known as **plasma**. Blood functions mainly as a transport medium throughout the body for respiratory gases (oxygen and carbon dioxide), nutrients, hormones, metabolic waste products and cells. Plasma consists of 90 per cent water and 10 per cent solutes, including proteins, nutrients, excretory products, dissolved gases, hormones, enzymes and other substances. Plasma proteins are of three types: albumins, globulins and fibrinogen. Albumins and fibrinogen are important in the blood-clotting mechanism; globulins are essential parts of the immune system.

There are three varieties of cells present in blood:
• erythrocytes, or red blood cells
• leucocytes, or white blood cells
• thrombocytes, or platelets.

All blood cells develop from multipotential stem cells, which are present in the bone marrow. Stem cells divide to replicate themselves and to give rise to separate cell types, each of which divides and develops to form one of the

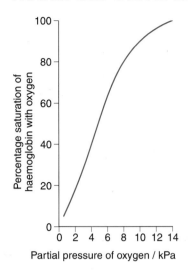

Figure 2.27 The oxygen dissociation curve

QUESTION

Under what circumstances might the amount of haemoglobin present in the blood change?

main blood cell types. White blood cells are subdivided into two main groups: **granulocytes** and **agranulocytes**. Granulocytes have prominent granules in their cytoplasm and a multilobed nucleus. There are three types of granulocytes: **neutrophils**, **eosinophils** and **basophils**. Agranulocytes, which are either **monocytes** or **lymphocytes**, have nongranular cytoplasm and their nuclei are not lobed, although the nucleus of a monocyte may be strongly indented. The structures and functions of blood cells are summarised in Table 2.1.

Transport of oxygen and carbon dioxide

Oxygen combines with haemoglobin, present in red blood cells, to form oxyhaemoglobin. Each gram of haemoglobin can combine with 1.34 cm^3 of oxygen, so the total amount of oxygen which can be carried in the blood depends mainly on the amount of haemoglobin present. The relationship between the partial pressure of oxygen and the quantity of oxygen combined with haemoglobin is an S-shaped curve, referred to as the **oxygen dissociation curve** (Figure 2.27).

The exact position of this curve depends on a number of factors, including the partial pressure of carbon dioxide, temperature and pH. For example, if the partial pressure of carbon dioxide increases, the curve moves to the right (known as the Bohr effect). This decreases the affinity of haemoglobin for oxygen, which will therefore be released more readily.

Fetal haemoglobin (haemoglobin F), has a higher affinity for oxygen than adult haemoglobin at any given partial pressure of oxygen. This means that fetal haemoglobin will receive oxygen from the maternal haemoglobin at the same partial pressure of oxygen.

Myoglobin is a pigment found in muscles, particularly the leg muscles and hearts of large mammals. Like haemoglobin, myoglobin can combine reversibly with oxygen, but myoglobin takes up oxygen much more readily than haemoglobin does. When blood reaches muscle tissue, oxygen is transferred from oxyhaemoglobin to myoglobin, which acts as a temporary oxygen store in the muscles.

Carbon dioxide, produced in respiration, diffuses from body tissues into the blood, where most of it is taken up by red blood cells. In the red blood cells, carbon dioxide combines with water and forms hydrogencarbonate ions (HCO_3^-):

$$CO_2 + H_2O \rightarrow H_2CO_3 \rightarrow H^+ + HCO_3^-$$

The hydrogencarbonate then diffuses into the plasma in exchange for chloride ions. The majority of carbon dioxide is transported in the form of hydrogencarbonate. Carbon dioxide also reacts with haemoglobin and other proteins to form carbamino compounds, and a relatively small percentage of carbon dioxide is transported in simple solution.

Table 2.1 *Cell types present in the blood of humans*

Cell type	Size / μm	Number per mm^3	Function
erythrocyte	6 to 8	4 to 6 million	transport of respiratory gases
leucocyte (neutrophil)	10 to 12	2800 to 5250	phagocytosis of pathogenic microorganisms
leucocyte (eosinophil)	10 to 12	70 to 420	secrete 'major basic protein' which is involved in defence against certain parasitic worms
leucocyte (basophil)	9 to 10	0 to 70	secrete heparin and histamine
leucocyte (lymphocyte)	7 to 8	1400 to 3150	secrete antibodies
leucocyte (monocyte)	14 to 17	140 to 700	migrate out of blood to form macrophages: phagocytic cells which engulf bacteria and cell debris
platelets (thrombocytes)	2 to 3	150 000 to 400 000	release thromboplastin, which is important in blood clotting

Carbon monoxide

Carbon monoxide (CO), a pollutant gas present in car exhaust fumes and cigarette smoke, can combine with haemoglobin to form carboxyhaemoglobin. Carbon monoxide has an affinity for haemoglobin about 250 times greater than that of oxygen and combines with the haem group, preventing oxygen from doing so. Death occurs in humans who are exposed to concentrations of carbon monoxide of around 1000 ppm (parts per million), which corresponds to a blood carboxyhaemoglobin concentration of 60 per cent. Adverse effects, including dizziness, headaches and mental confusion, are experienced at concentrations considerably lower than this. The actual concentration of carboxyhaemoglobin in the blood of cigarette smokers varies from 1.2 to 9 per cent. Because carbon monoxide blocks the transport of oxygen, it has been suggested that carbon monoxide is a contributing factor in heart disease.

Interchange of materials between capillaries and tissue fluid

The walls of capillaries consist of a single layer of flattened epithelial cells, which act as a selectively permeable membrane, allowing water and solutes of low molecular mass to pass through. Proteins remain in the capillaries. Tissue fluid is formed in the same way as the initial filtrate in the Bowman's capsule (Chapter 1), that is, by ultrafiltration. Tissue fluid contains water, glucose, amino acids, fatty acids, glycerol, mineral salts, dissolved gases and vitamins (Figure 2.28).

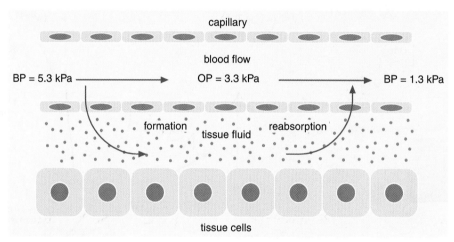

Figure 2.28 The exchange of materials between a capillary and tissue cells.
BP = blood pressure; OP = osmotic pressure.

At the arteriolar end of the capillary bed, the blood pressure within the capillaries is about 40 mm Hg (5.3 kPa) and this forces water out of the capillaries. However, this is opposed by the osmotic effect of the plasma proteins, which tends to draw water back into the capillaries. The osmotic pressure due to the plasma proteins is about 25 mm Hg (3.3 kPa) so the overall outward force is the difference between these two values, that is, 15 mm Hg (2.0 kPa). At the venular end of the capillary bed, the blood pressure has dropped to about 10 mm Hg (1.3 kPa) but the osmotic pressure due to the plasma proteins remains at 25 mm Hg. There is, therefore, a net inward pressure of about 15 mm Hg, which draws water back into the capillaries by osmosis.

Tissue fluid is continually being produced at the arteriolar end of the capillary beds and reabsorbed at the venular end. However, not all of the water is reabsorbed in this way. Some drains into blind-ended lymphatic capillaries, which are similar to blood capillaries, except their walls are more permeable. Excess tissue fluid, and some excretory products, enter the lymphatic system, where it is known as **lymph**. This is eventually returned to the blood system via the lymphatic ducts.

<table>
<tr><td>**PRACTICAL**</td><td>**Determination of water potentials**</td></tr>
</table>

Introduction

The water potential of a cell (ψ_{cell}) is the overall tendency for water to enter the cell, from outside, by osmosis. The two factors which determine the water potential of a plant cell are the solute potential of its cell sap (ψ_s) and the pressure exerted by the cell wall (ψ_p, or pressure potential). Thus the overall water relations for a plant cell can be represented by the equation

$$\psi_{cell} = \psi_s + \psi_p$$

If a plant cell is in equilibrium with an external solution, so that there is no net loss or gain of water, then the solute potential of the external solution with be equal to the water potential of the cell, or

$$\psi_{solution} = \psi_{cell}$$

Use of this fact can be made to find the water potential of a plant tissue, such as potato, by immersing pieces in a range of solutions (referred to as graded osmotica) and determining the changes in mass of the tissue.

Materials

- Large potato
- Cork borer (1 cm diameter)
- Graded sucrose solutions (0.2 mol dm^{-3}, 0.4 mol dm^{-3}, 0.6 mol dm^{-3} and 0.8 mol dm^{-3})
- Sharp knife
- Petri dishes
- Filter paper
- Ruler
- Electronic balance

Method

1 Set up five Petri dishes containing the above sucrose solutions. A zero ψ treatment should also be included using tap water, rather than distilled water. Label each dish on its base.
2 Using the cork borer, cut cores of potato tissue then slice into discs 1 mm thick. Place six discs on each of five pieces of filter paper.
3 Gently blot and weigh each group of discs. Record the mass of each group then place into each of the labelled dishes.
4 After *at least 30 minutes*, remove the discs, blot carefully and reweigh.

Results and discussion

1 Record all your results in a table and calculate the percentage change in mass (change in mass multiplied by 100, divided by the original mass) for each group of discs.
2 Using the information in Table 2.2, plot a graph of the percentage change in mass (vertical axis) against the solute potential of the bathing solution (horizontal axis).
3 Where this curve cuts the horizontal axis, $\psi_{tissue} = \psi_{solution}$.
4 Record the ψ_{tissue} from your graph.
5 If the curve has a kink below the horizontal axis, the kink will be approximately in the region of ψ_s for the cell sap. This is because, once incipient plasmolysis has been reached, very little further changes in mass occur.
6 What are the sources of error in this experiment?

Table 2.2 *Solute potentials of sucrose solutions*

Concentration of sucrose solution / mol dm^{-3}	Solute potential ($\psi_{solution}$) / kPa
0.2	− 540
0.4	− 1130
0.6	− 1800
0.8	− 2580

Further work

1 If a suitable balance is not available, satisfactory results can be obtained by measuring changes in the dimensions of a strip of tissue. Strips should be no less than 5 cm in length and about 0.5 cm thick.
2 If sufficient time is available, the groups of discs should be removed from their bathing solutions, blotted carefully, weighed and replaced in their bathing solutions. Readings should be taken every 30 minutes for 2.5 hours and changes in mass of each group can be plotted against time until equilibrium is reached.
3 Investigate tissue water potentials using other plant materials, such as other storage roots and tubers, leaf discs or hypocotyl sections of seedlings.

PRACTICAL ## Determination of the solute potential of cell sap

Introduction

Incipient plasmolysis is the point at which the plant cell contents (known as the protoplast) are *just* about to lose contact with the cell wall as water is lost from the cell by osmosis. At the point of incipient plasmolysis, the pressure potential (ψ_p) is zero therefore, from the general equation

$$\psi_{cell} = \psi_s$$

If plant cells are immersed in a graded osmotica, then examined microscopically, it is likely that signs of plasmolysis will be seen in cells immersed in one of these solutions. Cells in other solutions will either be turgid or fully plasmolysed.

In practice, the point of incipient plasmolysis is taken to be when half the number of cells observed show signs of plasmolysis.

Materials

- Rhubarb petioles (rhubarb epidermis is preferable to onion epidermis as the cytoplasm in rhubarb is strongly pigmented and plasmolysis is therefore easier to see)
- Graded sucrose solutions, as in previous experiment
- Scissors
- Watch glasses or other suitable containers
- Pipettes
- Microscope slides and coverslips
- Mounted needles
- Microscope

Method

1 Label small dishes appropriately and add sucrose solutions separately to each. One dish should contain tap water as a zero ψ control.
2 Carefully peel the pigmented epidermis from a rhubarb petiole and, using scissors, cut into squares with sides approximately 5 mm.
3 Immediately place one square of tissue into each of the osmotica.
4 Leave the tissue in these solutions for 10 minutes.
5 After 10 minutes, remove each strip one at a time using a mounted needle and mount on a microscope slide in a drop of the same solution in which it had been immersed.
6 Apply a coverslip and examine using a microscope, first with low power, then high.
7 Count all the cells which are visible within the field of view, then count all the cells which show signs of plasmolysis. Include all cells in which it is possible to see separation of the cell contents from the cell wall, no matter how slight this may be. If you are unsure of the appearance of plasmolysed cells, look at your preparation from 0.8 mol dm^{-3} sucrose solution first.
8 For each preparation, count three separate fields of view.
9 Make a labelled drawing to show the appearance of a plasmolysed cell.

Results and discussion

1 Calculate the mean percentage of cells which show signs of plasmolysis in each of the osmotica. Tabulate your results clearly.
2 Using the information in Table 2.2, plot a graph of the mean percentage of cells plasmolysed (vertical axis) against the solute potential of the bathing solution (horizontal axis).
3 From your graph, read off the solute potential of the sucrose solution which corresponds to 50 per cent plasmolysis.
4 Explain why this solution may be regarded as having the same solute potential as the cell sap.

PRACTICAL | **Preparation of an epidermal peel and observation of stomata**

Introduction

The use of *Commelina communis* is recommended for the preparation of epidermal peels, as it is possible to remove the lower epidermis relatively easily, with little or no damage to the stomata. As an alternative, leaves of *Vicia faba* (broad bean) may be used. *C. communis* can be easily grown from seed, which should be sown about 6 weeks before the leaves are required. If sown individually in 100 mm pots, the seeds will germinate after about 1 week at 20 to 25 °C, and after another 4 weeks the plants should have up to 10 mature leaves. It is important to keep the compost well watered.

An initial supply of *C. communis* seed can be obtained by sending a stamped, self-addressed envelope to: Dr J. Weyers, Department of Biological Sciences, University of Dundee, Dundee DD1 4HN, Scotland.

Materials

- *Commelina communis* plants, or a suitable alternative
- Scalpel or single-edged razor blade
- Microscope slides and coverslips
- Microscope
- Stage micrometer

Method

1 Carefully tear a detached leaf, using a slight twisting action, to remove the lower epidermis.
2 Cut the epidermis into pieces about 5 mm × 5 mm.
3 Mount each piece separately in a drop of water on a microscope slide and apply a coverslip.
4 Use a stage micrometer to measure the diameter of the field of view, at high magnification   (40 × objective).
5 Observe the epidermal strip and, at high magnification, count the number of stomata per field of view. Repeat several times and find the mean number. Compare with the photograph in Figure 2.14 on page 37.

Results and discussion

1 Make a careful, labelled diagram to show the structure of the stomatal complex, including the guard cells, subsidiary cells and epidermal cells. The subsidiary and epidermal cells of *C. communis* may contain calcium oxalate crystals (raphides), the function of which is not known.
2 Calculate the area of the field of view, and determine the number of stomata per mm^2. This is known as the **stomatal frequency**.
3 Find the surface area of one typical leaf, for example by placing the leaf on graph paper and carefully drawing around it. How many stomata are there on the lower surface of the leaf?

Further work

1 Observe the arrangements of stomata and compare the stomatal frequencies on the upper and lower epidermis of leaves from different species.
2 Permanent preparations of leaf epidermis can be made using clear nail varnish replicas. This method is suitable for species from which it is difficult to remove the epidermis. A small area (about 1 cm^2) of the epidermis should be painted *thinly* with clear nail varnish, which is then allowed to dry completely. The nail varnish replica can be easily transferred to a microscope slide using a piece of transparent adhesive tape.
3 Positive replicas of leaf epidermis can be made using a dental silicone impression material, such as Provil®. The base and catalyst are mixed together in approximately equal proportions, then spread onto a leaf. The material sets rapidly and, after removing, can be used to prepare positive impressions using clear nail varnish. This method provides striking results.

Adaptations to the environment

Types of adaptations

All organisms are adapted to survive in particular environmental conditions. Such adaptations may be:

- structural, as in the organism's body shape, or the presence or absence of appendages; or
- physiological, as in osmoregulation in response to varying degrees of salinity.

Depending on the habitat in which they live, organisms may have a combination of structural and physiological adaptations.

Environmental factors affecting distribution and adaptation

Several physical factors affect the distribution of organisms in their habitats. These physical factors are often referred to as **abiotic**, to distinguish them from **biotic** factors, which involve the effects of other living organisms, including humans, on the distribution of species. Some physical factors, such as light, have widespread effects and are important in both aquatic and terrestrial situations. Others, such as wave action, are significant only in aquatic environments. The physical factors can be divided into:

- climatic – temperature, light, wind and water availability
- soil – often referred to as **edaphic** factors
- topographic – altitude, aspect (whether north-facing or south-facing), and inclination (steepness of slope)
- others, such as wave action, which are relevant in specific situations.

In **terrestrial habitats**, light, temperature, soil type and the availability of water are important factors governing the distribution of the plants and animals. In sand dunes, for example, xerophytic conditions exist initially and the colonising organisms are adapted to lack of water and unstable soil, as well as to exposure to wind. The first colonisers are plants that are salt-tolerant and able to develop extensive root systems in order to remain in position. A typical plant found in such situations is marram grass (*Ammophila arenaria*), which has many adaptations to deal with the lack of water, exposure and shifting soil.

In **aquatic habitats**, such as a pond or a stream, organisms are distributed in different locations according to environmental factors. If the water is flowing, for example, this might mean that some organisms are attached to the substratum or to rocks and stones, so that they remain in the same position. Others swim or move so that they remain in the most favourable conditions. There are many structural adaptations in both plants and animals associated with the effects of movements and currents in the water. Streamlining and the possession of fins in fish, flexible stems and the variations in leaf form in plants and the flattened shape of crustaceans are all examples of structural adaptations to the movement of the water in an aquatic habitat. Aquatic organisms also show structural adaptations to other factors, such as light, oxygen concentration and salinity.

Structural and physiological adaptations to dry conditions

Adaptations to water loss in flowering plants

Any feature that significantly reduces the evaporation of water from the aerial parts of a flowering plant can be considered to be a **xeromorphic** adaptation. Most of a plant's water loss occurs during transpiration (as water vapour diffuses out through the open stomata on the leaves), although some water is lost by evaporation through the cuticle. The rate of transpiration is affected by temperature, light intensity, humidity and air movements.

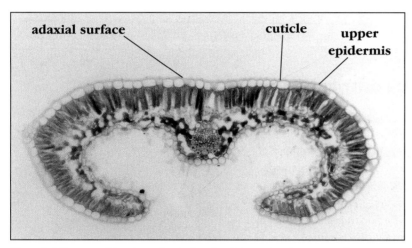

*Figure 3.1 Xeromorphic adaptation in heather (*Erica *sp.) reduces water loss through leaves*

Xeromorphic adaptations present in flowering plants include:

- thicker cuticles on leaves and herbaceous stems (Figure 3.1) – for example, on the upper (adaxial) epidermis of leaves of heather (*Erica* sp.) and holly (*Ilex* sp.) but also on the lower (abaxial) epidermis of marram grass.
- reduction in the size of leaves – there often is a reduction in the surface area to volume ratio, resulting in a decrease in the area of the leaf blade where most of the stomata are situated. There may be a corresponding increase in the thickness of the leaf blade. For example, heather has small leaves whilst in other plants, such as gorse and broom, the leaves are reduced to spines and photosynthesis takes place in the green stems.
- curling or rolling of the leaves into a cylindrical shape, to reduce the surface area of the leaves – for example, in marram grass, leaf rolling encloses the upper epidermis, where the stomata are situated. The lower epidermis has a thicker, waxy cuticle and no stomata. Humid air is trapped inside the rolled-up leaf, reducing the diffusion gradient and hence the rate of transpiration. Specialised epidermal cells, known as *hinge cells*, are present on the upper epidermis and lose water rapidly when the transpiration rate is high, causing the leaf to roll up (Figure 3.2).
- the number and distribution of the stomata – stomata may be confined to pits or grooves on the underside of the leaves, so that humid air is trapped and transpiration decreases.
- the presence of epidermal hairs – these trap humid air and reduce the effects of air movement on the rate of transpiration.

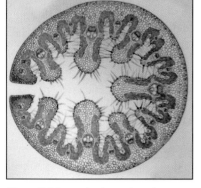

*Figure 3.2 Several adaptations in marram grass (*Ammophila arenaria*) reduce water loss*

In addition to these adaptations, there may be an increase in the quantity of supporting tissues, such as collenchyma and sclerenchyma. In habitats where water loss due to excessive transpiration is high, wilting may occur and extra supporting tissues can prevent the collapse of the herbaceous tissues, allowing time for the water balance to be restored. Many flowering plants lose their leaves during the season of the year when water is in short supply. These plants are known as **deciduous**. Evergreen plants retain their leaves throughout the year and often show xeromorphic adaptations, such as thicker cuticles.

Structural and physiological adaptations to aquatic conditions

Adaptations in flowering plants

Hydrophytes grow in situations where water is freely available, such as in and around ponds, lakes and streams. Some are adapted to being totally submerged, such as Canadian pond weed (*Elodea canadensis*) and water milfoil (*Myriophyllum spicatum*), whilst others may be rooted in the water with their stems, leaves and flowers projecting above the surface, such as water lilies (*Nymphaea alba*) and water crowfoot (*Ranunculus aquatilis*).

Totally submerged hydrophytes usually have:
- no cuticle (Figure 3.3)
- no stomata (Figure 3.3)
- reduced vascular and supporting tissues
- small leaves or leaves with a dissected lamina (Figure 3.4)
- air spaces or air bladders
- reduced root systems.

These adaptations enable the plants to carry out gaseous exchange efficiently, whilst offering little resistance to the movements of the water. Large expanses of leaf blade or rigid stems could be damaged by water movements, whereas air spaces and air bladders provide buoyancy, keeping the plants near the surface of the water and in the best position for efficient photosynthesis. Anchorage is not always of great importance and water uptake occurs all over the surface, so reduced root systems are common in totally submerged hydrophytes.

Some hydrophytes, such as water lilies, are rooted at the bottom of ponds and have leaves that float on the water surface (Figure 3.5). These leaves have several special adaptations including:
- stomata on the upper surface
- absence of stomata on the lower surface
- elongated lignified cells, called *sclereids*, that span the leaf between the upper and lower epidermises and prevent the leaf from rolling up
- a thick palisade mesophyll layer.

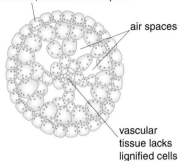

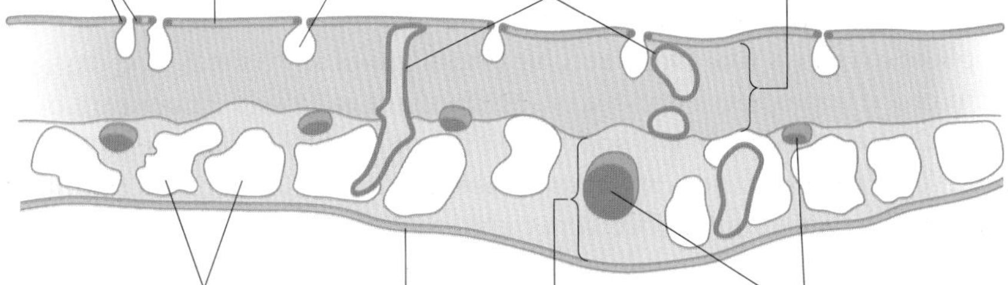

*Figure 3.3 Transverse section through leaf of water milfoil (*Myriophyllum sp.), *showing adaptations in totally submerged hydrophyte.*

epidermis lacks cuticle, stomata; contains chloroplasts

air spaces

vascular tissue lacks lignified cells

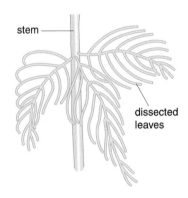

stem

dissected leaves

*Figure 3.4 Dissected leaves of water milfoil (*Myriophyllum sp.) *enable efficient gas exchange in an aquatic habitat*

stomata | upper epidermis with stomata | sub-stomatal air chamber | sclereids giving mechanical support | multilayered palisade tissue for photosynthesis

large air cavities | lower epidermis lacking stomata | spongy mesophyll tissue | leaf veins

*Figure 3.5 Transverse section through a leaf of water lily (*Nymphaea sp.). *The upper epidermis consists of thin-walled cells with a very thin cuticle.*

ADAPTATIONS TO THE ENVIRONMENT

*Figure 3.6 The aerial and submerged leaves of water crowfoot (*Ranunculus aquatilis*) have different adaptations because of their environment*

In addition, the petioles help to keep the leaf floating on the surface of the water.

Some hydrophytes, such as water crowfoot, have both aerial and submerged leaves (Figure 3.6). The submerged leaves often resemble those of plants such as Canadian pond weed or the water milfoils, being either small or dissected, and lacking a cuticle and stomata. The aerial leaves resemble those of mesophytes, with broad leaf blades, cuticles on the epidermis, and stomata.

Adaptations to salinity in flowering plants

Plants that can tolerate high levels of salt are referred to as **halophytes**, and typically are found growing in estuaries and salt-marshes, where their roots may be immersed in sea water. The degree of salinity to which they are exposed can vary, depending on their location and on the tides. Compared with sea water, salinity levels can be lower in a tidal estuary, but higher in a salt-marsh, because of the evaporation of water from the soil at low tides. Adaptations to these changing conditions often involve the maintenance of high salt concentrations in the plant tissues or the development of special tissues in which water can be stored.

Some animals can adapt to changes in salinity but, as many animals are motile, they generally will move to an area where they are best suited to the prevailing conditions.

Adaptations to water movements in aquatic organisms

Water movements include currents, and the ebb and flow of tides (the latter possibly interacting with air movements to bring about wave action). Any movement of water has an eroding action on soil and rocks and moves living organisms from one place to another, unless they are rooted or attached to a substratum. The churning action of water creates aeration of the water and also may contribute to the water's turbidity. Organisms in aquatic habitats show a wide range of adaptations to life in water.

Rate of flow in streams or rivers is an important parameter because of its influence on the organisms inhabiting the water. As the current increases, organisms that are unable to swim against it, or to take hold, are likely to be washed away. Faster flowing water is likely to be better oxygenated than sluggish or still water because of the mixing effect.

Adaptations to changing oxygen concentration in aquatic animals

A supply of oxygen is vital for all aerobic organisms in any habitat. The oxygen content of the atmosphere is more or less constant at around 21 per cent by volume. Oxygen content of the soil atmosphere is slightly lower, due to the respiration of soil organisms. In aquatic habitats, oxygen concentration can be very variable. In still, undisturbed water, the oxygen content may be very low, with anaerobic conditions in the mud at the bottom. Any disturbance of the water brings about aeration, so the water in a fast-flowing stream has a greater oxygen concentration than that in a pond. Also, the presence of actively photosynthesising plants and algae in the water can add significantly to the oxygen content, particularly on warm, bright days.

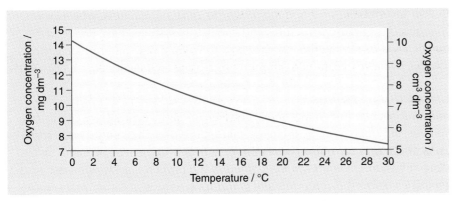

Figure 3.7 The oxygen content of water decreases as water temperature increases

Oxygen is soluble in water only to a limited extent; therefore, it is less available to aquatic organisms than to terrestrial organisms. In addition, as the temperature increases, the solubility of oxygen decreases. At 30 °C, the oxygen content of water decreases to about one half of that at 0 °C (Figure 3.7).

Another factor to consider is that oxygen diffuses more readily in air than it does in water. At 20 °C, the diffusion constant for oxygen in air is 11.0, whereas it is only 0.000034 in water. As air is less dense than water, convection currents are more easily established and ventilation movements associated with gaseous exchange require less energy.

There are many ways in which animals living in freshwater obtain the oxygen they require, and there are several adaptations to the varying oxygen concentrations found in aquatic habitats. Amongst invertebrates, oxygen may be obtained by diffusion over the entire body surface, or via specialised respiratory structures, such as gills, tracheae or lungs. The presence of respiratory pigments and circulatory systems enhances the distribution of oxygen from the respiratory surfaces to the metabolising cells.

Body size and surface area

In the smallest aquatic invertebrates, such as the protoctistans and cnidarians, there is a large surface area to volume ratio and the passive uptake of oxygen by diffusion from the surrounding water is sufficient to supply their needs. In a protoctistan, such as *Amoeba*, there is a lower concentration of oxygen inside the organism, due to aerobic respiration during metabolism, and a higher concentration of oxygen in the surrounding water. A diffusion gradient exists, but high metabolic rates can be maintained only if such organisms are 1 mm or less in diameter. The rate of diffusion through an organism decreases as the bulk increases.

In cnidarians, such as *Hydra*, the ectodermal and endodermal layers are thin: the endodermal layer is bathed by the water that circulates around the enteron, and gaseous exchange can occur here as well as in the ectodermal layer. In water fleas, such as *Daphnia*, oxygen diffuses in over the entire body surface when the oxygen concentration is high but, during winter, haemoglobin is synthesised to compensate for the reduction in the oxygen content of the water. This gives the organisms a pink colour.

Bulkier invertebrates, such as the flatworms (Platyhelminthes), which lack specialised respiratory structures and circulatory systems, have flattened bodies, thus increasing their surface area to volume ratio and reducing the internal distance over which diffusion takes place (see Figure 2.2 on page 28).

Circulatory systems

Annelids, such as the oligochaetes, polychaetes and leeches, have circulatory systems, although gaseous exchange takes place over their entire body surface. The surface area to volume ratio enables sufficient oxygen to be taken up and steep diffusion gradients are maintained as the oxygen quickly diffuses into the capillaries below the epidermis and is transported away to other parts of the body by the blood system. The respiratory pigment, haemoglobin, is present in the blood and enhances the oxygen-carrying capacity of the blood. This enables oxygen to be picked up readily in situations where it is more abundant and released where it is needed.

Respiratory pigments

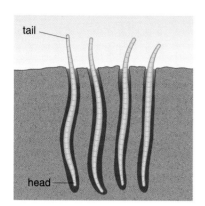

Tubifex is an oligochaete (Figure 3.8), which is well adapted to aquatic habitats where the oxygen concentration is in short supply. It lives, head downwards, in the mud at the bottom of rivers, where anaerobic conditions prevail as a result of oxygen depletion due to the activities of aerobic bacteria following high levels of organic pollution. Oxygen is obtained by diffusion through the posterior body wall and is taken up by the respiratory pigment, haemoglobin, present in the blood. *Tubifex* wave their tails rhythmically in the water: the lower the concentration of oxygen in the water, the greater the rate of tail-waving.

Figure 3.8 Tubifex *sp. obtain oxygen by diffusion; the lower the oxygen concentration in the water, the greater the rate of tail-waving*

Respiratory pigments are also present in the larvae of some of the members of the genus *Chironomus*. These larvae are known as 'blood worms' (Figure 3.9) and are able to survive in conditions where the oxygen concentration is low. In addition to the respiratory pigment, these larvae have gills, which are extensions of the body through which the blood flows and which are in contact with the water. These gills increase the surface area over which gaseous exchange can occur.

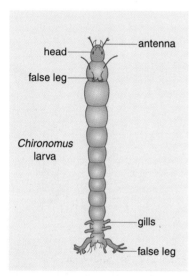

Figure 3.9 Gills in Chironomus *increase the surface area over which gaseous exchange can occur*

Respiratory structures

Tracheal systems

Adult insects have a well-developed tracheal system (Figure 3.11). Tracheae are formed by ingrowth of the ectodermal layer and are lined with cuticle, thickened to form rings or spiral ridges and thus keeping the tubes open for the passage of gases. Typically, these tubes open to the outside by means of **spiracles**, located on the thorax and abdomen. In fully aquatic insects and the aquatic larvae of insects, such as dragonflies and mayflies, spiracles are absent and so-called '**tracheal gills**' are present (see Figure 1.6 on page 7). These are plate-like structures, containing many fine branches of the tracheal system, and are situated immediately below the cuticle. In some dragonfly nymphs, these tracheal gills are situated in the rectum and are ventilated by muscular movements that also contribute to the locomotion of the nymph. There is no circulatory system or respiratory pigment involved in gaseous exchange in these organisms.

Breathing tubes or siphons

Aquatic insects that live in still water rely on the atmosphere for their oxygen supplies. These insects are able to rise to the water surface, in order to obtain air through spiracles, without being washed away by water currents. Adaptations such as breathing tubes or siphons (Figure 3.10) are found in the larvae of gnats (*Culex pipiens*) and drone flies (*Eristalis* sp.). In the gnat larvae, the siphons pierce the surface layer, whereas in the drone fly larvae (known as 'rat-tailed maggots'), which live on the bottom of shallow bodies of water, the siphons are telescopic and can be extended to 6 cm or more. The openings of the siphons are often surrounded by a fringe of hairs to prevent waterlogging.

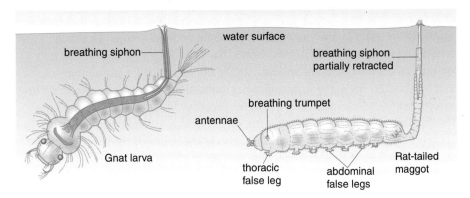

Figure 3.10 Different adaptations in these larvae allow for gas exchange

A number of beetles and water bugs transport air bubbles down into the water. The water boatman, *Notonecta glauca* (Figure 3.11), traps a single bubble among the hairs at the base of the abdomen. When this air has been used, the insect returns to the surface to obtain a fresh supply. In this way, sufficient oxygen is obtained for the organism's needs.

Lungs

Common pond snails, such as *Limnaea* and *Planorbis*, are adapted to life in still water with varying oxygen concentrations. In these gastropods, the inner surface of the mantle cavity functions as a lung, and they come to the surface to replenish their air supplies. The frequency with which they need to do this depends on the oxygen levels in the water. *Planorbis* has haemoglobin in its blood and thus is better adapted to poorly oxygenated conditions than *Limnaea*. The haemoglobin acts as an oxygen store and enables the animal to remain submerged for long periods of time. In contrast, *Limnaea* has no haemoglobin and the oxygen content of its blood decreases quite quickly, with a consequent decrease in its metabolic activity, so it must return to the surface more frequently.

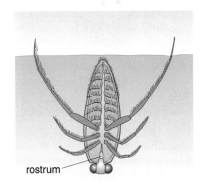

*Figure 3.11 The water boatman (*Notonecta glauca*) obtains oxygen by trapping bubbles of air under its abdomen*

4 Human ecology

Figure 4.1 Humans live in and tolerate a wide range of physical conditions, from the heat and aridity of the desert in Egypt (top) to the sub-zero temperatures of the North West Territories of Canada (bottom)

Figure 4.2 Ranulph Fiennes and Mike Stroud completing their 2050 km journey, on foot, across the Antarctic

The human species – distribution and tolerances

Human beings (*Homo sapiens*) are remarkably versatile in their living or habitat tolerances. Other animal species are often quite precise in their niche or habitat requirements and this is reflected in their distribution on a local and broader geographical scale. To illustrate this, we can look at desert lizards. In a small area there will be certain lizard species associated exclusively with sandy areas, other species will only be found clambering in the spiny bushes and yet others will be seen in and out of the crevices in rocky outcrops. The daily behaviour pattern of these lizards shows that they differ in their tolerance to the heat of the sun, with some being totally nocturnal. Their physiology enables them to conserve water, allowing survival in situations of extremely low water availability. European lizard species probably would not last long in the deserts of Central Asia. We say that the desert lizards are successfully adapted to their environment. We could look at a wide spectrum of animal species and find similar limits to their tolerance of a range of physical factors, such as light, temperature, altitude, salinity, oxygen concentration and pH.

By contrast, humans exist in a wide range of terrestrial environments, having extended their territories by use of buildings and clothing which protect them from unsuitable or extreme environmental conditions (Figure 4.1). Historically, regions inhabited by human populations have been determined largely by accessibility to land for food production and by the need for water – for people, for their crops and for their animals. Nevertheless, human populations show tolerance to wide temperature ranges, for example, from a hot 50 °C in July in the Sahara in Africa to a cold –65 °C in January in Yakutsk (in the former USSR). Most, however, prefer to live well away from these extremes. There are variations too in daylength in different parts of the globe. Arctic and Antarctic winters are totally dark for several weeks in the year, but have continuous light for a corresponding period in the summer. The upper limit for permanent settlements at high altitude is about 4500 m, though inside aircraft people are now able to cruise regularly at 10 000 m. Space travel has taken people to the moon, introducing space travellers to the experience of weightlessness. Travel in both aircraft and spacecraft is possible only by creating an artificial environment inside. Back on Earth, we spend a considerable part of our lives in artificially modified environments – houses, shops and offices – and sometimes go a short depth underground in mines, in road and rail tunnels or under cities.

Occasional exceptional feats have taken a few individuals outside the normally inhabited areas, but if the adverse conditions are too extreme or the human is subjected to them for too long, there comes a point when the body can cope no longer. We can look at the endurance shown by Ranulph Fiennes and Mike Stroud in the Antarctic during the winter of 1992 to 1993. For 97 days they journeyed on foot, dragging all their own supplies and equipment in their attempt to walk across the Antarctic continent (Figure 4.2). We can contrast their success with the failure of the Antarctic expedition in 1912, led by Robert Scott. One by one the men failed physically or mentally and though they reached the South Pole, none survived. All were beaten by starvation, cold and frostbite before they could reach safety and the ship home.

The human species has thus colonised a wide range of habitats and has shown its ability to tolerate considerable variation in the physical factors of the external environment. Nevertheless, the **internal environment** of the human body is maintained within quite narrow limits. The ability of an organism to control its internal environment is referred to as **homeostasis**. This is the result of internal physiological mechanisms which regulate factors such as body temperature, body water content, ionic composition, blood glucose concentration and oxygen concentration in the blood. The areas populated by the human species and the behavioural patterns which have evolved are such that the body regulatory mechanisms can operate satisfactorily.

This chapter on human ecology looks at humans in their environment and explores some of the ways in which the human body responds to variations in temperature and to the special effects of high altitude.

Temperature variations

Body temperature and thermoregulation

Human beings are described as **endotherms** and, like other mammals, are able to maintain a constant high body temperature independently of the external environmental temperature. In humans, normal body temperature is about 37 °C. With a clinical thermometer, we usually take the oral temperature (in the mouth) but we can also take a person's rectal temperature. The two values would be slightly different. The oral temperature is less reliable as it may vary according to recently consumed hot or cold foods and drinks, or because of breathing activities. If we were to use a thermocouple to measure temperature with greater precision, we would find that the body temperature is not the same throughout the tissues. The rectal temperature is close to the temperature of the deeper structures in the body, or the body **core**. Thus, when we speak of a constant body temperature, strictly speaking the term refers to the core temperature of the body, that is, the temperature inside the head, thorax and abdomen.

In humans, the temperature of the core fluctuates within a narrow range, normally between 36 and 37.5 °C. There is a clear diurnal (or daily) rhythm, with temperatures reaching a peak from midday to early afternoon and a trough during the night after midnight (Figure 4.3). This rhythm gradually becomes reversed if daily activity patterns change, for example, in workers on night shifts. In women the temperature is lowest during menstruation and rises noticeably at about the time of ovulation. Exercise may lead to a rise in core temperature, with a temperature as high as 41 °C being recorded in an athlete after a marathon race. Core temperature may also rise in response to emotional situations.

QUESTION

The estimated average energy requirement for a man aged between 19 and 50 years is about 20.6 MJ per day (1 MJ = 1000 kJ). The energy expenditure of Dr Mike Stroud and Sir Ranulph Fiennes, during their expedition across Antarctica, was between 23 and 44 MJ per day. What sort of diet would be required to provide this energy?

HUMAN ECOLOGY

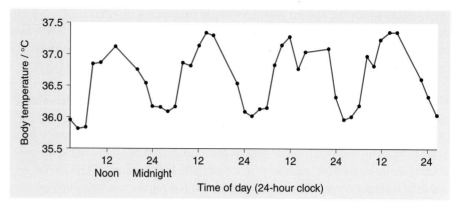

Figure 4.3 Diurnal variation in body temperature: mean body temperature of a group of 14 men, measured over a period of 4 days in a temperate climate. All were carrying out the same task.

If a steady temperature is to be maintained in the human body, heat loss must equal heat gain. Most of the heat gained is generated internally from metabolic activities (thermogenesis), though there may be some gain from the surroundings. Heat is produced at a fairly constant rate from metabolic activities in various organs in the body, such as the liver and heart. For a person at rest, the heat produced is approximately 4 kJ per kg body mass per hour. This is equivalent to about 170 kJ per square metre per hour, or about the same as a 40 watt light bulb. Activity in skeletal muscles increases heat production and short bursts of vigorous exercise may increase the heat produced by more than 10 times the level at rest. A brisk walk (or jog or game of squash) does a lot to warm the body on a cold day. Shivering is a specialised form of uncoordinated muscle activity which produces heat, to about five times the level at rest. Shivering thermogenesis may be initiated when the body becomes cooled and lasts for a few minutes at a time. Heat may be gained from the environment in situations where air temperature is higher than the temperature of the skin. The body also gains heat by direct radiation from the sun, from a fire or artificial heater, and indirectly from reflected radiation. Some heat is gained directly from the consumption of hot food and drink.

Figure 4.4 The balance between heat gain and heat loss in the maintenance of a stable body (core) temperature. Heat gain may be the result of internal generation (thermogenesis) from metabolism, including exercise and shivering, or external gain from the environment, hot food and drink. Heat loss involves the skin, through conduction, convection, radiation and evaporation through sweating.

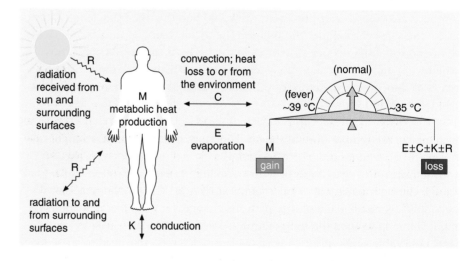

When the body is hotter than the surrounding environment, heat may be lost by direct radiation from the body, by conduction through areas of the body touching cooler objects or by convection to the surrounding air (Figure 4.4). The skin covers the surface of the body and plays a very important part in regulating the loss of heat from the body and thus in maintaining the required balance between heat gain and heat loss.

The role of skin in temperature regulation

To understand the role of the skin in temperature regulation, it is important to look at its general structure, shown in Figure 4.5. Heat loss from the skin occurs by conduction, radiation and evaporation of sweat. Heat loss by conduction and radiation can be varied by altering the blood flow to superficial capillaries. The diameter of arterioles in the skin is controlled by sympathetic nerves originating in the hypothalamus. External cold results in a decrease in the diameter of these vessels (vasoconstriction) and the blood flow to capillaries is reduced. This reduces the loss of heat. Conversely, in warm conditions, the diameter of skin arterioles increases (vasodilatation), resulting in increased blood flow in the peripheral circulation and leading to a considerable increase in heat loss.

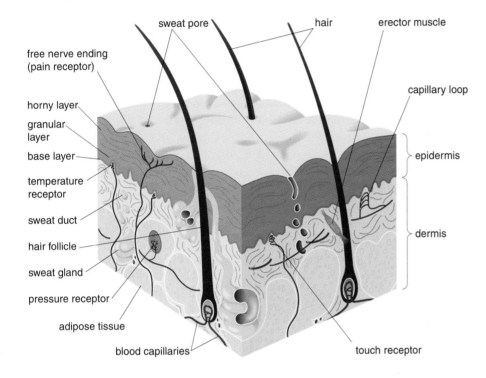

Figure 4.5 The structure of human skin showing structures involved in temperature regulation

In hot situations, an important means of heat loss is through evaporation of moisture from the sweat glands or from the inside surface of the lungs and mouth. When 1 g of water vapourises it requires 2.42 kJ of heat and this latent heat is taken from the immediate surroundings, resulting in cooling. Thermal sweating occurs when the external temperature or body temperature rises. Sweat glands secrete a dilute solution containing sodium chloride (salt), urea and lactic acid. Heavy sweating involves rapid loss of water and salt from the body. Dehydration and salt deprivation will occur unless enough water is drunk and adequate amounts of salt are taken to replace the losses.

In cold conditions, smooth muscles attached to hair follicles in the skin contract, raising the hairs. This is important in many mammals as it helps to trap a layer of air in their fur. Air is a poor conductor of heat so this helps to insulate the body against excessive heat loss. The insulating effect of hair is minimal in humans, except on the head, and lack of hair in bald adults and babies can lead to significant heat losses. We should all take heed of the advice to wear a hat in cold weather! The layer of adipose tissue also makes a contribution as a means of insulation because fat is a poor conductor of heat.

In most situations people wear clothes. This clothing has a protective effect which alters the exchange of heat between the body and the immediate environment. Clothes have an insulating effect when dry, so, to some extent, clothes modify the relationship of the skin with the immediate environment by creating a 'microclimate' close to the body. We spend a considerable proportion of our time indoors and the design of buildings also serves to protect us from the natural environmental temperature. Clothing and buildings are behavioural responses which help maintain the required balance between heat loss and heat gain.

The **thermoneutral zone** (TNZ) refers to the range of external (environmental) temperatures over which heat production by metabolism is at a minimum. The thermoneutral zone has been defined as 27 to 31 °C for a naked 70 kg man. The lowest temperature (27 °C) is known as the **critical temperature**. The thermoneutral zone is a useful concept in the understanding of the operation of body temperature control mechanisms, but in reality people usually wear clothing so the critical environmental temperature would be much lower than the defined temperature of 27 °C. Figure 4.6 indicates the relative importance of the different temperature regulation processes. Within the TNZ, any changes in body temperature are compensated by adjustment in blood flow in the peripheral vessels, that is, by vasoconstriction or vasodilatation. When the surrounding environmental temperature falls below the critical temperature, non-evaporative heat loss increases, so if the core temperature is to be maintained, the balance is restored by increased production of metabolic heat. At environmental temperatures higher than the TNZ, you can see that evaporative heat loss by sweating is the most important means of thermoregulation.

Figure 4.6 The thermoneutral zone (TNZ) refers to the range of environmental temperatures at which heat production by metabolism in the body is at a minimum. The graph gives values for a naked 70 kg man.

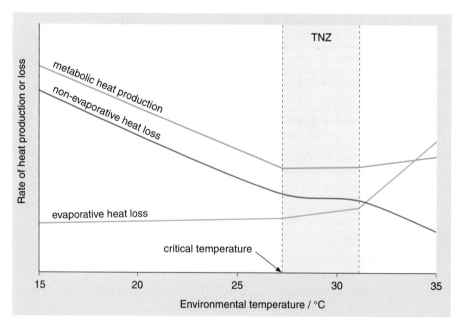

The next sections look at how humans respond to extremes in environmental temperatures in both hot and cold environments. Physiological and behavioural responses are seen, but when conditions are such that temperature regulation processes are inadequate or fail, the body suffers from stress.

Extremes of temperature

Response to high temperature – acclimatisation and heat stress

If you live in a cool or temperate climate and pay a visit to a much hotter place, in the tropics or hot desert, at first you feel very uncomfortable. For a few days you are likely to lack energy even for walking around, perhaps you find you cannot think very clearly and probably have little appetite. Then you begin to adjust, or **acclimatise**, and gradually find you can carry on your daily activities much as you did in the cooler place. You would, however, be wise to start your activities early in the morning when it is cooler, and be less active around midday and early afternoon when temperatures are at their highest. It would also be sensible to wear loose and generally light-coloured clothing, but you should not necessarily abandon all clothing and you should certainly not sunbathe in the direct heat of the sun.

In the hot climate, reduction of physical activity and reduced food intake mean that less heat is generated internally as a result of muscular and metabolic activity. A preference may develop for foods with high water content, such as fruit and salads, and this may be related to the thirst mechanisms attempting to prevent potential dehydration in the heat. In response to the high temperatures, blood vessels in the skin dilate, bringing more blood near the surface. But because the environmental temperature may be close to or higher than normal body temperature, there is likely to be little or no heat loss to the surroundings as a result of conduction, convection or radiation. Evaporation of sweat thus becomes the most important means of losing heat and so cooling the body.

We will consider the effects of sweating in two different extremes of hot climate: hot and humid (as in tropical regions or in factories, mines and other enclosed environments) and hot and dry (as in desert conditions). When humidity is high, less sweat evaporates and sometimes sweating may cease altogether. Inability to lose heat through evaporation of sweat in these situations is serious and quickly leads to rise of the body core temperature. At the other extreme, if humidity is low, sweating is an effective way of losing heat. In temperatures as high as 40 °C a person may feel perfectly cool and comfortable, particularly if the clothing is loose, thus allowing sweat to evaporate from the body surface. The danger comes after prolonged exposure to high temperatures if the components of sweat are not replaced. Excessive loss of water through sweating leads to dehydration of body tissues. Loss of ions in the sweat, particularly of sodium (Na^+) and chloride (Cl^-), depletes these from body fluids and is likely to lead to painful muscular cramps.

Alteration of sweat production appears to be the main response to hot conditions as the body acclimatises. This effect is shown in Figure 4.7. Data for this study were obtained from people doing physical work in an artificial environment, who were subjected to high temperatures for different lengths of time. Equivalent results are obtained when the body temperature is raised without the person indulging in physical work. It seems that similar increases in the rate of sweating occur in people of different ethnic groups, though females usually show lower rates than males. This may be because females tend to undertake less vigorous physical activity than men, though it is of interest that some female athletes do show rates of sweating which are comparable with those of men. People who normally live in hot climates appear to have an initially high rate of sweating compared with those from cooler climates but show a similar response when exposed to higher than normal temperatures. Another effect of acclimatisation is that the sweat produced has a lower salt concentration, thus reducing the harmful loss of salt from body fluids. People living in hot climates may find it advisable (and desirable) to take extra salt with their food or drinks.

Figure 4.7 Acclimatisation and sweating: a group of people exposed to hot conditions for 5 or 6 days at a time over a period of 4 weeks showed a noticeable increase in sweat loss. The dashed line on the graph shows the average sweat loss of the people in the group for approximately 4 weeks before the experiment.

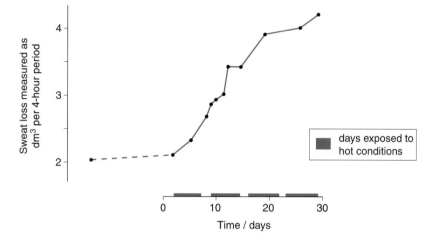

People living in hot climates have evolved traditional clothing and housing that are usually highly effective in helping them to tolerate heat. Clothing which covers the body minimises direct exposure of the skin to the radiation of the sun; loose clothing allows for evaporation of sweat and also keeps a still layer of air next to the skin, which insulates against excessive absorption of heat; light colours reflect the heat (Figure 4.8). Clusters of compact, thick-walled mud houses with only narrow slits for windows, characteristic of villages in deserts, remain remarkably cool inside (Figure 4.9). Modern buildings use air conditioning, with controlled temperature and ventilation, in an attempt to provide comfortable working and living conditions, particularly for visitors from a cold climate.

Figure 4.8 Traditional clothing of desert people: Bedouin in Sahara Desert

Figure 4.9 Typical desert village in Afghanistan, with thick-walled mud houses

When the body can no longer cope with excessively high temperatures, problems of **heat stress** arise. The skin may suffer from sunburn when exposed directly to excessive radiation from the sun. Redness, blistering and peeling of the epithelium occurs. Increased production of the pigment melanin, associated with a tan, gradually gives some protection from the sun's radiation. An irritation known as prickly heat may develop due to blocking or narrowing of the ducts from the sweat glands, with the result that sweat cannot reach the skin surface.

In some situations a person may feel dizzy or suffer from **heat collapse**, probably because blood is diverted away from the internal organs to the skin and skeletal muscles. Recovery usually occurs quickly if the person is taken to a cool environment or lies down. **Heat exhaustion** is a more serious condition which may be due to dehydration because fluid lost in sweating has not been replaced. With a loss of 5 to 8 per cent of the body fluid, fatigue sets in, and with a 10 per cent reduction in body fluid, mental and physical deterioration occur. With further decrease in body fluid, intracellular fluid is withdrawn and this starts to cause damage to cells. Heat exhaustion may also result when losses of sodium chloride are not replaced.

The most severe condition is known as **heat stroke**, characterised by a breakdown of the temperature regulation mechanisms. This appears to be associated mainly with a failure or inadequacy of the sweating mechanism. At core temperatures of 42 °C or higher, irreversible damage to cells and proteins occurs and the person is likely to go into a coma. Unless immediate steps are taken to lower the body temperature, death may follow. It should be appreciated that the upper limit of tolerance to temperature is only a few degrees above normal core temperature.

Response to low temperature – acclimatisation and cold stress

The body's response to extreme cold is not simply a reverse of its response to heat. To begin with, 'coldness' may be due to very low environmental temperatures but people can also suffer from cold in more moderate temperatures, particularly in windy conditions. Moving air blows away the warm layer of air immediately surrounding the body and increases the loss of heat by convection. This **wind chill** factor (Figure 4.10) is made worse if the body surface and any clothing being worn are wet, because further cooling occurs due to evaporation of water. Another difference when considering response to cold rather than heat is that the temperature gradient between the body surface and surrounding temperature is likely to be far greater in cold conditions. In many parts of the world, the surrounding temperature is well below the core temperature of 37 °C; indeed temperatures in the region of –40 °C may be experienced in some places normally inhabited by humans. The body can tolerate and recover from a lowering of core temperature by as much as 10 °C, whereas a rise in temperature of only 4 °C may prove lethal. If the body temperature is to be maintained close to 37 °C, the focus is on generation of internal heat and on protection and insulation of the body to **conserve** heat.

HUMAN ECOLOGY

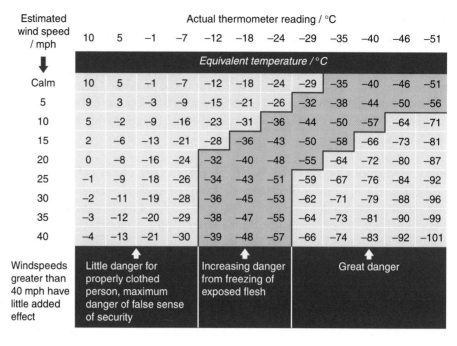

Figure 4.10 The wind chill effect: the table shows how increasing wind speed lowers the effective temperature on exposed skin. Look for the wind speed in the left-hand column and the actual temperature across the top. From this, you can find the equivalent temperature on exposed skin. Wind speeds are given in miles per hour (mph) in line with familiar usage.

Estimated wind speed / mph ↓	Actual thermometer reading / °C											
	10	5	−1	−7	−12	−18	−24	−29	−35	−40	−46	−51
	Equivalent temperature / °C											
Calm	10	5	−1	−7	−12	−18	−24	−29	−35	−40	−46	−51
5	9	3	−3	−9	−15	−21	−26	−32	−38	−44	−50	−56
10	5	−2	−9	−16	−23	−31	−36	−44	−50	−57	−64	−71
15	2	−6	−13	−21	−28	−36	−43	−50	−58	−66	−73	−81
20	0	−8	−16	−24	−32	−40	−48	−55	−64	−72	−80	−87
25	−1	−9	−18	−26	−34	−43	−51	−59	−67	−76	−84	−92
30	−2	−11	−19	−28	−36	−45	−53	−62	−71	−79	−88	−96
35	−3	−12	−20	−29	−38	−47	−55	−64	−73	−81	−90	−99
40	−4	−13	−21	−30	−39	−48	−57	−66	−74	−83	−92	−101

Windspeeds greater than 40 mph have little added effect

Little danger for properly clothed person, maximum danger of false sense of security	Increasing danger from freezing of exposed flesh	Great danger

Increased metabolic rate in response to cold conditions leads to increased heat production. This can be stimulated by the hormones adrenaline and thyroxine. A person is likely to have a better appetite for food in cold conditions, thus increasing food intake. Voluntary muscular movements during physical activity and involuntary shivering also contribute to the generation of heat, though shivering is likely to be sustained only for short periods.

Diversion of blood away from the body surface by **vasoconstriction** is an important means of conserving heat. Reduced blood flow to the skin means that less heat is lost by conduction and convection from the body surface. Vasoconstriction for a prolonged period would restrict blood flow to the extremities of the limbs, that is, the fingers and hands, toes and feet. This could cause damage to the tissues and is counteracted by occasional dilation of the blood vessels in what is described as the 'hunting reaction'. Without this reaction, fingers tend to become numb or paralysed and loss of manual dexterity would lead to serious difficulties. The tendency to curl up the fingers, or indeed the whole body, with arms folded, when it is cold reduces the surface area exposed and illustrates another way of reducing heat loss to the surroundings.

Fat present as a subcutaneous layer provides **insulation**. This cannot be turned on and off at short notice, but development of a fat layer in certain people may be an advantage, for example, to long-distance swimmers immersed in water for long periods. Young babies, up to about 6 months old, may benefit from 'brown fat', which generates additional heat by its metabolism rather than insulation effects. It is unlikely that brown fat plays a major part in the heat balance of adults.

Probably the most important way of protecting people from the cold is by conserving heat through **insulation** of the body, hence the importance of suitable clothing and buildings. In extreme temperatures and where wind chill might be significant, it is necessary for clothing to be windproof. Even though windproofing is important it can lead to discomfort due to condensation of moisture produced from the body. In extreme cold, this moisture may freeze inside the garment. Air is a good insulator, so the most effective clothing includes a number of layers which trap air, provided the air is dry (Figure 4.11). The design of clothing needs to allow for adequate physical activity and in this respect very heavy clothing may be cumbersome. In temperatures below freezing, the face and limb extremities become vulnerable if inadequately protected. Inside buildings additional heat is supplied artificially from fires, electrically or by other systems of central heating. An important economic consideration is the adequate insulation of the building as a means of saving energy and this is given high priority in the design of modern buildings. Traditional housing in cold climates usually has thick walls and small windows, thus minimising loss of heat, which is likely to be supplied from an open fire. The hard-packed snow used to construct Inuit (Eskimo) igloos has excellent insulating properties.

Figure 4.11 Clothing in an environment of extreme cold: an Inuit in the Arctic region of Canada

People living permanently in cold climates show certain physiological adaptations, though their main means of protection is through clothing and housing. One study showed that native Australians were able to sleep well, even though naked, in temperatures around freezing, whereas unacclimatised white people shivered violently and were unable to sleep properly in similar conditions. Inuit people have a greater blood flow through the hands and feet than do visitors in the same conditions, and the traditionally high protein diet of the Inuit may contribute to their high metabolic rate. Acclimatisation to cold by people who travel from warmer to colder climates does occur, but compared with acclimatisation to heat, it is less easy to define the mechanisms. It is likely that increased food intake, leading to increased metabolic rate, is an important response, though the most important consideration is to ensure adequate protection by means of suitable clothing and housing.

When the body can no longer cope with the effects of cold, problems of **cold stress** may result. **Cold injury** is characterised by actual damage to tissues, most often the hands, feet and face, because of their direct exposure to low temperatures. Severely reduced blood circulation deprives the tissues of nutrients and their normal metabolic reactions. In mild form, chilblains may develop as the parts become tender and itchy. In more severe conditions, tissues actually freeze and this is known as **frostbite** (Figure 4.12). If this is only superficial, the tissues are likely to recover and injured skin is replaced by new growth. If exposure is prolonged or tissues are deeply frozen, underlying tissues, including muscle and bone, may suffer permanent damage. This is caused by the mechanical action of ice crystals on the cell structure and also by the dehydrating effects of removing liquid water from body fluids. Gangrene may set in, resulting in loss of toes or fingers. The condition known as **trench foot** is usually a result of prolonged cooling in cold water. Trench foot is characterised by blackening of the skin of the toes and foot. The main damage is to the muscles and nerves and can lead to gangrene if the affected limbs are not warmed up quickly.

Figure 4.12 Frostbitten toes, post treatment. Frostbite refers to tissue damage due to freezing, from the destructive effects of the formation of extracellular ice crystals. Frostbitten parts need to be gently warmed in tepid water. Precautions are required against bacterial infection, to which frostbitten skin is susceptible.

Hypothermia develops when the core temperature falls to 35 °C or below. Down to 35 °C shivering increases, but already the muscles are likely to be at a lower temperature. Below 35 °C there are signs of muscle weakness and the person shows difficulty in walking and coordinating movements. By 34 °C the person becomes mentally confused and vision is disturbed. Loss of consciousness occurs between 32 and 30 °C and death usually follows at between 28 and 25 °C if the person is not warmed up. Probably the most important effect of the lowering of core temperature is the reduction of the heart rate. Cooler blood flowing through the heart affects the **pacemaker** (sinoatrial node) that initiates the heart beat. Reduced blood output from the heart means that the coronary circulation and flow to muscles and the brain may be inadequate, hence the symptoms associated with hypothermia. People suffering from hypothermia may also show a slower respiration rate and increased production of urine. The latter is linked to suppressed release of antidiuretic hormone (ADH).

Recovery from hypothermia can be complete provided the body is warmed quickly. A number of deaths from hypothermia, or **exposure**, do occur each year among walkers and mountain climbers, even on the hills of Britain, usually through a combination of physical fatigue and inadequate protective clothing. Immersion in cold water can quickly lead to hypothermia and accidental deaths in water are often due to hypothermia rather than drowning. Compared with air, water has a higher thermal conductivity so the body cools faster when surrounded by water. Survival time of a naked unprotected person is about 90 minutes in water at 15 °C, but only 30 minutes at 5 °C. Attempts to swim to safety after an accident in cold water are probably misjudged, since the movement disturbs any remaining layer of warm air adjacent to the skin and the activity uses up valuable metabolic reserves.

Young babies and old people are particularly vulnerable to hypothermia. Up to about 1 year old, babies are unable to shiver and also their behavioural responses are limited. Old people generally show less physical activity and have a lower metabolic rate, thus reducing internal heat generation. Their temperature control mechanisms, originating in the hypothalamus, are usually less effective with respect to the responses such as shivering, vasoconstriction and increase in oxygen consumption. In some cases the hypothalamus sets the temperature at too low a level. For those living on low incomes the situation may be made worse by inadequate heating and clothing.

In some surgical operations, involving the heart or brain for example, hypothermia may be deliberately induced by cooling the blood or body surface. This is used as a short-term means of reducing blood flow and use of oxygen in the tissues and allows the operation to take place. In these situations, body temperature can be lowered temporarily to about 25 °C.

QUESTIONS

A question of clothing

A manufacturer of specialist outdoor clothing advertises its garments by promoting the benefit of several layers of clothing (Figure 4.13). In their garments, they emphasise the following features:

- the 'wicking' properties of the inner layer (next to the skin);
- the choice of several different layers depending on external conditions;
- the importance of a windproof and/or waterproof outer layer;
- the overall light weight of their garments.

Imagine you are walking for several hours in the mountains, in wet, windy conditions with temperatures near to freezing, and you are wearing this type of clothing.

1. What do you think the manufacturer means by 'wicking' and why is this beneficial?
2. How do several layers keep you warm?
3. Why is it important that the outer layer is windproof?
4. Explain what features should be incorporated into the design of the waterproof material to make sure it is effective in these conditions.
5. Explain why it is important to pay attention also to the design of hats, gloves and boots worn in these conditions.
6. Why are lightweight garments preferable to heavy clothing?
7. How far do you think the manufacturer's claims about their garments are biologically sound?
8. Why don't you just stay at home? What benefits do you get from your walk? Is it really worth the effort?

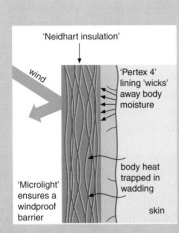

Figure 4.13 Clothing (from Rohan) designed to provide 'one stop insulation': an outer layer of 'Microlight', a middle layer of 'Neidhart insulation' (thin, stable, featherweight) and an inner layer of 'Pertex'. Successful insulation is achieved by trapping still air next to the body.

High altitude

Mount Everest, or *Chomolungma* ('Goddess Mother of the Earth') in Tibetan, was first climbed in 1953. The climbers were part of a large-scale expedition, with many people involved in the team. The whole expedition required considerable planning and meticulous attention to detail with regard to routes to be taken, specialised equipment required, food stores and oxygen supplies. When Hillary and Tenzing stood at 8848 m, on the summit of the highest peak in the world, their success showed that humans can overcome the extremes of physical conditions associated with the highest mountains, in terms of exposure to cold, low levels of oxygen and dangerously hazardous terrain (Figure 4.14).

Since then, very few people have climbed Mt Everest solo and without the help of extra oxygen: two who have achieved this are Reinhold Messner in 1980 and Alison Hargreaves in 1995. An increasing number of other climbers have now reached the summits of Everest and of the remaining peaks over 8000 m. Many, however, have endured the hardships without the success. Some have lost their lives in the attempt (including Alison Hargreaves a few weeks after her success on Everest); others have become victims of frostbite and sacrificed toes or fingers. Nobody can stay for long at those heights: realistically a few hours at the most. The urgent need is to summon both the physical energy and mental concentration to make a safe descent to lower altitudes.

Figure 4.14 Mountaineers face difficult terrain and are exposed to harsh physical conditions

People at high altitude

People **native** to high altitudes are seen as rugged, robust and sturdy, able to live successfully and in equilibrium with the particular conditions characteristic of high altitude. These qualities may be due partly to the outdoor lifestyle associated with the mountain environment, but also indicate that the natives are well adapted to the rigours of life at high altitude. For convenience, we will define 'high altitude' as being above 3000 m. Using this as an arbitrary limit, we find the main native high-altitude populations in the Himalayan region of Asia (notably Tibetans and Nepalese) and in the Peruvian Andes of South America (Quechua Indians) (Figure 4.15). The upper limit for permanent settlements is about 4500 m in both regions, though to some extent this is a reflection of historical events and of accessibility and not determined solely by the altitude itself.

Figure 4.15 Natives in high mountain regions: (left) shepherd in Himalayan region of north-west India (4000 m); (centre) Tibetan woman, western China (3200 m); (right) Quechua Indian woman and child, Peru (4000 m)

Visitors to these high altitudes from the lowlands may suffer varying degrees of discomfort and illness (Figure 4.16a). With increasing numbers of tourists visiting high mountain regions for short periods, these effects are becoming more familiar. If, on a quick trip up Mount Kenya, you spend a night below the peaks in a hut at about 4500 m, you are likely to have a persistent headache, probably slight nausea and an extreme disinclination to continue with your journey the next day. Trekkers in the Himalayan mountains, from altitudes of about 3000 m and higher, find that their movements become slower. They are likely to stop frequently and also experience difficulty in maintaining steady breathing, or may become very conscious of it. Similar difficulties have been encountered by military personnel unaccustomed to life at high altitude, for example, when controlling border disputes in the Himalayan region. The problems are worst during the first few days at high altitude and can be much more severe if the ascent is rapid, perhaps by motor vehicle or even by plane. Bus passengers in the Andes are sometimes supplied with oxygen when their journey takes them over high passes. Certainly, the best way to get into the mountains is a slow plod on foot. The effects usually disappear rapidly on descent to lower altitudes.

These symptoms described for visitors to high altitudes can be attributed primarily to the lower levels of oxygen, though some effects are a result of unfamiliar physical demands of mountain terrain and, at extreme heights, of the cold. The symptoms, collectively known as **acute mountain sickness**, include: headaches (mild to severe); lack of concentration and giddiness; coughing and difficulty with breathing; palpitation and very rapid beating of the heart; loss of appetite, feelings of nausea and vomiting; muscular weakness, exhaustion and poor coordination; reduced production of urine, swelling, particularly of the legs, and also development of excessive fluid in the lungs; a general disinclination for exertion or coherent thinking and frequent difficulty in sleeping (Figure 4.16b). At extreme heights, or in severe cases, loss of consciousness or death may occur, unless the sufferer is brought rapidly to a lower level. Development of symptoms of mountain sickness depends on the rate at which the ascent is made but the severity is unpredictable, and fit young males are often more prone to suffering than the middle-aged or females.

Environmental conditions at high altitude

The physical conditions in high mountains which lead to the symptoms of mountain sickness are dominated by low levels of oxygen, known as **hypoxia**. In addition, the body has to withstand low temperature, high winds, low humidity and increased solar radiation. These physical conditions impose considerable stress on the human body.

Oxygen and hypoxia

The percentage of oxygen in the atmosphere remains constant, at about 21 per cent, from sea level to the peaks of the highest mountains and up to at least 110 000 m. However, air is a compressible gas, which means that at sea level, there are more molecules per unit volume than there are at high altitude. Thus, at high altitude, there are fewer molecules per unit volume so the atmospheric pressure is less. The part of the pressure due to the oxygen molecules is called the partial pressure, or pO_2. It is the partial pressure of oxygen that effectively determines the amount of oxygen available at the lung surface for uptake and transport into the body tissues.

Figure 4.17 shows that, at sea level, atmospheric pressure is approximately 100 kPa so the partial pressure of oxygen is 21 per cent of this, or 21 kPa. At 3500 m, the atmospheric pressure is 65.5 kPa, giving a partial pressure of oxygen of 13.8 kPa. At 8500 m, approaching the summit of Everest, atmospheric pressure is reduced to 31.9 kPa and the partial pressure becomes 6.7 kPa. This is only 31 per cent of its value at sea level.

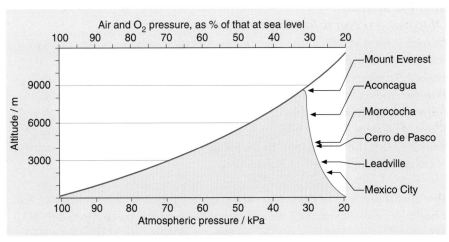

Figure 4.17 Changes in air pressure with altitude

(a)

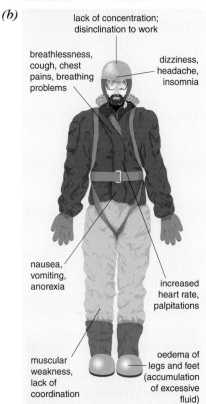

(b)

Figure 4.16 (a) Visitors on Mount Kenya at about 4000 m, already struggling and losing interest with still another 1000 m of height to climb to reach Point Lenana, one of the three summits; (b) mountain sickness and its symptoms

Cold temperatures, low humidity, high winds and solar radiation

Air **temperature** drops approximately 1 °C for each 150 m of ascent, though this varies in different mountain ranges around the world. However, a rough estimate indicates that, compared with sea level in a nearby area or equivalent latitude, the temperature at 3500 m is likely to be 23 °C lower, and at 8500 m 56 °C lower. This emphasises the need, at very high altitudes, to conserve body heat by providing good insulation in terms of clothing worn and housing, or portable tents in the case of mountaineers.

Humidity of the air is often low at high altitudes. This leads to an increased loss of heat from the body as a consequence of evaporation of sweat. Mountaineers frequently suffer from dryness and cracking of the lips or other exposed parts of the skin. There is also a tendency to develop a persistent cough, because breathing is usually through the mouth and the air is cold and dry. Loss of water from the body by evaporation brings a danger of dehydration. Plants found growing at high altitudes tend to show xeromorphic (water-conserving) features, giving further evidence of the low humidity in these regions. In addition, strong winds are frequently associated with mountain regions, which adds to the potential heat loss from the body due to the wind chill factor.

Solar radiation increases at high altitudes because there are fewer molecules (of oxygen, nitrogen and ozone) per unit volume of the atmosphere. These molecules effectively absorb and scatter radiation at various wavelengths. Ultraviolet radiation at 3000 m is about double that at sea level because of the reduced ozone at high altitude. Excessive ultraviolet radiation may damage the cornea of the eye, a condition known as **snow blindness**, and mountaineers frequently wear dark goggles to protect their eyes. Exposure to ultraviolet radiation may lead to a higher incidence of skin cancer; reflection from snow intensifies the effects of radiation on exposed skin. During the daytime the high solar radiation can provide additional heat for the body, though temperatures fall rapidly at night. A climber on Mt Everest at 8530 m was able to remove his down-filled clothing without suffering from cold when in the full sun and at low wind velocity.

Physiological responses of the body to hypoxia at high altitude
Obtaining oxygen for respiration

Oxygen is used in cells in the process of respiration, which releases energy for the many metabolic and physical activities of the body. Any reduction in available oxygen leads to impairment of a range of body functions, and, in extreme cases, to death. To reach the mitochondria in the cells where the respiratory reactions take place, the oxygen molecules must pass through a series of barriers. There is effectively an oxygen **cascade**, down a gradient of pressure from the atmosphere to the inside of the cells. The stages for transfer of oxygen are summarised in Figure 4.18.

The partial pressure of oxygen at each stage is a measure of its availability. For a healthy person at sea level, the difference between the partial pressure (pO_2) of inspired air and the final pO_2 in the blood capillaries surrounding the body cells is sufficiently great for there to be no difficulty for the oxygen to reach the mitochondria. However, at higher altitudes, because of the lower pO_2 of oxygen in the atmosphere, this gradient is reduced considerably. The body responds in several ways to overcome or compensate for the effects. Native high-altitude people have already adjusted to the lower pO_2 of oxygen, whereas visitors beome **acclimatised** and usually adjust after a number of days.

DEFINITION

Hypoxia is the term used to describe a low partial pressure of oxygen which is insufficient for haemoglobin to become fully saturated. This may be due to a low partial pressure of oxygen in the air, for example, at high altitude where although the percentage of oxygen in the air is normal, the air pressure is low.

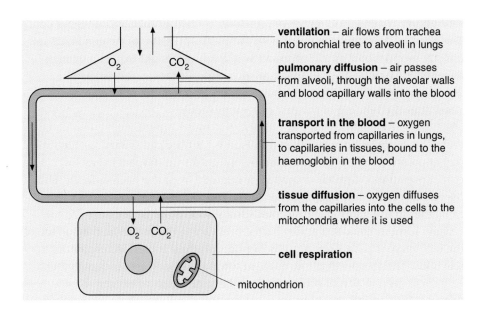

The gradient in pO$_2$ at these different stages is shown in Figure 4.19. It compares the fall in pO$_2$ for a person living at sea level with that of a native highlander living at 4540 m and a 'visiting' climber at 6000 m. When air enters the bronchial tree inside the lungs, it becomes saturated with water vapour, which itself exerts a partial pressure. Expired carbon dioxide in the lungs also exerts a partial pressure and these two gases account for the immediate steep fall in pO$_2$ inside the alveoli.

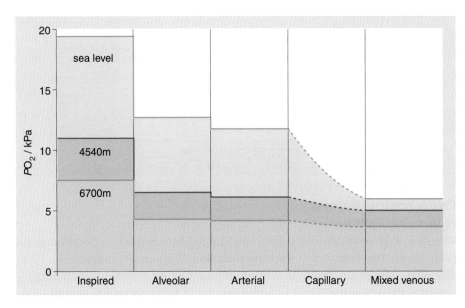

Figure 4.19 Oxygen cascade from inspired air to venous blood. Changes in the partial pressure of oxygen (pO$_2$) for three groups of people: natives living at sea level, natives living at 4540 m and visitors (climbers) at 6700 m. The small gradient at high altitude makes it more difficult for oxygen to be taken up by the cells.

Haemoglobin in the red blood cells combines with oxygen to form oxyhaemoglobin. The reaction between haemoglobin and oxygen is summarised in the equation

$$\underset{\text{haemoglobin}}{\text{Hb}} + 4O_2 \rightleftharpoons \underset{\text{oxyhaemoglobin}}{\text{HbO}_8}$$

The term **percentage saturation** is used to give a measure of the amount of oxyhaemoglobin in relation to (deoxy)haemoglobin in the blood. In practice, saturation of haemoglobin with oxygen is rarely higher than about 95 per cent. The percentage saturation varies with the partial pressure of oxygen but is not directly proportional to it. Expressed as a graph, we might expect a straight line, but the typical sigmoid shape of such curves (known as dissociation curves) is due to the way in which the affinity of haemoglobin for oxygen alters after the binding of the first oxygen molecule.

From the dissociation curve shown in Figure 4.20, we can see that at high partial pressures of oxygen the haemoglobin takes up oxygen, but at low partial pressures oxygen is unloaded or released from the haemoglobin. Thus oxygen is collected by haemoglobin in the blood flowing through the capillaries in the lungs at the alveolar surface where partial pressure are high. Oxygen is then off-loaded at low partial pressure in the tissues at the surface of the cell; there it passes to the mitochondria where it is used in respiratory reactions. The steepness of the curve at low partial pressures indicates that a very small drop in partial pressure allows large amounts of oxygen to be released. The critical partial pressure of oxygen needed at the mitochondria for oxidative reactions to take place is less than 0.4 kPa. If we look at the flat part of the curve, we can also see that the partial pressure of oxygen in the alveoli can drop from 13.3 to 8 kPa without making any appreciable difference to the degree of saturation of the haemoglobin. Thus, at moderate altitude, people do not suffer from a reduced uptake of oxygen by haemoglobin.

Figure 4.20 Oxygen dissociation curve of haemoglobin showing the percentage saturation with increasing partial pressure of oxygen, at 37 °C and pH 7.4

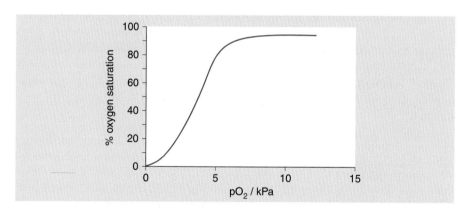

Overcoming hypoxia
Hyperventilation

Visitors to high altitudes notice an immediate increase in their rate of breathing, even at rest. This is known as **hyperventilation**. The response may be observed from about 3000 m upwards and is also found in native highlanders. Quechua Indians in the Peruvian Andes breathe at a rate about 30 per cent higher than people at sea level, though visitors maintain a rate higher than that of the native highlanders. As well as more rapid breathing, the breaths may be deeper. This hyperventilation increases the ventilation inside the alveoli and increases the pO_2 of oxygen at the boundary between the alveoli and the blood.

Another consequence of hyperventilation is increased exhalation of carbon dioxide, which results in a degree of **alkalaemia**, or abnormally high pH in the blood. (Carbon dioxide dissolves in the blood to form carbonic acid, which increases the acidity, or lowers the pH.) The acid–alkali balance in the blood must be restored to avoid further physiological effects. A complication arises because the level of carbon dioxide in the arterial blood is one factor which controls the rate of breathing (hence ventilation). As the carbon dioxide level in the blood falls, the ventilation rate decreases until a high carbon dioxide level builds up and the rate increases again. This may lead to irregularity in breathing. The low carbon dioxide level in the blood (or high blood pH) triggers the symptoms of nausea and dizziness.

Increased pulmonary diffusing capacity

The pulmonary diffusing capacity is a measure of the rate of exchange of gases between the alveoli and the (pulmonary) capillaries surrounding them. The capacity can be improved by an increase in surface area of the lung and by an increase in blood flow in the surrounding capillaries. There is some evidence that native highlanders have a lung volume larger than that of comparable lowlanders. This enlargement gives an increased alveolar surface area, thus allowing a higher rate of diffusion of oxygen from the alveoli into the surrounding blood capillaries. Native highlanders also show a relatively higher total volume of blood, which results in a greater flow through the pulmonary capillaries. Visitors to high altitudes do not seem to develop a similar increase in lung capacity; if anything there at first appears to be a decrease in vital capacity (maximum volume that can be exhaled), though this change is reversed after a few weeks at high altitude.

Increased transport of oxygen in the blood

The total quantity of oxygen transported in the blood to the cells depends on three factors: the **cardiac output**, the **haemoglobin concentration** and the **saturation of the haemoglobin** with oxygen.

Cardiac output (Figure 4.21) may be altered by changes in both the **heart rate** (number of heart beats in a given time) and the **stroke volume** (volume of blood pumped out at each beat). Increases in one or both of these attributes will result in more blood being pumped through the pulmonary capillaries, allowing an increase in the collection of oxygen from the alveoli and increased delivery to the cells. Visitors to high altitudes show an immediate increase in heart rate, though stroke volume remains steady at first then appears to fall. Overall cardiac output thus increases for the first few days then returns to about the same as that at sea level. In native highlanders the resting cardiac output is about the same as that for comparable lowlanders.

Native highlanders, compared with equivalent lowlanders, show higher levels of both the haemoglobin concentration in the blood and the total number of red blood cells (Table 4.1). A similar increase is noted when lowlanders visit high altitudes. The response is due to increased production of red blood cells,

Table 4.1 *Red blood cell (rbc) counts and haemoglobin (Hb) concentration at different altitudes (all values are for male subjects)*

Altitude	Rbc count / dm^{-3}	Hb concentration / $g\ dm^{-3}$
Sea level (normal values)	5.0×10^{12}	148
4540 m (natives in the Andes)	6.4×10^{12}	210
5790 m (mountaineers on Mt Everest)	5.6×10^{12}	196

which takes place in the bone marrow, stimulated by the hormone erythropoietin. Increased secretion of erythropoietin occurs in conditions of low oxygen. There is also an overall increase in blood volume. At 4500 m, these values are about 25 to 30 per cent above the corresponding values at sea level. In visitors, the higher red blood cell count is noticeable about 3 to 4 days after arrival at high altitude, though the increase in haemoglobin and blood volume continues for several weeks. With more haemoglobin in the blood, the capacity for carrying oxygen is increased, provided the pO_2 of oxygen is high enough for the haemoglobin to collect the oxygen (become saturated). The increased blood volume noticed at higher altitudes is due to the increased red blood cell volume. Plasma volume actually decreases. A potential danger of the raised red blood cell count is that the blood becomes more viscous (thicker), which in extreme situations may reduce the flow of blood through the capillaries.

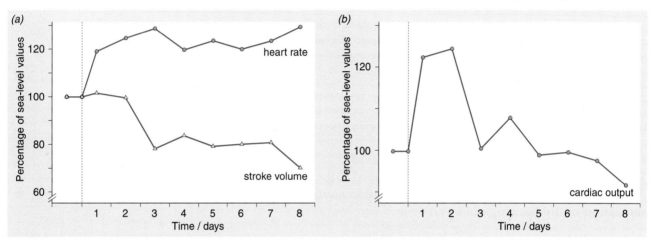

Figure 4.21 Changes in cardiac output of a group of people during the first 8 days after exposure to an altitude of 3800 m (cardiac output = heart rate × stroke volume): (a) heart rate and stroke volume; (b) cardiac output

A closer look at the oxygen–haemoglobin dissociation curves reveals how readily the haemoglobin collects oxygen and how easily it gives it up again to the cells. If the curve shifts to the right, it means that oxygen is released more easily, but there is some loss in percentage saturation of the haemoglobin with oxygen. This shift would provide some advantage at moderate high altitude (3000 m to 5500 m). Quechua Indians living in the Peruvian Andes do show such a shift to the right, as do visitors to high altitudes (Figure 4.22). At very high altitudes, a shift to the left would be favoured because it increases the saturation of haemoglobin with oxygen, though there is a corresponding disadvantage in terms of the point at which oxygen is released to the cells. A shift to the left has been found in the Sherpa people at high altitudes in the Himalayas. It is also of interest that some mammals characteristic of high altitudes, such as the llama, show a shift to the left of the oxygen–haemoglobin dissociation curve.

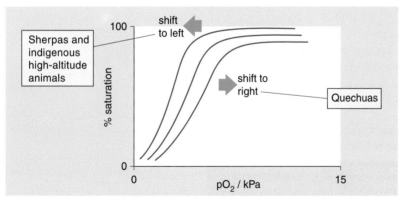

Figure 4.22 Oxygen dissociation curve for high-altitude inhabitants (Quechuas and Sherpas). A shift to the left suggests adaptation; a shift to the right indicates acclimatisation. Visitors to high altitude are likely to show a shift to the right.

Redistribution of body fluids

Distribution of fluids in the body is influenced by a number of interacting factors, including blood pressure, blood volume, salt balance and hormones. The changes are complex and some are affected by hypoxia as experienced at high altitude.

One of these hormones is antidiuretic hormone (ADH), secreted by the posterior pituitary gland. ADH increases the reabsorption of water by the kidneys. This results in more water being retained in the body and a smaller volume of urine being produced. In **mild hypoxia**, there is probably a decrease in secretion of ADH, which will result in more urine being produced, a situation known as **diuresis**. However, in conditions of **severe hypoxia**, increased secretion of ADH has the opposite effect, leading to retention of water in the blood and reduced urine production. At high altitude there is a redistribution of the circulation of the blood, with a reduced flow to the extremities. The excess fluid retained in the body tends to accumulate outside the blood vessels, particularly in the lungs and brain. The condition is known as **oedema**. In severe **pulmonary oedema**, fluid collects in the lungs and the sufferer may froth at the mouth and become very breathless. In **cerebral oedema**, the brain swells with fluid and then presses against the cranium (the part of the skull which contains the brain). This induces severe headaches, leading to loss of consciousness and sometimes to death. For recovery, in both situations, it is essential for the person to be taken rapidly to a lower altitude. Milder forms of oedema show as a puffiness in the face, particularly around the eyes, and as swelling in the legs and feet.

Mental reactions at high altitude

Visitors to moderately high altitudes frequently show slower mental reactions and weaker decision-making ability than would be expected from the same people at lower altitudes. This can be tested by a variety of memory tests. There are many stories of mountaineers making foolish mistakes at high altitudes, which may often have been the cause of serious accidents in this difficult terrain. These mental reactions may have been influenced by a combination of the direct effect of hypoxia on brain function as well as stress imposed on the body by the onset of symptoms of mountain sickness. At altitudes over about 5500 m, the hypoxia has yet more severe effects on the activity of the brain, leading to loss of concentration and inability to carry out calculations or make reliable judgements. At still higher altitudes, hallucinations may become apparent, often manifesting themselves as the presence of another companion on the mountain. Habeler and Messner, when they climbed Mt Everest without oxygen in 1979, experienced a feeling of euphoria, somewhat dangerous at a height of 8848 m, surrounded by snow, ice and precipitous slopes. To quote from Habeler, 'I felt somehow light and relaxed, and believed nothing could happen to me. Undoubtedly, many of the men who have disappeared for ever in the summit region of Everest have also fallen victim to this treacherous euphoria'.

Acclimatisation or adaptation?

Native highlanders, such as the Quechua Indians in the Andes or Tibetans and Sherpas in the Himalayas, are able to lead active and physically demanding lives at altitudes in excess of 3000 m. Newly arrived lowland visitors to high altitudes notice an immediate decline in their normal physical activity, and though their performance gradually improves, it may never reach that of the native highlander, or at least not for a considerable time. Athletes competing in the 1968 Olympic Games in Mexico City (2380 m) experienced difficulties in reaching their maximum performance. However, athletes who have trained at moderate or high altitudes, or who are normally resident there, may show superior performance (at low or at high altitudes), particularly in middle-distance or long-distance running events. Sherpas are known for their support as porters in mountaineering expeditions: at about 3000 m they can carry loads of about 60 kg and even at 7000 m can manage loads of about 18 kg. This is more than would be expected from a newly arrived lowlander and is certainly related to the Sherpa's superior capacity to utilise oxygen.

If native highlanders were **genetically adapted** to high altitude, the features which allow normal activity in the hypoxic conditions at high altitudes would be inherited and irreversible. There is little evidence to support this, nor is there evidence that the features would persist if the highlander went to live at sea level. It is preferable to consider both the natives and the visitors as showing different degrees of **acclimatisation** to the high altitudes. Acclimatisation implies that reversible non-inherited changes are shown in structural and physiological features in the body, in response to the conditions experienced at high altitude, and these changes help survival. Thus the features which allow success in hypoxic conditions are of the same kind in both native highlanders and lowland visitors. However, in the native highlander these features probably developed during normal growth and in the early years of childhood, and so appear to be permanent, whereas in the visitor the features are acquired over a period of time after arrival at high altitude.

A few examples (discussed earlier in this chapter) will help to illustrate this.
- Native highlanders show an increased lung volume which contributes to a higher pulmonary diffusing capacity. This would develop in childhood, though perhaps the feature is partly a response to the physical exercise associated with the lifestyle in mountainous regions. A lowland visitor is unlikely to show an increase in lung volume.
- A 'barrel-shaped' chest with large lung volume is a characteristic of Quechua Indians. (This feature may have already existed and given this group an advantage when they first colonised the high regions in the Andes.)
- Both highlanders and visitors hyperventilate, though the visitor maintains a higher rate for a longer period than the native highlander.
- At high altitudes both groups show a higher red blood cell count and higher haemoglobin concentration compared with similar groups living at sea level.

On descent to sea level, several of the features apparent at high altitude, including hyperventilation, haemoglobin level and cardiac output, fall to a normal level. Native highlanders and visitors to high altitudes are affected in a similar way.

Certain species of mammals, including yaks and llamas, live permanently at high altitudes, so it may help to look at their features in comparison to native highlanders to understand the extent to which each is adapted or acclimatised. Comparing llamas with Quechua Indians at similar altitudes, llamas do not hyperventilate, nor do they show as much increase in haemoglobin concentration. However, llamas are efficient in their extraction of oxygen by the tissues at low partial pressures and show a shift to the left of the oxygen dissociation curves. Sherpas show a similar shift, but the Quechua Indians do not. The llama is considered to be adapted, the Sherpas are on their way to being fully adapted rather than acclimatised, and the Quechua Indians can best be described as acclimatised. The degree of adaptation is relative and related to the length of time the group has lived at high altitude. The lowland visitor is always at a disadvantage during the first few days at high altitude, but becomes at least partially acclimatised after a period of time.

QUESTIONS

Turning your theory into practice – some practical questions!
Some university students studying biology are planning an expedition in the Himalayan mountains. They will do some botanical work, surveying distribution of plants and studying their ecology, and also aim to climb some of the peaks in the area. They expect to spend about 6 weeks at altitudes between 2000 m and 6000 m.

Write about a page of 'advice' which can be circulated to the students intending to join the expedition. The advice should include:
• an indication of the conditions expected as they reach the higher altitudes
• how the body is likely to react at the higher altitudes and over the period of time spent there
• a biological explanation of the changes taking place in response to the higher altitudes
• how best to prepare for the journey and how to take care of themselves during the expedition.
Don't forget it can be cold at high altitudes, so include reference to suitable clothing.

Then list some simple measurements they could take or observations they could make during the expedition to monitor the responses of the body to higher altitudes.

Remember that the students will be carrying most of their own baggage so will not be able to take heavy or complex equipment with them, but you can include some measurements which could be taken before they depart and again on their return.

5 Sexual reproduction

The production of new individuals of the same species is a fundamental characteristic of living organisms. Reproduction allows for the replacement of individuals that die and ensures the continuity of the species. If conditions are favourable, it can also result in an increase in numbers. Genetic information from the individuals of one generation, the **parental generation**, is passed on to the next generation, the **offspring**, ensuring that the characteristic features of a species are perpetuated.

Reproduction may be asexual or sexual. **Asexual reproduction** usually involves a single individual and no gamete formation occurs. The offspring inherit identical genetical information from the parent and may be referred to as clones. New individuals are formed from mitotic divisions and the only genetic variation possible arises as a result of random mutation. Few animal species reproduce naturally in this way, although both animals and plants have been successfully cloned using artificial techniques. **Sexual reproduction** involves the formation and fusion of **gametes** from two individuals of the same species. The process of gamete formation includes meiotic division, halving the chromosome number. The resulting offspring are likely to show genetic variation, due to the events of meiosis and the random fusion of gametes at fertilisation.

The cell cycle

Sexual reproduction involves the fusion of nuclei with the **haploid** (n) number of chromosomes to form a **diploid zygote** (2n). These haploid nuclei are usually contained within special cells called **gametes**. The diploid zygote then undergoes mitotic divisions (see *Molecules and Cells*, Adds, Larkcom and Miller, Nelson, 2000) and grows into a new individual which, when mature, will be capable of producing gametes. In order to prevent chromosome doubling, **meiosis** occurs at some stage in the life cycle, reducing the chromosome number from diploid to haploid. A combination of the events which take place during prophase I of meiosis and the random nature of fertilisation leads to genetic variation in the offspring and ensures that each new individual is unique.

Meiosis

Before considering the process of meiosis, it is helpful to understand the origin and nature of the chromosomes in a diploid cell. In a diploid organism, one set of chromosomes will have come from the male parent and the other set from the female parent, so that the chromosomes occur in pairs in the cells. These pairs of chromosomes are called **homologous** pairs.

The members of a pair have the following characteristics:
- they are exactly the same length
- they have the centromere in the same position
- they contain the same number of genes
- the genes are arranged in the same linear order.

When mitosis occurs, the homologous chromosomes act independently, but in meiosis, pairing of homologous chromosomes takes place during the first stage, prophase I, and their subsequent separation ensures that one of each pair is present in the gametes or spores that are formed.

Meiosis differs from mitosis in that it involves a reduction in the number of chromosomes from the diploid number (2n) to the haploid number (n). Replication of the DNA takes place in interphase, but this is followed by two cycles of nuclear division, one in which separation of homologous chromosomes occurs and the other in which the chromatids are separated. These are usually referred to as the first and second meiotic divisions and result in the production of four haploid nuclei from one diploid nucleus. This type of nuclear division occurs during **gametogenesis** (the production of sperm and ova) in animals and in spore formation in the sporophyte generations of plants. As mentioned earlier, the gametes will have a single set of chromosomes, but these will not be identical. During prophase I, when the chromosomes pair up, there is the possibility of exchange of sections of non-sister chromatids, leading to variation.

The events that take place during meiosis form a continuous process, but as with mitosis, they are separated into different stages for ease of description. The same stages occur, but as there are two divisions of the nucleus, each stage occurs twice (see *Practical: Meiosis in pollen mother cells*). For example, prophase I refers to the first meiotic division and prophase II to prophase in the second meiotic division.

Prophase I

In prophase I, the chromosomes become visible as single threads. It is not possible to distinguish their double structure in the early stages, but initially each chromosome appears to have a beaded appearance due to localised coiling of the DNA forming regions called **chromomeres**. Homologous chromosomes pair up precisely along their length, a process known as **synapsis**, and more condensation makes them appear shorter and fatter. Each pair of chromosomes is called a **bivalent**. As the chromatids of each homologous chromosome become visible, the members of a pair seem to repel each other in some regions but remain attracted at others. At the points of attraction, non-sister chromatids break and rejoin at exactly corresponding locations. This is known as **crossing over** and results in the formation of **chiasmata** (sing. **chiasma**, from the Greek for 'cross-arrangement').

More than one chiasma can form and it may involve the same pair or another pair of non-sister chromatids. If one chiasma forms, the bivalents have a cross shape, if two a ring shape and if more than two a series of loops arise at right angles to each other. Chiasmata hold the two homologous chromosomes together and this leads to their orderly separation during anaphase I. During the later stages of prophase I, the nucleoli disappear, the centrioles migrate to opposite poles of the cell and the nuclear envelope breaks down. Spindle formation begins as microtubules become arranged across the middle of the cell from pole to pole (Figures 5.1, 5.2).

Figure 5.1 Photomicrograph of prophase I of meiosis in Lilium, *showing the chromosomes as threads, with some regions of contact between chromatids*

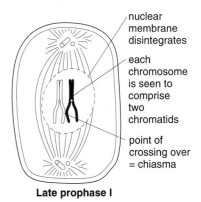

nuclear membrane disintegrates

each chromosome is seen to comprise two chromatids

point of crossing over = chiasma

Late prophase I

Figure 5.2 Diagrammatic representation of prophase I of meiosis, showing that the regions of contact between chromatids (chiasmata) are points where genetic material crosses over when the chromatids break and rejoin

Metaphase I

The bivalents become attached to the spindle in metaphase I (Figures 5.3a, 5.4a). The centromeres attach to individual spindle fibres and the bivalents are moved so that they are arranged along the equator of the spindle. They are orientated so that the centromere of one homologous chromosome will move to one pole and the other will move to the opposite pole. At this point, the centromeres of each homologous pair repel each other strongly, but the sister chromatids are closely associated.

Anaphase I

In anaphase I, the homologous chromosomes are separated (Figures 5.3b, 5.4b). The centromeres are pulled by the spindle fibres towards opposite poles. The attraction between sister chromatids ceases. The reduction in the number of chromosomes is achieved by this separation.

Telophase I

Telophase I does not always occur, but in most animal and some plant cells, the chromatids begin to uncoil and a nuclear envelope forms around each group of chromatids (Figures 5.3c, 5.4c). In many plants, this stage does not occur and the nucleus passes straight into metaphase II of the next stage of division. There may be a short interphase between the two stages, but there is no replication of the DNA.

Prophase II

There is no prophase II if interphase is lacking, as the chromosomes will already be condensed. If nucleoli and nuclear envelopes were reformed in telophase I then these will disappear and two new spindles will form at right angles to the plane of the original spindle (Figures 5.3d, 5.4d).

Metaphase II

At metaphase II, each of the chromosomes attaches by its centromere to a spindle fibre and the chromosomes are brought into line up the equators of the spindles (Figures 5.3d, 5.4e).

Anaphase II

Separation of the sister chromatids is achieved at anaphase II (Figures 5.3d, 5.4f). The centromeres divide and the chromatids, now called daughter chromosomes, are pulled by the spindle fibres to opposite poles of the spindle.

Telophase II

During telophase II, the daughter chromosomes despiralise and become less visible. The nucleoli reappear and new nuclear envelopes form around the groups of chromosomes (Figures 5.3e, 5.4g).

The first and second telophases are usually accompanied by division of the cytoplasm.

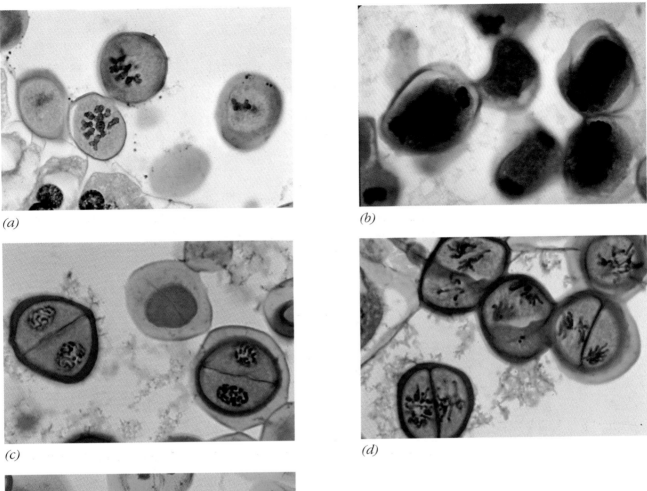

(a)

(b)

(c)

(d)

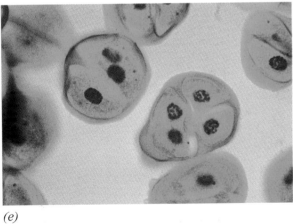

(e)

Figure 5.3 Photomicrographs of meiosis in Lilium *pollen mother cells, showing the remaining phases of division to form haploid cells: (a) metaphase I, (b) late anaphase I in which the cytoplasm becomes very dense and (c) telophase I and first cell cleavage, followed by (d) metaphase II and anaphase II in different cells, and (e) telophase II and second cell cleavage*

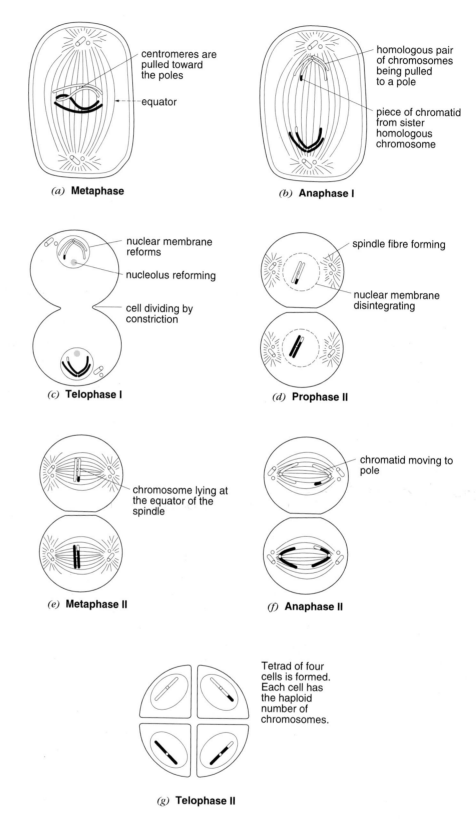

Figure 5.4 Diagrammatic representations of the remaining phases of meiotic division to form haploid cells: (a) metaphase I, (b) anaphase I and (c) telophase I, followed by (d) prophase II, (e) metaphase II, (f) anaphase II, and (g) telophase II

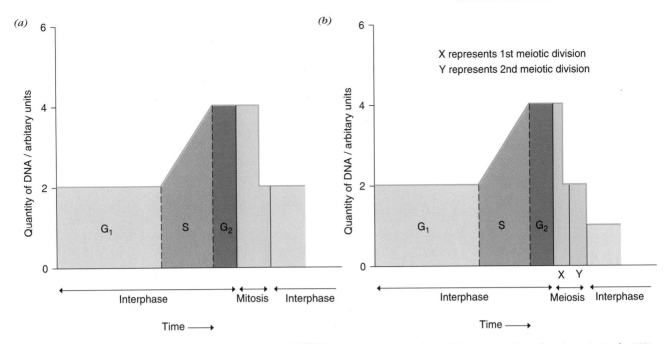

Figure 5.5 Graphs to illustrate changes in DNA content of a cell during (a) the cell cycle, and (b) meiosis. Note that, in meiosis, the DNA content of each daughter cell is only half that of the parent cell.

As mentioned earlier, replication of the DNA occurs during interphase before prophase I. At that time, the DNA content of the nucleus doubles. The amount of DNA in each nucleus is half the original amount after the first stage of the meiotic division. By the end of the second meiotic division, the amount in each nucleus is halved again (Figure 5.5).

Significance of meiosis

It is significant that meiosis offers a mechanism for some genetic variation in a species, whereas mitosis maintains genetic stability. In meiosis, the separation of homologous chromosomes, resulting in the reduction of the diploid (2n) to the haploid (n) number means that each gamete or spore will only carry one form of the gene for a particular characteristic. The crossing over that occurs in prophase I, before the separation of the homologous pairs in anaphase I, results in the exchange of genetic information between maternal and paternal chromosomes, leading to the possibility of new combinations of genes in the gametes. In addition, the orientation of the bivalents on the spindle at metaphase I is completely random, so that the products of the first meiotic division will contain a mixture of chromosomes of maternal and paternal origin. Similarly, during metaphase II, orientation of the pairs of chromatids is random. All these events result in the possibility of a large number of different chromosome combinations in the gametes. This is referred to as **independent assortment of chromosomes** and makes a contribution to the way in which particular characteristics are inherited.

Mitosis and meiosis compared

There are a number of similarities between the two processes. They both involve:
- replication of the DNA in interphase
- replication of cell organelles
- similar stages of prophase, metaphase, anaphase and telophase, during which similar events take place
- formation of a spindle.

SEXUAL REPRODUCTION

Mitosis and meiosis differ in a number of ways, which are summarised in Table 5.1.

Table 5.1 *Summary of differences between mitosis and meiosis*

Mitosis	Meiosis
consists of one division separating sister chromatids	consists of two divisions: separation of homologous chromosomes followed by separation of chromatids
homologous chromosomes do not associate	homologous chromosomes pair up
no chromomeres visible in prophase	chromomeres often visible in prophase
no crossing over occurs	crossing over occurs
no chiasmata formation	chiasmata formation
daughter nuclei have same number of chromosomes as parent nucleus	daughter nuclei have half the number of chromosomes as the parent nucleus
no genetic variation in daughter nuclei	genetic variation possible in daughter nuclei
can occur in haploid, diploid or polyploid cells	occurs in diploid and some polyploid cells
associated with increase in numbers of cells, replacement and repair, asexual reproduction and with gamete formation in the gametophyte generation of plants	associated with gametogenesis in animals and with spore production in the sporophyte generation of plants

PRACTICAL

Meiosis in pollen mother cells

Introduction

Tradescantia spp. provide very useful material for the demonstration of meiosis, as they give a succession of flowers from May to October. The chromosomes are large and relatively small in number. Very small buds should be selected and the anthers stained using aceto-orcein. This stain is made up by dissolving 1 g of orcein in 99 cm³ of 45 per cent (aqueous) ethanoic acid. Filter the stain after several hours to remove any undissolved residue.

Materials

- *Tradescantia* flower buds
- Fine forceps
- Aceto-orcein
- Watch glasses
- Forceps to hold watchmaker's forceps
- Bunsen burner
- Microscope slides and cover slips
- Small glass rods
- Blotting paper
- Microscope

CORROSIVE
aceto-orcein

Method

1 Use fine forceps to remove anthers from flower buds. Watchmaker's forceps are ideal.
2 Place in a watch glass containing 2 cm^3 of aceto-orcein and add a couple of drops of 1.0 M hydrochloric acid.
3 Hold the watch glass firmly with forceps and warm gently over a low bunsen flame until the liquid just begins to steam. Do not allow it to boil.
4 Leave for 10 minutes to take up the stain, then place the anthers on a microscope slide. Add three or four drops of fresh stain and break up the anthers using a small glass rod.
5 Carefully apply a coverslip and place the slide between several sheets of blotting paper. Squash firmly, avoiding any sideways movement.
6 Examine the preparation using a microscope, first with low magnification, then high. Look carefully for cells with visible chromosomes, which should be stained darkly.

Results and discussion

1 Make labelled drawings of representative stages of meiosis from your preparation.
2 Summarise the differences between mitosis and meiosis.
3 How does the process of meiosis contribute to genetic variation?

Reproduction in flowering plants

Floral structure

The reproductive organs of flowering plants are borne in **flowers**, which are often hermaphrodite, possessing both male and female structures. The male parts are the **stamens**, forming the **androecium**, and the female parts are the **carpels**, forming the **gynaecium**. All the flower parts arise from the enlarged apex of the flower stalk, a region known as the **receptacle**. In addition, there may be accessory structures, such as **sepals**, **petals** and **nectaries**, arranged in whorls, or circles, around the reproductive organs. These accessory structures may show wide varieties of form and are often associated with the way in which pollination is achieved. Each stamen is made up of a stalk, called the **filament**, supporting the lobed **anthers**, in which there are usually four **pollen sacs**. Each carpel consists of a receptive **stigma** connected to an **ovary** by the **style**. In the ovary, one or more **ovules** develop (Figure 5.6a, b).

Flowering plants are divided into two major subgroups: Monocotyledones and Dicotyledones. There are differences in the internal arrangement of tissues, but members of the two groups can generally be distinguished from each other by their leaves and flowers. Monocotyledonous plants usually have long, thin leaves with parallel veins, whereas dicotyledonous plants show a wide range of leaf forms, both simple and compound, and the venation is described as reticulate as it forms a dense network. The flower parts in monocotyledons are arranged in threes or sixes and there is often no distinction between the calyx and the corolla, the petals and sepals being referred to as the **perianth segments**. In dicotyledons, the flower parts are often in fours or fives, or multiples of four and five, and there is usually a clear distinction between the

SEXUAL REPRODUCTION

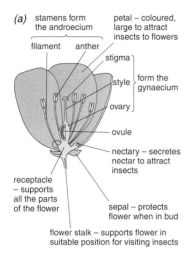

(a) stamens form the androecium

filament anther

petal – coloured, large to attract insects to flowers

stigma ⎤
style ⎬ form the gynaecium
ovary ⎦

ovule

nectary – secretes nectar to attract insects

receptacle – supports all the parts of the flower

sepal – protects flower when in bud

flower stalk – supports flower in suitable position for visiting insects

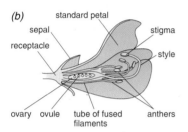

(b)

standard petal

sepal

receptacle

stigma

style

ovary   ovule   tube of fused filaments

anthers

This flower does not have a nectary, but produces masses of pollen which insects collect

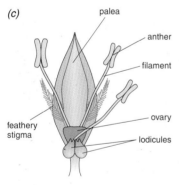

(c)

palea

anther

filament

ovary

lodicules

feathery stigma

The palea and lodicules are bracts. The lemma, another bract, has been removed. They are green.

Figure 5.6 (a) Generalised structure of a dicotyledonous flower; (b) flower structure in the family Papilionaceae; (c) flower structure in the family Gramineae

calyx and the corolla. In the Gramineae (grasses) (Figure 5.6c), a large monocotyledonous family, there are no petals or sepals; the accessory structures consist of small structures called bracts.

Development of pollen and ovules

In the early stages of their development, each pollen sac contains a central mass of microspore mother cells surrounded by a nutritive layer called the **tapetum**. The microspore mother cells undergo meiosis to produce tetrads of haploid cells, each of which develops into a pollen grain, or microspore (Figure 5.7). The haploid nucleus divides by mitosis to produce a generative nucleus and a pollen tube nucleus. The generative nucleus represents the male gametophyte generation and will undergo a further mitotic division to produce two nuclei which function as male gametes. The pollen grains secrete a thin inner wall, called the **intine**, and a thick outer wall, the **exine**. In wind-pollinated species of flowering plants, the exine of the pollen grains is smooth, but in insect-pollinated species it is often sculptured or pitted.

As the pollen grains mature, the cells of the nutritive layer surrounding each pollen sac shrink and break down and fibrous layers develop in the anther wall. Drying of the anther sets up tensions in the wall, which eventually splits along a longitudinal line of weakness, the two edges curl away and the mass of mature pollen grains is exposed.

Inside the ovary of the carpel, each ovule begins as a small outgrowth from the placenta. This tiny structure is called the **nucellus** and at its apex a megaspore mother cell undergoes meiosis, producing four haploid megaspores. Normally, only one of these will continue to develop by undergoing three successive mitotic divisions, resulting in the formation of an embryo sac containing eight haploid nuclei. The embryo sac represents the female gametophyte generation in the life cycle and is completely enclosed and nourished by the sporophyte generation. As the nucellus gets bigger, it becomes surrounded by two layers of cells, called the **integuments**, which grow from the base of the ovule. In a mature ovule, these layers do not completely surround the nucellus, but a small opening, the **micropyle**, is left.

As the ovule matures, each of the eight nuclei becomes surrounded by cytoplasm and they are arranged in a definite pattern in the embryo sac. The three nuclei situated at the micropylar end are referred to as the **egg apparatus**. The female gamete, or **egg cell**, is in the centre with a **synergid** on either side. At the opposite end of the embryo sac is another group of three cells, referred to as the **antipodal cells**. The remaining two nuclei, called the **polar nuclei**, are found in the centre, where they may remain as separate nuclei or fuse to form a central diploid nucleus. Before pollination and fertilisation, each ovule consists of the nucellus, containing an embryo sac, surrounded by two integuments (Figure 5.8).

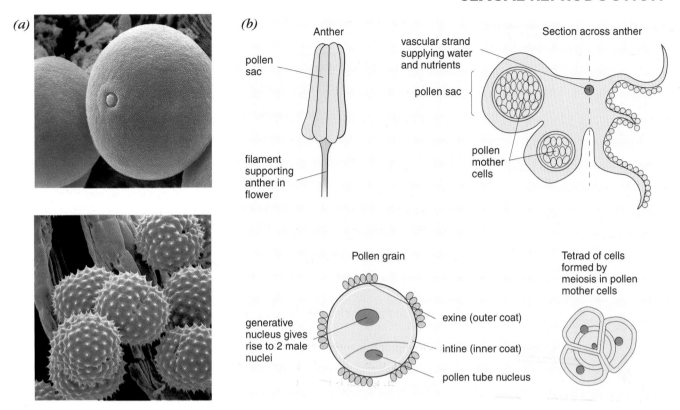

Figure 5.7 (a) Pollen grains from (top) wind-pollinated and (bottom) insect-pollinated flowers; (b) development of pollen grains

Pollination and fertilisation

Before fertilisation can occur, mature pollen grains containing the male gametes must be transferred to the receptive stigma in a process referred to as pollination. In some species, **self-pollination** occurs. Pollen from the anthers is transferred to the stigma of the same flower or another flower on the same plant. In other species, **cross-pollination** is achieved, where pollen from the anthers of one flower is transferred to the stigma of a flower on another plant of the same species.

Pollination is usually achieved by wind or insects transferring the pollen from the anthers to the stigmas. Many flowering plant families, such as the Gramineae (grasses) and most trees, are **wind-pollinated**. This mechanism necessitates the production of vast quantities of light, smooth pollen to maximise the chances of some landing on the mature stigmas of the flowers. **Insect pollination** involves the insect as a vector and increases the chances of pollen reaching the stigmas. Insect-pollinated flowers are adapted to this mechanism in that they are coloured and scented to attract the insects, they produce nectar and/or pollen as food for the insects and there are often structural modifications which ensure that pollination is achieved. Table 5.2 summarises the major differences between wind-pollinated and insect-pollinated flowers.

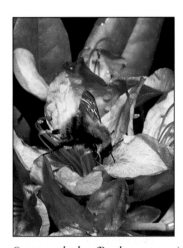

*Queen carder bee (*Bombus agrorum*) feeding on a flower of the common rhododendron (*Rhodedredron ponticum*), Betwys-y-coed, North Wales. Nectar guides, stamens and stigma of the flower are clearly shown.*

SEXUAL REPRODUCTION

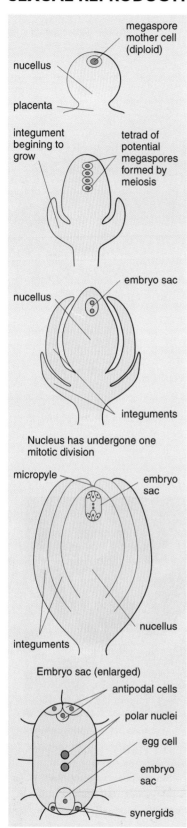

Figure 5.8 Development of embryo
sac

Table 5.2 *The differences between wind-pollinated and insect-pollinated flowers*

Feature	Wind-pollinated flowers	Insect-pollinated flowers
position of flowers	above leaves (grasses) or produced before leaves appear (many trees such as hazel, willow)	often, though not always, above leaves; either solitary and large or smaller and in clusters so conspicuous
petals	small, inconspicuous, sometimes absent (grasses); if present, not brightly coloured	large, brightly coloured, conspicuous; attractive to insects
nectaries	absent	present; insects feed on nectar
scent	not scented	often scented; attracts insects
stamens	hanging outside flower (pendulous)	enclosed within flower
anthers	move freely (versatile) so that pollen is easily dispersed	fixed to filaments; positioned so that they come into contact with visiting insect
pollen	produced in large quantities; light, smooth pollen grains	less produced; pollen grains larger, sculptured walls to aid attachment to insects and to stigma
stigma	large, often branched, often feathery, hanging outside flower to trap pollen	small, enclosed within flower; positioned so that it comes into contact with visiting insect

Following successful pollination, the epidermal cells of the stigma secrete a solution of sucrose, which stimulates the germination of the pollen grain. A **pollen tube** grows out through one of the pores in the wall of the pollen grain and rapidly penetrates the tissue of the style. The growth of the pollen tube is controlled by the **tube nucleus**, which is located at the tip of the tube, and involves the secretion of digestive enzymes, allowing the penetration of the tissues. The enzymes soften the cutin of the stigma and the middle lamella of the cell walls. Pollen tubes also produce auxin, which is involved in the initiation of fruit development. Pollen tubes are positively hydrotropic (growing towards water) and negatively aerotropic (growing away from oxygen). As the pollen tube approaches the ovule, it becomes positively chemotropic to a substance produced by the micropyle and so grows in that direction.

The generative nucleus in the pollen grain undergoes mitosis, forming two **male nuclei**. This division may occur before the mature pollen is shed from the anthers or it may occur during the growth of the pollen tube. The tip of the pollen tube enters the ovule through the micropyle and comes into contact with the embryo sac near the site of the synergids. The male nuclei are released through a pore which develops in the tip of the pollen tube. One male nucleus will fuse with the egg nucleus to form a **diploid zygote** and the other fuses with the two polar nuclei in the centre of the embryo sac (Figure 5.9). The diploid zygote gives rise to the **embryo** and the nuclei in the centre fuse to form a triploid nucleus, the **primary endosperm nucleus**, which gives rise to the nutritive tissue known as the **endosperm**. This type of fertilisation is called **double fertilisation** as it involves two fusions. It is also worth noting that the transfer of gametes and the process of fertilisation is an adaption to life on land because no water is needed. In the less adapted groups of plants, such as the mosses and the ferns, water is needed for the transfer of gametes from the male to the female organs.

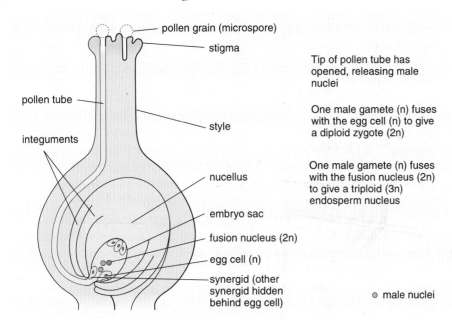

pollen grain (microspore)

stigma

Tip of pollen tube has opened, releasing male nuclei

pollen tube

style

One male gamete (n) fuses with the egg cell (n) to give a diploid zygote (2n)

integuments

One male gamete (n) fuses with the fusion nucleus (2n) to give a triploid (3n) endosperm nucleus

nucellus

embryo sac

fusion nucleus (2n)

egg cell (n)

synergid (other synergid hidden behind egg cell)

⊙ male nuclei

Figure 5.9 A mature carpel showing fertilisation

Mechanisms for ensuring cross-pollination

Self-pollination leads to **self-fertilisation**, where the offspring will only show limited variation due to the recombination of genes from a single parent. Self-fertilisation results in **inbreeding**. If an individual plant, heterozygous at a single locus (**Aa**), is repeatedly selfed, the resulting population becomes homozygous at that locus and two pure-breeding lines, **AA** and **aa**, become established. There is a large number of gene loci in the genome and there will be many ways in which the lines become homozygous, so natural populations of such inbreeding plants will contain different pure lines all breeding true. Self-pollination and self-fertilisation may favour the survival of uncommon or widely-dispersed species, as successful seed production does not depend on wind or insects to disperse the pollen. Common species which show self-pollination are the garden pea (*Pisum sativum*), groundsel (*Senecio vulgaris*) and chickweed (*Cerastium arvense*). In some species, self-pollination is allowed to occur if cross-pollination fails.

Cross-pollination, leading to cross-fertilisation and **outbreeding**, occurs in many species and has the advantage of maintaining heterozygosity and variation, because two different parent plants are involved. Each ovule in a gynaecium must be fertilised by the male nuclei from separate pollen grains.

QUESTION

List the advantages and disadvantages of inbreeding and outbreeding.

These pollen grains may come from different parent plants, a feature which has the effect of increasing variation still further. A number of different mechanisms have evolved which prevent self-pollination and improve the chances of cross-pollination. Such mechanisms may involve separation of the male and female reproductive organs, dichogamy, self-sterility (self-incompatibility) or heterostyly.

Although the flowers of most plant species are hermaphrodite, several have separate male and female flowers. **Dioecious** species, such as poplar (*Populus* sp.), willow (*Salix* sp.) and holly (*Ilex* sp.), have male and female flowers on separate plants, so self-pollination is impossible. In **monoecious** species, such as hazel (*Corylus* sp.) and oak (*Quercus* sp.), male and female flowers occur on the same plant, but self-pollination is avoided by a difference in the timing of their development.

In hermaphrodite flowers, self-pollination can be avoided if the male and female organs mature at different times, a condition known as **dichogamy**. In **protandry**, the stamens ripen and the pollen is released from the anthers before the carpels are mature, so the stigmas of the flower are not receptive to pollen at this stage. This mechanism is found in white deadnettle (*Lamium alba*), Canterbury bell (*Campanula medium*), rose-bay willow-herb (*Epilobium angustifolium*) and sage (*Salvia* sp.). In the reverse situation, known as **protogyny**, the carpels mature before the stamens, so the stigma of the flower is receptive to pollen before the anthers have dehisced.

*Figure 5.10 Protogyny in ribwort plantain (*Plantago lanceolata*)*

An example of protogyny is seen in the ribwort plantain (*Plantago lanceolata*), where the inflorescence is an erect spike (Figure 5.10). The lower flowers open first and initially the stigma is receptive to pollen. Later in the same flower, the anthers ripen and release mature pollen. The mature pollen will always be released at a lower level than the receptive stigmas, so it is unlikely that self-pollination will occur.

Many wind-pollinated flowers, such as members of the Gramineae, are protogynous, but the condition is generally less common than protandry. Among insect-pollinated flowers showing protogyny are wild arum (*Arum maculatum*), bluebell (*Endymion non-scriptus*) and figwort (*Scrophularia nodosa*).

QUESTION

Work out why pollen from plant A is needed to pollinate plant B when plant A has alleles S_1 and S_2 at the incompatibility locus and plant B has alleles S_3 and S_4.

Self-incompatibility, or **self-sterility**, occurs if pollen from the same flower, or another flower on the same plant, lands on the stigma and fails to germinate. Sometimes germination may occur, but the pollen tube grows very slowly and fails to reach the ovules. Proteins are produced on the surfaces of pollen grains and stigmas. Physiological mechanisms enable the stigmas to distinguish between the proteins on pollen from the same plant and pollen from different plants of the same species. When pollen lands on the stigma of the same plant, the proteins are identical and the pollen fails to germinate, so pollen and stigmas are incompatible. Pollen from a different plant of the same species, carrying different surface proteins, will germinate and is said to be compatible. Different forms of these surface proteins are determined by alleles of an incompatibility gene. This recognition system prevents inbreeding and encourages outbreeding.

ADDITIONAL MATERIAL

Heterostyly describes the situation where different kinds of floral morphology exist within a species. One of the best known examples is seen in the primrose (Primula vulgaris), where there are differences in the length of the style and the positioning of the anthers. In the thrum-eyed flower, the style is short, placing the stigma low down in the corolla tube. The anthers are situated high up in the corolla tube, above the stigma. In the pin-eyed type, the anthers are low down the corolla tube, but the style is long and the stigma is above the anthers.

Insects visiting the thrum-eyed flowers have pollen deposited high up on the proboscis as they reach inside the flower for nectar. When a pin-eyed flower is visited, the pollen from the thrum-eyed flower gets brushed against the stigma. Pollen from the pin-eyed flower is deposited about half-way along the proboscis, just in the right position to come into contact with the style of the next thrum-eyed flower visited. However, this mechanism is not particularly effective as, when the insect withdraws from the pin-eyed flower, pollen from the anthers can be drawn up onto the stigma. Similarly, pollen from the anther of the thrum-eyed flower can get taken down to the stigma as the insect enters. Additionally, pollen from the anthers of the thrum-eyed flower can just fall onto the stigma. There is incompatibility between the pollen and the stigmas of the same flower, so self-fertilisation is prevented. Investigation of the pollination mechanism found in the primrose has shown that the development of the pin- and thrum-eyed flowers is controlled by two linked genes determining style length and anther position. These two genes also determine the form of the stigma, pollen grain size and the production of the surface proteins involved with the incompatibility reaction.

QUESTION

Make drawings to show the position of the anthers and stigmas in pin-eyed and thrum-eyed flowers to help you work out what happens at pollination.

Reproduction in humans

Reproductive systems

The reproductive systems in the male and female differ in both their structure and their physiology. The female system produces a gamete, the **ovum** (oocyte), which is fertilised by the male gamete, or **spermatozoon**. The resulting zygote develops and is implanted in the wall of the uterus where it grows and develops until the baby is born after a gestation period of approximately 38 weeks, from fertilisation to delivery.

The **male reproductive system** consists essentially of four major components:

- the **testes**, or male gonads, situated in the scrotum, which are responsible for producing the male gametes, and for secreting male sex hormones.
- a system of **ducts**, including the epididymis and ductus deferens (sperm duct), which collect and store spermatozoa from each testis. The ejaculatory ducts converge on the urethra, through which spermatozoa are expelled.
- exocrine glands, including the **seminal vesicles** and **prostate gland**, which secrete a nutritive and lubricating fluid, called seminal fluid, with which spermatozoa are mixed. **Semen** consists of spermatozoa, seminal fluid, mucus and cells which are lost from the lining of the duct system.
- the **penis**, which contains the urethra and erectile tissue. During sexual arousal, this erectile tissue fills with blood and the penis becomes rigid and increases in both length and diameter. The result is termed an erection which enables the penis to function as a penetrating organ during sexual intercourse.

The functions of the **female reproductive system** are to produce gametes, (the ova), to receive the male gametes, to provide a suitable environment for fertilisation and the development of the fetus and to provide a means of expelling the developed fetus during the process of parturition, or birth. The internal organs of the female reproductive system consist of:

- the **ovaries**, which are the sites of both the production of ova and the secretion of the hormones oestrogen and progesterone.
- a pair of **oviducts** (or Fallopian tubes) which convey the ovum from the ovary to the uterus. Fertilisation of the ovum usually takes place in the oviduct.
- the **uterus**, a hollow, pear-shaped, muscular organ. The lining of the uterus, the **endometrium**, undergoes cyclical changes under the influence of the ovarian hormones oestrogen and progesterone. The **cervix** is part of the uterus which projects through the upper part of the vaginal wall.
- the **vagina**, a muscular tube which is adapted both for the reception of the penis during sexual intercourse, and for the passage of the baby out of the mother's body during birth.

The structures of the male and female reproductive systems are illustrated in Figure 5.12.

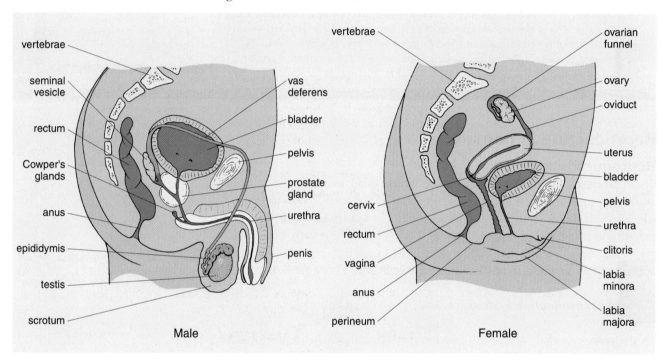

Figure 5.12 The male and female reproductive systems

Gametogenesis and the menstrual cycle

Gametogenesis is the process which results in the formation of gametes. It involves a special form of cell division – meiosis – in which the number of chromosomes is halved. The significance of meiosis in sexual reproduction is described on page 91. Each human testis is packed with numerous coiled **seminiferous tubules**, within which the process of spermatogenesis occurs. **Spermatogenesis** begins at about the time of puberty and normally continues through life. Figure 5.13 shows the major steps in spermatogenesis.

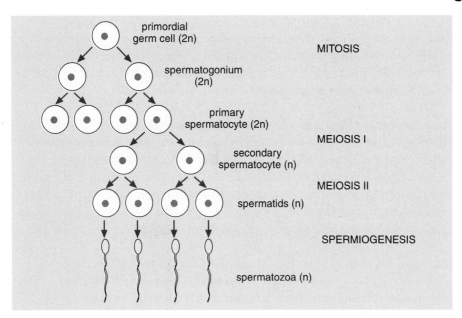

Figure 5.13 Spermatogenesis

Spermatogonia, also known as germ cells, line the seminiferous tubules and divide by mitosis, giving rise to further spermatogonia (known as spermatogonia Type A) and to spermatogonia which will undergo meiosis to form spermatozoa (Type B). Spermatogonia Type B are also known as **primary spermatocytes** and undergo the first meiotic division to form **secondary spermatocytes**. In humans, this first division takes about 3 weeks to complete. The secondary spermatocytes then rapidly undergo the second meiotic division to form **spermatids**, which undergo a process of development, known as **spermiogenesis**, to form **spermatozoa** (Figure 5.14).

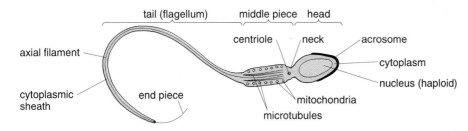

Figure 5.14 Structure of a spermatozoon

Spermatogenesis occurs in waves throughout the seminiferous tubules; at any given time some areas are active whilst others are at rest. Studies of spermatogenesis in humans have shown that the entire process takes 74 days. Spermatozoa in the seminiferous tubules are not motile (they only become motile after ejaculation) and are pushed onwards to the epididymis, partly by ciliary activity of cells lining the ducts and partly by contraction of smooth muscle. The mature human spermatozoon is 55 to 65 μm long and is often described as having a head and a tail. The head, 4 to 5 μm long and 3 μm wide, consists of a nucleus and an acrosome – a membrane-bound structure containing lytic enzymes. The first part of the tail is packed with mitochondria which provide energy for movement of the spermatozoon.

SEXUAL REPRODUCTION

During the process of spermatogenesis, the cells are supported by **Sertoli cells** within the seminiferous tubules. Sertoli cells are described as acting as 'nurse cells' and provide mechanical and metabolic support for the developing spermatozoa. Sertoli cells are also phagocytic and take up excess cytoplasm which is lost during spermatogenesis.

The main function of the testes is spermatogenesis, but they also have an important endocrine role: secreting the male sex hormone **testosterone**. Testosterone is secreted by cells known as Leydig cells, which are situated in the spaces between the seminiferous tubules. Testosterone controls the rate of spermatogenesis and is responsible for a wide range of male characteristics, including aspects of behaviour, increased growth of muscle tissue and changes in the larynx which cause the voice to 'break' at puberty.

The testes are controlled by the anterior pituitary gland which secretes two gonadotrophic hormones: **follicle stimulating hormone** (**FSH**) and **interstitial cell stimulating hormone** (**ICSH**). ICSH is identical in structure to luteinising hormone (LH) which, as described later, has an important role in the menstrual cycle. ICSH stimulates the Leydig cells to secrete testosterone, which has an inhibitory effect on the secretion of FSH and ICSH. In other words, a negative feedback mechanism operates between the anterior pituitary and the testes. FSH acts with testosterone to stimulate the process of spermatogenesis.

Oogenesis (Figure 5.15) is the process by which primordial germ cells, known as oogonia, become mature ova. This process begins during early fetal development, where oogonia divide by mitosis. By the fourth and fifth months, some of these oogonia will have enlarged and have the potential to develop into mature gametes. At this stage they are known as **primary oocytes** and begin the first stage (prophase I) of meiosis. By the seventh month of fetal development, the primary oocytes have become surrounded by a layer of flattened follicular cells to form **primordial follicles**. The first stage of meiosis then ceases and no further development occurs until after the female reaches puberty. Then, approximately once a month, a few of the primary oocytes resume meiosis and begin to move towards the surface of the ovary. Usually only one follicle reaches full maturity; the others undergo degeneration (atresia). As the follicle develops, it enlarges and fluid begins to accumulate within the follicle. During this stage, the first meiotic division is completed and the oocyte is known as a **secondary oocyte**. At ovulation, the mature follicle (or **Graafian follicle**) ruptures and the secondary oocyte, surrounded by cells from the follicle, is released from the ovary. After the oocyte is released it is usually referred to as an ovum and the second meiotic division will not be completed until the head of a spermatozoon enters during fertilisation.

Notice that during oogenesis the meiotic divisions are unequal, that is, the cytoplasm is not distributed equally between the daughter cells. Only one mature ovum is produced from each primary oocyte, plus three polar bodies, which disintegrate. This process ensures that the ovum has a large store of cytoplasm with all of its organelles and nutrients for early development.

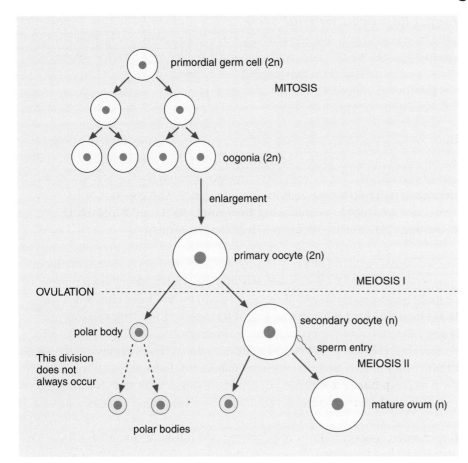

Figure 5.15 Oogenesis

After ovulation, the ruptured follicle fills with a blood clot and cells remaining within the follicle enlarge. This forms a temporary endocrine structure, the **corpus luteum**, which grows for 7 or 8 days. During this time, the corpus luteum secretes **progesterone** and **oestrogen**. If fertilisation and implantation do not occur, the corpus luteum degenerates 12 to 14 days after ovulation to form the functionless corpus albicans (Figure 5.16).

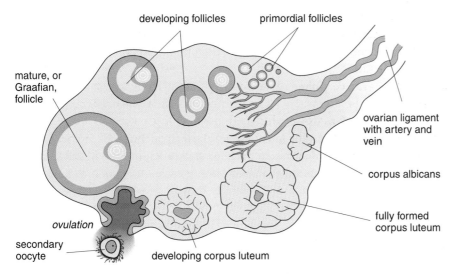

Figure 5.16 Stages of ovarian follicle development

Control of the menstrual cycle

Ovulation is a cyclical process and this is accompanied by corresponding cyclical changes which occur throughout the female reproductive system. These changes depend on two interrelated cycles:

- the ovarian cycle, and
- the uterine (menstrual) cycle.

Both of these cycles are variable, but both last approximately 28 days. The menstrual cycle is controlled by the ovarian cycle, via the hormones oestrogen and progesterone. The ovarian cycle, in turn, is controlled by gonadotrophic hormones secreted by the anterior pituitary gland. The gonadotrophic hormones are **follicle stimulating hormone (FSH)** and **luteinising hormone (LH)** and are secreted in a cyclical pattern.

An initial increase in the blood FSH level stimulates the development of one or more of the primordial follicles and also stimulates follicular cells to secrete oestrogen and small amounts of progesterone. The levels of oestrogen in the blood therefore gradually increase for a few days, then suddenly rise to a peak on about the 12th day of the cycle. About 12 hours afterwards, there is a rise in the levels of both LH and FSH which triggers ovulation. LH also causes the formation of the corpus luteum from the ruptured follicle, which secretes oestrogen and progesterone. If pregnancy does not occur, the lack of FSH and LH causes the corpus luteum to degenerate and the levels of progesterone and oestrogen fall.

The changing concentrations of oestrogen and progesterone during the cycle are responsible for cyclical changes in the uterus. The wall of the uterus has three layers:

- a thin outer layer in contact with the body cavity
- a thick, smooth muscle layer, the **myometrium**
- an inner lining, called the **endometrium**, which provides the environment for development of the fetus.

During the uterine cycle, the endometrium undergoes cyclical changes in structure, which can be divided into three phases (Figure 5.17):

- the **menstrual phase**, which occurs on days 1 to about 5 of a new cycle. During this phase, the outer layers of the endometrium are lost (menstruation).
- the **proliferative phase** (or follicular phase), which lasts from about day 6 to day 13 or 14 in a 28 day cycle. During this phase, the endometrium becomes thicker as tissue which was lost in menstruation is repaired.
- the **secretory phase** (or luteal phase) during which glands in the endometrium start to secrete a thick, glycogen-rich mucus. In this phase, which lasts from ovulation to the end of the cycle, the endometrium is prepared for implantation of the fertilised ovum.

As the blood oestrogen levels rise during the proliferative phase, they produce several changes in the endometrium, including repair and thickening, and an increase in the water content of the endometrium. Increasing blood progesterone levels during the secretory phase are responsible for

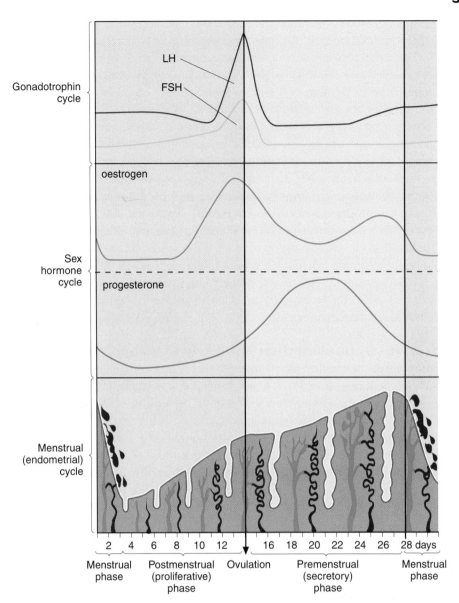

Figure 5.17 Female reproductive cycles

maintenance of the endometrium, secretion by the endometrial glands and a further increase in the water content. The drop in levels of both oestrogen and progesterone, due to degeneration of the corpus luteum towards the end of the ovarian cycle, is responsible for loss of the outer layers of the endometrium which characterises the menstrual phase.

Feedback and control of the ovarian cycle by gonadotrophins

So far, we have described cyclical changes in the ovary and in the endometrium, and how these changes are, in turn, controlled by the gonadotrophic hormones FSH and LH. The secretion of these gonadotrophins depends on the activity of the **hypothalamus**, which is one reason why female reproductive cycles can be affected by emotional influences, including stress (psychogenic influences).

The hypothalamus controls the secretion of both FSH and LH by means of **gonadotrophin releasing hormone** (GnRH), sometimes referred to as

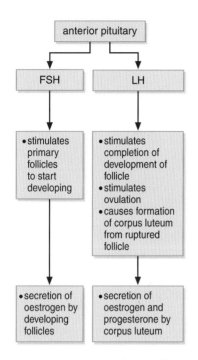

Figure 5.18 Summary of main effects of gonadotrophic follicle stimulating hormone (FSH) and luteinising hormone (LH) on the ovaries

luteinising hormone releasing hormone (LHRH). Both negative and positive feedback mechanisms help to control the secretion of FSH and LH (Figure 5.18). These mechanisms depend on the secretion of oestrogen and progesterone by the ovaries, and the secretion of GnRH by the hypothalamus. Remember that at the start of the menstrual cycle, the blood level of FSH starts to rise, which in turn stimulates the secretion of oestrogen by follicular cells in the ovary. Oestrogen exerts two types of feedback on the secretion of gonadotrophins: at low levels it inhibits secretion (negative feedback), but at relatively high concentrations it stimulates secretion of gonadotrophins (positive feedback). This effect is responsible for the mid-cycle peak in LH and FSH which triggers ovulation. After ovulation, the level of LH remains relatively high, which stimulates the formation of the corpus luteum. Towards the end of the cycle, however, secretion of LH is inhibited as a result of negative feedback exerted by rising levels of progesterone. As the corpus luteum degenerates, the levels of progesterone fall, and the concentrations of FSH gradually increase again. Oestrogen and progesterone probably exert their effects by affecting the secretion of GnRH by the hypothalamus and changing the sensitivity to GnRH of cells in the anterior pituitary.

Fertilisation, implantation and early development

Transfer of sperms into the vagina involves erection of the penis and ejaculation of semen. Erection is a parasympathetic nervous reflex initiated by various tactile, visual and psychological stimuli. As a result of dilatation of arteries and arterioles in the penis, spaces in the erectile tissue become distended which compresses the veins. More blood enters the penis than leaves it through the veins and it becomes larger and rigid. Ejaculation of semen is also a reflex involving the same stimuli that initiate erection. Rhythmic contractions of the bulbocavernosus and ischiocavernosus muscles at the base of the penis propel semen into the vagina.

Normal sperms are motile and can move at a rate of about 1 mm per minute. Assisted by muscular movements of the uterus, sperms make their way through the cervix and uterus and into the oviducts (Fallopian tubes). Fertilisation occurs most frequently in the outer one third of the oviduct, as shown in Figure 5.19.

Of the 10^8 to 5×10^8 sperms released into the vagina at ejaculation, fewer than 100 reach the oviduct. Only one sperm fertilises the ovum and, as soon as the head of one sperm enters the ovum, complex mechanisms in the ovum are activated to prevent further sperm entry. The 23 chromosomes from the sperm combine with the 23 chromosomes present in the ovum to restore the diploid number of 46 chromosomes.

After ovulation, the ovum lives only for about 24 hours. Sperms may live for up to a few days after entering the female reproductive tract and sexual intercourse from about 3 days before ovulation occurs, to 1 day after ovulation, may result in fertilisation.

The fertilised ovum is referred to as a **zygote** and it immediately begins to divide, by mitosis, as it travels down the oviduct. In about 3 days, a mass of about 16 cells, known as a **morula**, is formed. The morula enters the uterus

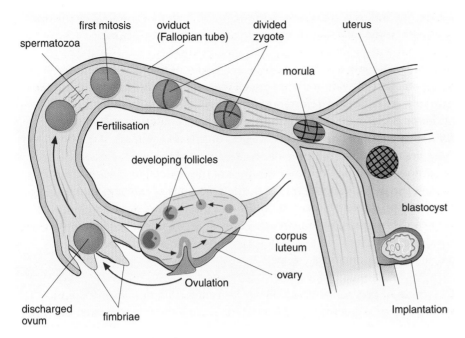

Figure 5.19 Fertilisation and implantation

and fluid from the uterine cavity enters the morula. The cells rearrange themselves to form a hollow structure, known as a blastocyst. The **blastocyst** begins to implant in the endometrium and, in about 10 days from fertilisation, the blastocyst is completely implanted.

The blastocyst consists of an outer layer of cells and an **inner cell mass**. The outer wall of the blastocyst is referred to as the **trophoblast** and gives rise to structures which support the embryo during development. As the blastocyst develops further, the inner cell mass forms a structure with two cavities: the **yolk sac** and the **amniotic cavity**. Cells within the yolk sac produce blood cells until this function is taken over by the embryonic liver. The amniotic cavity becomes filled with fluid, mainly derived from maternal blood, which physically cushions the developing embryo, maintains a constant temperature and allows free movement of the fetus.

The chorion develops from the trophoblast to form the **placenta** (Figure 5.20). The surface of the chorion becomes covered with chorionic villi which connect blood vessels of the chorion to the placenta. The placenta has several functions, including the transfer of oxygen and carbon dioxide, nutrients, metabolic

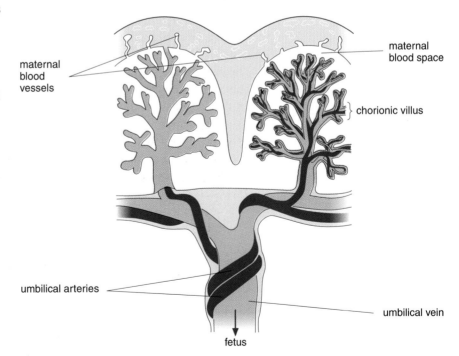

Figure 5.20 Diagrammatic structure of the placenta

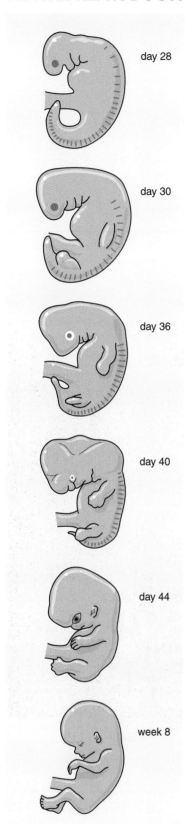

day 28

day 30

day 36

day 40

day 44

week 8

Figure 5.21 Stages of development of the human embryo and fetus

wastes, antibodies and hormones between the maternal and fetal circulations. Drugs and some infectious organisms can also cross the placenta.

The inner cell mass develops to form the tissues of the baby itself. Early in development, cells within the inner cell mass differentiate to form the three **primary germ layers**, referred to as the endoderm, mesoderm, and ectoderm. Cells within each of these germ layers continue to divide and differentiate to give rise to all the tissues, organs and systems of the body. As examples, the endoderm gives rise to the lining of the digestive and respiratory tracts; mesoderm forms most of the skeletal muscles and bones, kidneys and gonads; ectoderm forms the epidermis of skin and various components of the nervous system. During the third week of development, the process of **neurulation** occurs, in which the neural tube is formed, from ectoderm, along the dorsal axis of the embryo. The neural tube is the precursor of the nervous system.

The length of pregnancy, about 38 weeks from fertilisation, is divided into three 3-month segments called trimesters. During the first trimester, the term **embryo** is used to describe the developing individual. Towards the end of the first trimester, from about week 8 until birth the term embryo is replaced by the term **fetus**. Stages of embryonic and fetal development are illustrated in Figure 5.21.

Birth and lactation

Birth, or **parturition**, is the point of transition between the prenatal and postnatal periods of life. The term **labour** is used to describe the processes which result in the birth of a baby. Labour is divided into three stages:

- Stage 1: period from the onset of uterine contractions until dilation of the cervix is complete
- Stage 2: from the time of maximal dilation of the cervix until the baby exits through the vagina
- Stage 3: process of expulsion of the placenta through the vagina.

The processes which initiate and control parturition are not fully understood, but can be summarised as follows:

- the sensitivity of the uterine muscle to oxytocin increases towards the end of pregnancy
- in sheep and goats, parturition is triggered by the release of corticotrophin releasing hormone from the fetal hypothalamus, which stimulates the secretion of adrenocorticotrophic hormone (ACTH)
- ACTH acts on the fetal adrenal glands and cortisol is secreted which passes from the fetus to the placenta, where it stimulates oestrogen secretion and inhibits progesterone secretion
- as a result, the synthesis of prostaglandin F2α is increased in the placenta and uterus
- this increases the sensitivity of the uterine muscle to oxytocin
- oxytocin from the mother's posterior pituitary gland stimulates contraction of the uterine muscle until the baby is pushed out through the cervix and vagina.

Lactation consists of two processes: milk secretion, and milk ejection. Milk secretion involves the synthesis of milk by secretory cells in the mammary glands. This is stimulated by prolactin, or lactogenic hormone, secreted by the anterior pituitary gland. Milk ejection involves suckling by the baby and a contractile mechanism within the mammary glands which helps to express milk. Suckling stimulates the secretion of oxytocin (and prolactin) by the mother's pituitary gland. Oxytocin is then carried in the blood stream to the mammary glands where it stimulates contraction of myoepithelial cells. This propels milk into ducts where it is accessible for the baby to remove by suckling.

The fluid secreted by the mammary glands during the first 3 days after parturition is termed **colostrum**. This is deep yellow in colour and rich in protein and salts. Milk formed during the first few weeks of lactation is termed transition, or intermediate, milk. Mature milk is produced at the end of the first month. Milk is a rich source of proteins, fat, calcium, vitamins and other nutrients needed by the developing infant. It also provides passive immunity to the baby in the form of maternal antibodies present in the milk.

ADDITIONAL MATERIAL

Passage through the placenta of potentially harmful substances and of viruses
Potentially harmful substances in the mother's blood can cross the placenta and have a number of adverse effects on the developing fetus. Such substances include nicotine, alcohol and heroin. Some viruses are also able to cross the placenta.

- Cigarette smoke contains numerous harmful substances including nicotine, tar and carbon monoxide. Maternal smoking adversely affects the fetus and decreases the chances of survival of the newborn infant, by decreasing the availability of oxygen to the fetus. It has been suggested that oxygen deprivation may be responsible for more than 30 per cent of the deaths of all stillborn infants and is a major cause of intrauterine growth retardation (IUGR).
- Alcohol is freely soluble and easily crosses the placenta. Consumption of alcohol during pregnancy can have tragic effects on the developing fetus. when alcohol enters the fetal blood, the result, called fetal alcohol syndrome (FAS) can cause congenital abnormalities such as microcephaly (abnormally small head), low birth weight, slow physical and mental development of the infant, or fetal death.
- Heroin. If the mother is addicted to heroin, then her baby probably will also be addicted. Such babies are very likely to be born underweight, or prematurely.
- Transmission of infection can also occur across the placenta, an example of vertical transmission. Microorganisms which can be transmitted in this way include the rubella virus, HIV, and the hepatitis B virus. The fetus is particularly susceptible to the rubella virus when maternal infection occurs during the first three months of pregnancy. The virus interferes with the development of the brain, heart, eyes and ears, resulting in a number of malformations, low birth weight, failure to thrive and increased infant mortality.

QUESTIONS

A recent survey in the USA showed that 20 to 25 per cent of women who smoked before pregnancy continued to do so. What are the public health issues associated with smoking (or drinking alcohol) during pregnancy? What factors might influence a woman's decision to continue to smoke during pregnancy?

Growth and physical development

The postnatal period begins at birth and lasts until death. Although it is often divided into four major periods, it is important to recognise that growth and development are continuous processes which occur throughout life. Gradual changes in the physical appearance of the body as a whole and in the relative proportions of the head, limbs and trunk are particularly noticeable between birth and adolescence. Figure 5.22 shows the changes in the relative proportions of the body parts of a boy from birth to 16 years.

SEXUAL REPRODUCTION

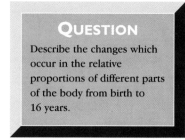

QUESTION

Describe the changes which occur in the relative proportions of different parts of the body from birth to 16 years.

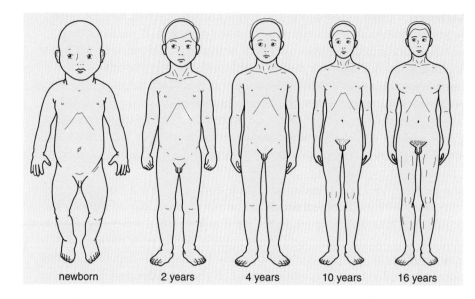

| newborn | 2 years | 4 years | 10 years | 16 years |

Figure 5.22 Changes in the proportions of body parts from birth to 16 years

Briefly, the postnatal periods are as follows:

1 Infancy, which begins at birth and lasts about 18 months.
2 Childhood, which extends from the end of infancy to sexual maturity, or puberty.
3 Adolescence and adulthood. The average age range of adolescence varies, but generally the teenage years (13 to 19) are used. This period is marked by rapid physical growth, resulting in sexual maturity.
4 Older adulthood, characterised by a gradual decline in every major organ system in the body.

Puberty is the age at which the reproductive organs reach maturity. In females, the ovaries are stimulated by the gonadotrophic hormones from the anterior pituitary, to secrete increasing amounts of oestrogen. Oestrogen, with progesterone, produces the changes of puberty. This occurs between the ages of about 10 and 14 years and the physical changes include:

• maturity of the uterus, oviducts and ovaries
• start of the menstrual cycle and ovulation
• development and enlargement of the breasts
• growth of pubic and axillary hair
• increase in the rate of growth in height
• widening of the pelvis
• increase in the amount of fat deposited in subcutaneous tissue.

Puberty in the male occurs between the ages of about 10 and 14 years. The gonadotrophic hormone ICSH (interstitial cell stimulating hormone) from the anterior pituitary stimulates production of testosterone in the testes. This hormone influences growth and development of the body to maturity. The physical changes which occur during puberty in the male include:

• growth of muscle and bone resulting in a marked increase in height
• the voice 'breaks', or deepens, due to growth of the larynx
• growth of pubic and axillary hair and of hair on the face, chest, abdomen
• enlargement of the penis and scrotum
• production of spermatozoa.

A **growth curve** shows the relationship between, say, body mass and the age of the person. Figure 5.23 shows such a growth curve for humans and, after birth, four distinct phases can be recognised:

1 A rapid increase during infancy, especially during the first year.
2 A slower, progressive increase from 3 to about 12 years of age.
3 A marked increase in growth from the time of puberty (the 'adolescent spurt').
4 Even after puberty, there is a slight increase in growth during early adulthood.

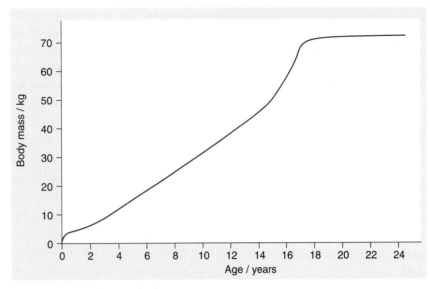

Figure 5.23 Growth curve for humans

Adulthood

Most body systems are in a peak condition and function efficiently during the early years of adulthood. As we grow older, a gradual decline takes place in the functioning of all major organ systems in the body. For example, during older adulthood, the bones undergo changes in their extent of calcification and texture. With increasing age, changes in calcification may result in a decrease in bone size and in bones which become porous and prone to fracture. Degenerative joint diseases, such as **osteoarthritis**, are common in the elderly. Osteoarthritis is a degenerative change in the articular cartilage in joints, which in the early stages loses its smooth appearance and becomes flaky. The damaged cartilage is gradually worn away until the underlying bone is exposed. These changes lead to joint pain and reduced movement at the joint. The knees and hips are the most commonly and severely affected.

Degenerative diseases of the heart and blood vessels are a common and serious effect of ageing. Fatty deposits may build up in the walls of blood vessels, resulting in **atherosclerosis**, which may affect all arteries, but the aorta, cerebral and carotid arteries tend to be the most severely affected. The consequences of atherosclerosis include narrowing of the lumen of the artery, which obstructs blood flow, and weakening of the vessel wall.

Ageing also affects the reproductive system. Men may continue to produce gametes as they age, but in women between the ages of about 45 and 60 years, ovulation and the menstrual cycle become less regular and eventually stop. This is known as the **menopause** (Figure 5.24) and results from a decrease in the secretion of sex hormones, particularly oestrogen. Follicle stimulating hormone (FSH) and luteinising hormone (LH) continue to be secreted at higher levels than normal. This results in a number of both physiological and psychological effects, including disturbance of temperature control ('hot flushes') and mood swings including anxiety and loss of confidence. The decrease in oestrogen levels may contribute to a condition known as

osteoporosis. This is due to a reduction in the density and mass of bone, leading to increased risk of fracture, back pain, weight loss and curvature of the spine. Osteoporosis results in about 60 000 hip fractures a year in the UK, 90 per cent of which occur in people over the age of 50, and 80 per cent of whom are women. Hormone replacement therapy (**HRT**) has been shown to reduce bone loss and to reduce the risk of hip and spinal fractures in postmenopausal women. HRT is administered in the form of tablets or skin patches, containing either oestrogen or a combination of oestrogen and synthetic progesterone.

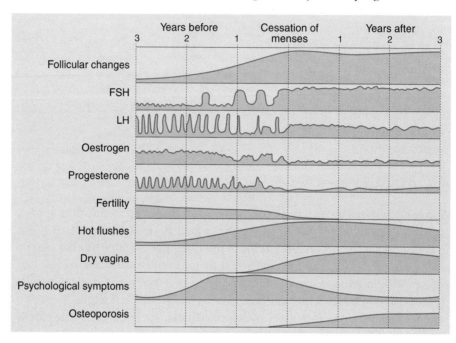

Figure 5.24 Hormonal and other changes associated with the menopause

Energy and the Environment

Bluebells in a woodland.

6 Modes of nutrition

All living organisms need energy for growth and maintenance. **Autotrophic** organisms are able to use external sources of energy in the synthesis of their organic food materials, whereas **heterotrophic** organisms must be supplied with ready-made organic compounds from which to derive their energy. Algae, green plants and certain prokaryotes can obtain the energy for synthesis directly from the sun's radiation. It is then used to build up essential organic compounds from inorganic molecules. Such organisms are called **photosynthetic** and possess special pigments which can absorb the necessary light energy. A few specialised prokaryotes are able to use energy derived from certain types of chemical reaction in the synthesis of organic molecules from inorganic ones. These organisms are called **chemosynthetic** and include the nitrifying bacteria *Nitrosomonas* and *Nitrobacter*, which are important in the nitrogen cycle (see Chapter 7). All other organisms are heterotrophic and are dependent on autotrophic organisms for their energy supplies, so must feed on plants or on other animals which have eaten plants. Photosynthesis is the source of energy and organic materials for other organisms besides plants. So it can be seen that the ultimate source of all metabolic energy is the Sun and photosynthesis is responsible for the maintenance of life on Earth.

The different types of heterotrophic nutrition

Heterotrophic organisms need to be supplied with food consisting of complex organic molecules, which they use to obtain energy for metabolism and the

Figure 6.1 All these organisms are heterotrophic: (top) lionesses feeding at a kill; (left) parasitic bracket fungi; (right) hermit crab with anemone attached to its shell

materials required for growth, repair and replacement of tissues. These organic molecules are obtained either directly from green plants or from organisms that have fed on green plants. The ways in which heterotrophic organisms obtain their food vary greatly (Figure 6.1), but once obtained, the complex organic compounds have to be broken down into simpler, soluble molecules before they can be absorbed.

Within an ecosystem, heterotrophic organisms are the **consumers** in food chains. Green plants, known as **primary producers**, are autotrophic and able to synthesise the organic molecules which are required by consumers. Primary consumers are **herbivores**, feeding directly on green plants. Secondary consumers are **carnivores** and feed on the herbivores. Tertiary consumers are also carnivores as they feed on the secondary consumers. Heterotrophic organisms that feed on both plant and animal material are known as **omnivores**.

Four main types of heterotrophic nutrition are recognised:
- **holozoic**, in which complex food is taken into a specialised digestive system, broken down into smaller pieces, and absorbed – this type of nutrition is characteristic of free-living animals
- **saprobiontic/saprotrophic**, in which organisms feed on dead organic remains of other organisms
- **parasitic**, in which an organism obtains food from another living organism, called the **host**
- **mutualism**, a form of **symbiosis**, in which there is a close association between two organisms, each contributing to and benefiting from the relationship.

Holozoic nutrition

Holozoic nutrition is characteristic of higher animals, including humans, and consists of five stages:
- **ingestion** – food is taken into the body through the mouth
- **digestion** – the food is first mechanically broken down by the teeth in the mouth and then chemically broken down by **hydrolysing enzymes** in the **stomach, duodenum and ileum**
- **absorption** – the smaller soluble molecules are taken up into the **bloodstream** from the **duodenum** and **ileum**
- **assimilation** – the absorbed products of digestion are incorporated and used by the body
- **egestion** – the undigested parts of the food are eliminated from the body through the **anus** during **defaecation**.

Herbivores

Cattle and sheep are herbivores (Figure 6.2). Their ruminant digestive system allows a high proportion of the cellulose in fibrous foods to be digested and become available as energy. They also benefit from features of their nitrogen metabolism and their ability to synthesise water-soluble vitamins. The alimentary canal is more complex than that of humans due to three additional compartments, the **rumen**, **reticulum** and **omasum**, which come before the true stomach, known as the **abomasum** (Figure 6.3).

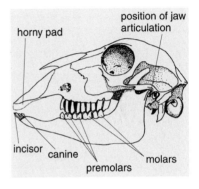

Figure 6.2 Side view of skull showing dentition of a sheep, illustrating typical herbivore features.
- *small sharp incisors and canines on lower jaw – cut against pad of gum for cropping*
- *diastema (gap between incisors and molars) – for manipulation of food bolus*
- *premolars and molars – for grinding*
- *ridges of enamel – provide efficient cutting edge as grinding surfaces of premolars and molars get worn down*
- *open roots – allow for continuing growing of the tooth*
- *loose jaw articulation – allows sideways movement of lower jaw against upper jaw (related to cud chewing)*

Dental formula $i\frac{0}{3}$ $c\frac{0}{1}$ $pm\frac{3}{3}$ $m\frac{3}{3}$

(i = incisors, c = canines, pm = premolars, m = molars. The line separates the upper and lower jaw)

MODES OF NUTRITION

After swallowing, food passes to the rumen for up to 30 hours. Here it is mixed mechanically and fermented by populations of microorganisms. Coarse material is regurgitated into the mouth, rechewed, then swallowed again. Chewing the cud in this way may continue for up to 8 hours in a day if the diet is very fibrous. The microorganisms in the rumen are mainly bacteria but also include protoctists and yeasts. These microbes become established soon after birth when the calf begins to pick up solid food. The species mixture depends on the food consumed so changes to the diet should be made gradually to ensure rumen microorganisms adjust accordingly. The microorganisms digest carbohydrates, particularly polysaccharides with b-links, and this contributes to the breakdown of cellulose. The resulting hexoses are further broken down, by fermentation under anaerobic conditions, to short-chain organic acids (ethanoic, propionic and butyric) with the release of the gases carbon dioxide and methane.

> example of rumen fermentation reaction
> $$C_6H_{12}O_6 \rightarrow 2CH_3COOH + CO_2 + CH_4$$

Energy released in these reactions is utilised by the microorganisms for their own biosyntheses. The gases escape from the animal by belching and are wasted. The acids, known as volatile fatty acids (VFAs) are absorbed through the walls of the rumen and contribute to the energy requirements of the animal. High fibre foods rich in cellulose produce mainly ethanoic acid, whereas feeding of concentrates increases the proportion of propionic acid produced. In dairy cows, a shift towards more propionic acid results in deposition of body fat with a reduction in fat content of milk and a lowered milk production. The composition of the rumen microflora can be altered artificially so that the carbohydrate, when broken down, produces more or less methane.

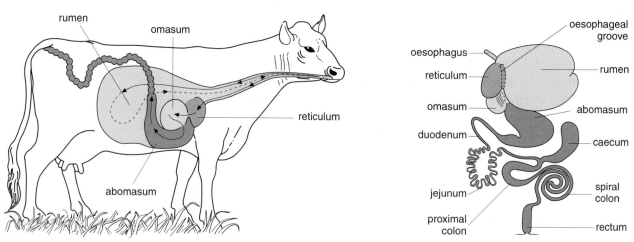

Figure 6.3 Ruminant digestive system in a cow– the arrows show the pathway taken by food, including chewing the cud

- the **reticulum** has no digestive function – concerned with the passage of boluses of food to the oesophagus and digested material from the rumen to the omasum
- the **rumen** is the chamber in which fermentation of food material takes place. Capacity is about 150 litres. Microorganisms in the rumen synthesise vitamins of the B-complex
- the **omasum** – main function is to remove water and organic acids from digested material passed from the rumen; produces no digestive secretions. Capacity is about 15 litres.
- the **abomasum** functions as a 'true' stomach, secreting gastric juices. Digestion here and in the rest of the alimentary canal is similar to that in humans
- fibre slows down the passage of food in the gut and adequate amounts in the diet are essential to maintain rumen function.

Protein is also broken down in the rumen by microbial activity, first to amino acids then deaminated to release ammonia. Some ammonia is incorporated into microbial protein and the rest is absorbed into the blood of the animal. It may then either be excreted or recycled to the rumen by means of the saliva and thereby gain another chance of being synthesised into microbial protein. Non-protein nitrogen, in the form of chemicals such as urea, can be supplied with the diet and is utilised by microorganisms to synthesise protein (Figure 6.4). This protein becomes available to the animal when they pass from the rumen into the abomasum and are digested. Some of the protein in the food by-passes the rumen and is then digested with the animal's digestive enzymes in the abomasum, duodenum and rest of the alimentary canal.

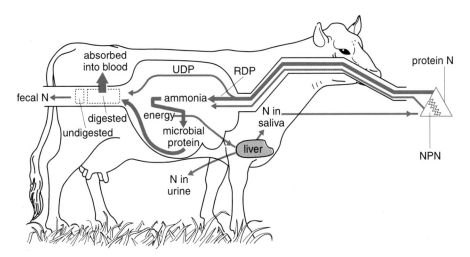

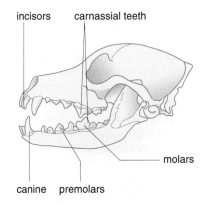

MODES OF NUTRITION

QUESTION

Gas production from carbohydrates fermenting in the rumen can account for loss of about 7% of the energy contained in feeds. Why might it be desirable to reduce the methane production? Think about the diet and economics of feeding the cow or sheep as well as about wider environmental implications.

Figure 6.4 Ruminants and their utilisation of nitrogen in the diet. Note how ruminants benefit from microbes in the rumen which convert non-protein and low-quality protein into relatively high-quality protein. NPN = non-protein nitrogen, such as urea, RDP = rumen degradable protein, UDP = undegradable protein

Carnivores

Carnivores are meat eaters and their teeth are adapted for catching and killing their food, as well as for shearing the flesh, cutting through tendons and ligaments, and crushing bones. The teeth of the carnivores show many adaptations to their diet (Figure 6.5), including:

- sharp incisors, which can hold the prey and also remove flesh from bones
- large, often curved, pointed canines which assist in holding prey and tearing flesh
- the fourth premolars on each side of the upper jaw and the first molars on each side of the lower jaw are especially modified to form the carnassial teeth, which are effective at slicing through the flesh
- sharply pointed premolars and molars.

In addition, the jaw articulation is tight, with larger chewing muscles than the herbivores (where there is more of a rotational chewing movement).

The gut of a carnivore is not significantly different from the human gut, but there are other adaptations shown. The carnivore is a hunter and depends on good vision and speed in order to catch live prey. Comparison of the skull of a dog or cat with that of a herbivore reveals the difference in the position of the eyes. The carnivore has eyes at the front, positioned quite close together to give stereoscopic vision, thus enabling distances to be judged accurately. The herbivore's eyes are on the side of its head and give a more all-round view, detecting movement of predators more easily. Some carnivores have good night vision, which enables them to hunt at night and surprise their prey.

Figure 6.5 Skull of a domestic dog showing features of carnivore dentition.

Other adaptations that may be seen in the carnivores include:
- the ability to run fast in order to chase their prey
- camouflage (coat colour or markings) so that they can stalk their victims without being seen
- powerful claws on their limbs to hold their prey.

Members of the Order Carnivora include leopards, cheetahs and the domestic cat which usually hunt their prey singly; others, such as the wolves and hyenas, hunt in social groups called packs. Lions may hunt singly or in packs. Not all carnivores hunt large prey that have to be chased and caught. Some, like badgers, eat earthworms which they collect from the surface of the soil. Otters hunt and catch fish underwater.

Saprobiontic nutrition

So far in this chapter we have been considering in detail the type of heterotrophic nutrition shown by most animals, namely **holozoic** nutrition. **Saprobiontic**, or **saprotrophic**, organisms obtain their nutrition from dead or decaying organic remains of plants and animals. They are **primary consumers** in **detritus food chains** and are often referred to as **decomposers**. Saprobionts secrete enzymes onto the organic matter and absorb the soluble products of this **extracellular** digestion. Any substances released by this digestion which are not taken up by the saprobionts are made available for uptake by plants, so contributing to the circulation of nutrients. Many bacteria and fungi are saprobiontic.

Rhizopus – a saprobiontic organism

Rhizopus stolonifera is a member of the Zygomycota, which are fungi lacking cross-walls in their hyphae. *Rhizopus* (Figure 6.6) is commonly found growing on damp wholemeal bread, where it can be seen as cotton-like white threads on the surface. After a few days, masses of tiny black sporangia appear, resembling pin heads and giving the fungus its common name 'pin mould'. Closer observation, using a microscope, reveals that the fungus consists of a **mycelium** made up of much-branched **hyphae**, which are **aseptate** (lacking cross-walls). Aerial hyphae, called **stolons**, spread over the food substrate and produce tufts of branched hyphae, or **rhizoids**, where they touch down. The rhizoids penetrate the substrate, secreting enzymes which digest the complex substances in the food. The soluble products of this digestion are absorbed by the rhizoids and either used in metabolic activities or stored. Three main groups of enzymes are secreted as in other types of heterotrophic organisms: carbohydrases, proteases and lipases.

Parasitic nutrition

A **parasite** is an organism which lives in close association with another living organism, the **host**. In this relationship, the parasite is dependent on the host for its food and usually causes the host some degree of harm. **Ectoparasites** live on the outside of their hosts while **endoparasites** live inside their host. Most endoparasites, such as gut parasites, spend their entire lives within their host, but some ectoparasites, such as the tsetse fly, only become attached during feeding. Most parasites are highly adapted to their particular mode of life.

> ### QUESTIONS
> What are the differences between parasites and saprophytes?
> Do they have any features in common?
> Think about how they fit into food chains and food webs.

(a)

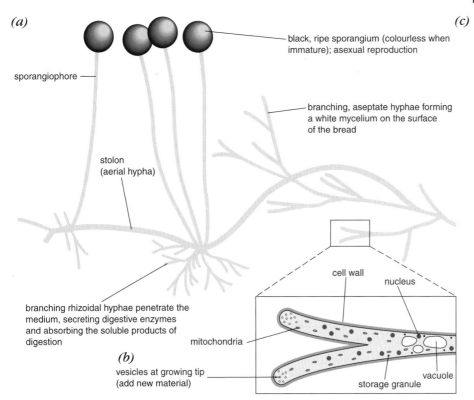

(c)

black, ripe sporangium (colourless when immature); asexual reproduction

sporangiophore

branching, aseptate hyphae forming a white mycelium on the surface of the bread

stolon (aerial hypha)

cell wall

nucleus

branching rhizoidal hyphae penetrate the medium, secreting digestive enzymes and absorbing the soluble products of digestion

mitochondria

(b)

vesicles at growing tip (add new material)

storage granule

vacuole

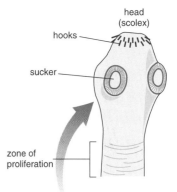

head (scolex)

hooks

sucker

zone of proliferation

Figure 6.6 (a) Rhizopus *on bread, showing sporangia; (b) diagram of* Rhizopus *showing mycelial structure; (c) photomicrograph of sporangia of* Rhizopus

Taenia – a parasitic organism

Taenia solium, the pork **tapeworm** (Figure 6.7), is an endoparasite with two hosts. Its primary host is man, and the adult stage is found attached to the wall of the small intestine of an infected individual. The secondary host is the pig, in which the larval stage develops. The adult stage consists of a flattened, ribbon-like body, made up of a large number of 'segments' called **proglottides** (sing. **proglottis**). It must be emphasised that the proglottides are not true segments, such as those found in earthworms or in the Chordates. The tapeworm can be up to 3.5 m long and is approximately 6 mm wide and 1.5 mm thick. At its anterior end, it has a tiny knob known as the **scolex** which has a double row of hooks and four suckers. Just behind the scolex is a region called the **proliferation zone** where new proglottides form. The rest of the organism consists of proglottides containing both male and female reproductive structures. At the posterior end, after self-fertilisation has occurred, these proglottides contain a greatly enlarged uterus full of fertilised eggs, the rest of the structures having been reabsorbed. These proglottides become detached from the organism and pass out with the faeces of the host. If ingested by the secondary host, a pig, the life cycle proceeds to the next stage, giving rise to a larval stage in muscular tissue.

Taenia has no mouth or alimentary canal, as it absorbs the digested food of its host all over its body surface. Simple, soluble products of digestion of the host's food will be present in the small intestine, so the tapeworm can absorb the food it requires and has no need of a digestive system of its own, nor does it need to secrete digestive enzymes. It has a thick outer covering, known as

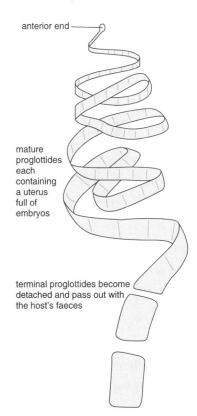

anterior end

mature proglottides each containing a uterus full of embryos

terminal proglottides become detached and pass out with the host's faeces

Figure 6.7 Taenia, *adult stage with detail of anterior region*

the **tegument**, consisting of protein and chitin, which protects it from the digestive enzymes of its host. Other adaptations to its mode of life are:
- its ability to live in the low oxygen concentrations present in the human gut
- a reduction in the nervous system and a lack of sense organs
- the possession of suckers and hooks for attachment to the gut wall of the host
- the production of very large numbers of offspring.

If the human host is healthy, little damage is caused by the tapeworm apart from depriving the host of some of its food. The long thin shape of the tapeworm does not block the small intestine. In children and adults already debilitated by other diseases, it can cause problems. Individuals may become less resistant to other diseases and suffer from abdominal pain, vomiting, constipation and loss of appetite.

Mutualism

The term **mutualism** describes a close association between two organisms in which both contribute and both benefit. This type of association can be illustrated by reference to the relationship between the bacterium *Rhizobium* and members of the flowering plant family Papilionaceae.

Rhizobium is a nitrogen-fixing bacterium. In this process, hydrogen ions from carbohydrates, such as glucose, are combined with nitrogen to form ammonia. The ammonia then combines with glutamate to form the amino acid glutamine, from which other amino acids can be synthesised. The fixation reaction takes place in anaerobic conditions in the cytoplasm of the bacterial cells, catalysed by the enzyme **nitrogenase** (Figure 6.8).

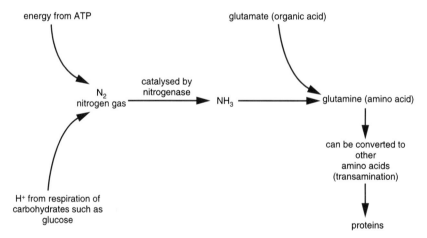

Figure 6.8 Stages in nitrogen fixation

Rhizobium bacteria are present in the soil. Those near the roots of leguminous plants, such as clover, peas or beans, are attracted towards the roots and are able to penetrate the root hair cells. This attraction has been found to occur in response to a hormone secreted by the roots of the plant. The bacteria also secrete substances which cause the root hair cells to bend around, possibly encouraging penetration. Once inside the root, the bacteria move to the cortex and stimulate the production of auxins and cytokinins by the root tissue. This causes cell division to occur and a nodule of tissue is formed in the cortex, composed of cells containing large numbers of the bacteria. The bacteria become Y-shaped and have a banded appearance. These forms of the bacteria are called **bacteroids**. The bacteroids are able to fix nitrogen in the nodules, where the anaerobic environment is suitable for the efficient functioning of their nitrogenase enzymes. Oxygen molecules are absorbed by a special pigment, **leghaemoglobin**, which surrounds the bacteroids and gives a pinkish colour to the tissues of the nodule. Figure 7.14 on page 131 shows root nodules in the bean, *Phaseolus multiflorus*, and a TS through a nodule is shown in Figure 6.9.

The bacteria benefit from this association by obtaining their supplies of carbohydrate from the photosynthetic activities of the plant. The plant benefits by receiving a supply of ammonia from the bacteria. This enables the leguminous plants to grow in nitrogen-deficient soils.

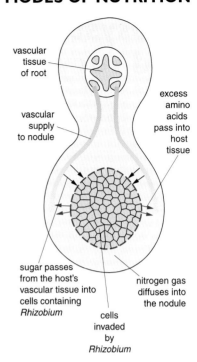

Figure 6.9 TS through a root nodule

7 Ecosystems, energy flow and recycling of nutrients

The biosphere and its ecosystems

Figure 7.1 A deciduous woodland (in the UK) in April – an example of a habitat

Ecosystems are complex associations of plants, animals and microorganisms which interact with each other and with their non-living environment. The flow of energy and flow of nutrients within ecosystems are regulated by the organisms living there. Through photosynthesis, green plants incorporate about 1 per cent of the sun's energy falling on them into organic compounds. The plants may then be eaten by herbivores (primary consumers), which in turn may be eaten by carnivores (secondary consumers). This type of sequence forms a **food chain** and the different levels within it are called **trophic levels.**

The term **biosphere** encompasses the part of the Earth and its atmosphere inhabited by living organisms. Within the biosphere are many different ecosystems. These represent a complex series of interrelationships between the rock, soil, water, air and living organisms.

An **ecosystem** was first defined in 1935 by Sir Arthur Tansley as 'the living world and its habitat'. This definition includes both the organisms within the ecosystem (the **biotic** component) and the physical and chemical factors (the **abiotic** component) which influence them. Different ecosystems may have more or less clearly defined boundaries, but they also merge into one another, so it may not always be easy to see the boundaries. For example, there is a gradual transition from a freshwater ecosystem, such as a pond, through the surrounding marshy ground to a field.

An ecosystem will contain a number of different **habitats**. A habitat is the place within an ecosystem where an organism lives. The pond shown in Figure 7.2 is a habitat for a whole range of different species, including pond snails and phytoplankton. Many organisms occupy one particular part of the total habitat, for example, the pea mussels living in the mud at the bottom of the pond. This location within the overall habitat is sometimes referred to as a **microhabitat**.

> ### DEFINITION
> The term **biosphere** refers to the part of the Earth which is inhabited by living organisms. An **ecosystem** consists of communities of organisms which interact with each other and their physical and chemical environment. The place where an organism lives is known as the **habitat**, such as a pond or rocky shore.

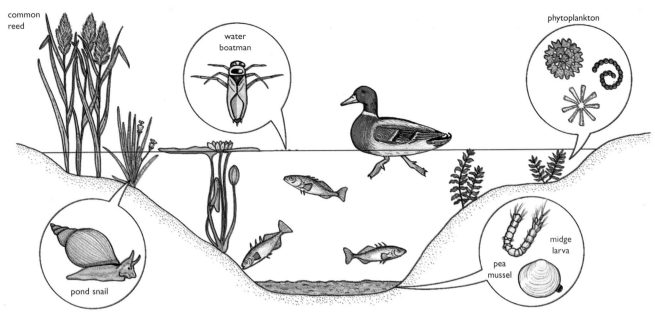

Figure 7.2 A freshwater ecosystem. Organisms in the inserts are shown enlarged, but not to the same scale.

An ecosystem thus comprises several habitats with their communities of organisms, and includes both biotic and abiotic components. A useful way of thinking of an ecosystem is as a network of habitats interlinked by the flow of energy and nutrients. Abiotic components are the non-living factors that influence the distribution of organisms within an ecosystem. These components include physical factors (such as light intensity, temperature, rainfall, wind and water currents) and chemical factors (including all the elements and compounds in the ecosystem). Biotic components also affect the populations of organisms in an ecosystem; these include the availability of food, competition and predation.

Flow of energy through an ecosystem

All organisms in an ecosystem depend on an adequate supply of energy for their survival. Energy from the sun, trapped by photosynthesis, provides the source of energy for all living organisms. Carbohydrates, which are produced in photosynthesis, are used as both building blocks for the growth of green plants and an energy source for the plant. Carbohydrate is respired in plant cells to provide adenosine triphosphate (ATP) for endergonic reactions, such as protein synthesis (see Figure 7.3 for an illustration of this energy cycle).

Heterotrophs cannot fix carbon dioxide by photosynthesis and therefore depend on obtaining ready made organic compounds from their food. In heterotrophs, these organic compounds serve the same functions as they do in **autotrophs**, that is, they provide building blocks for the synthesis of new cell compounds for growth and provide substrates for respiration and the production of ATP.

Producers and photosynthesis, consumers and decomposers

We have already stated that energy from the sun enters an ecosystem through organic compounds produced, in photosynthesis, by green plants. Green plants are described, in this context, as **primary producers**. The Earth's surface receives between 0 and 5 joules of solar energy per square metre every

> **DEFINITION**
>
> **Autotrophs** are organisms which are able to synthesise complex organic substances from inorganic substances, such as carbon dioxide and water. Green plants are autotrophs, using light energy to produce carbohydrates in the process of photosynthesis.

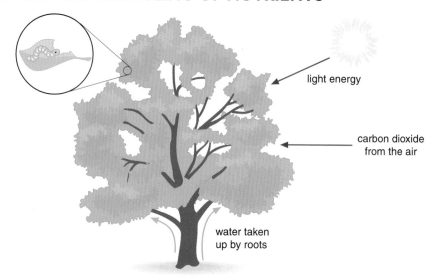

light energy

carbon dioxide
from the air

water taken
up by roots

Figure 7.3 The flow of energy through an ecosystem. Green plants use light energy to synthesise organic substances from carbon dioxide and water, in the process of photosynthesis. These organic substances are used for growth and as an energy source. Heterotrophs use the organic compounds from the plant for growth and for energy.

minute. However, only a small percentage of this energy is captured by chlorophyll and converted into chemical energy of newly synthesised organic compounds. Some of the light striking a leaf is reflected, or passes straight through, and about half is made up of wavelengths which are not used in photosynthesis. There is also some wastage of energy due to biochemical inefficiency of the reactions of photosynthesis.

The bodies of all the living organisms within a unit area constitute the standing crop, or **biomass**. Biomass is defined as the mass of organisms per unit area of ground (or water) and is usually expressed either in units of energy (for example $J\,m^{-2}$) or as units of dry organic matter (tonnes per hectare). The **primary productivity** of an ecosystem is the rate at which biomass is produced per unit area by green plants. It is expressed either in units of energy (such as $kJ\,m^{-2}\,yr^{-1}$) or as the mass of dry organic matter produced (such as $kg\,ha^{-1}\,yr^{-1}$). The total fixation of energy by photosynthesis is referred to as **gross primary production (GPP)**; the most commonly used units for GPP are $kJ\,m^{-2}\,yr^{-1}$. Some of the GPP is used by the plant for respiration and will ultimately be lost as heat energy. The rate at which organic compounds are used in this way is referred to as **plant respiration (R)** and is also measured in $kJ\,m^{-2}\,yr^{-1}$. The difference between GPP and R is known as the **net primary production (NPP)**. This represents the actual rate of production of new biomass that is available for consumption by heterotrophic organisms.

We can summarise the relationship between GPP, NPP and R by the equation:

$$GPP = NPP + R$$

This relationship and the fates of solar radiation falling on a leaf are shown in Figure 7.4.

DEFINITION

Biomass refers to the mass of living material per unit area, or per unit volume in an aquatic habitat. **Gross primary production** (GPP) is the rate of formation of organic material by green plants. Some of this material will be used by the plants in the process of respiration and ultimately lost as heat energy. The remainder is referred to as the **net primary production** (NPP).

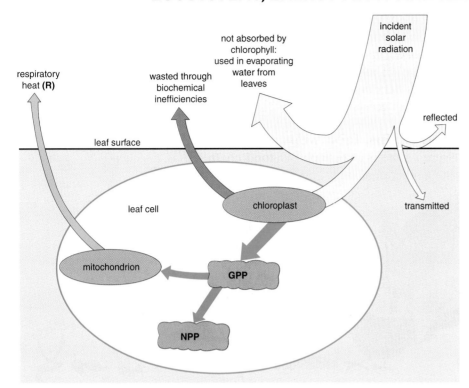

Figure 7.4 Fates of solar energy falling on a leaf

It is estimated that the global terrestrial net primary production is 110 to 120×10^9 tonnes dry mass per year, and in the sea, 50 to 60×10^9 tonnes per year. Since only the NPP is available for consumers to eat, NPP values are often used to compare the **productivity** of ecosystems. Productivity varies widely in different ecosystems, as shown in Table 7.1.

Table 7.1 *Mean values for net primary production (NPP) in a range of ecosystems*

Ecosystem	Mean NPP / kJ m^{-2} yr^{-1}
extreme desert	260
open ocean	4700
temperate grasslands	15 000
temperate deciduous forest	26 000
intensive agriculture	30 000
tropical forest	40 000

> ### QUESTION
> Apart from the availability of light energy, what factors will influence the primary productivity of different ecosystems?

What happens to the NPP in an ecosystem? Some NPP will remain stored within plants and increase plant biomass, and some may be eaten by herbivores. This energy input to herbivores is referred to as **herbivore consumption**. In a grass field, about 40 per cent of the annual production may be eaten by cows, but in a forest only about 2 per cent of the NPP passes to herbivores. Herbivores may themselves be preyed upon by predators, the first carnivores. The energy input to these animals is termed **carnivore consumption**. A final part of the NPP, contained in, for example, dead leaves and flowers, reaches the ground where it forms litter or **detritus**. This provides a source of food for a variety of organisms. Some of these are earthworms, termed **detritivores**; others are soil fungi and bacteria. These soil microorganisms are collectively known as **decomposers** and are the ultimate consumers of all dead organic matter in an ecosystem.

Food chains, food webs and trophic levels

Figure 7.5 shows an example of a **food chain**, that is, a sequence of organisms eating other organisms.

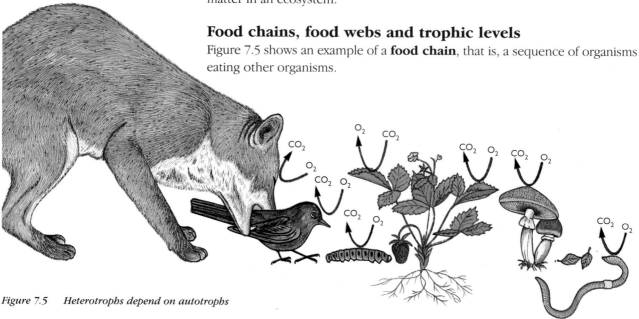

Figure 7.5   Heterotrophs depend on autotrophs

One sequence shown is:

$$\text{plant} \rightarrow \text{caterpillar} \rightarrow \text{bird} \rightarrow \text{fox}$$

Each organism within the chain occupies a particular **trophic level**. The food chain 'plant to fox' shown above has four trophic levels and can be written in general terms as:

$$\text{primary producer} \rightarrow \text{herbivore} \rightarrow \text{first carnivore} \rightarrow \text{second carnivore}$$

There are very large numbers of different food chains in the range of ecosystems on Earth, but it is rare to find chains with more than five trophic levels. Green plants fix only about 1 per cent of the sun's energy that falls on their leaves, and successive members of a food chain incorporate into their own biomass about 10 per cent of the energy available in the organisms they consume. The loss of energy at each trophic level is so great that very little of the original energy remains in the chain after it has been incorporated successively into the biomass of organisms at four trophic levels.

> ### DEFINITION
>
> A **food web** illustrates the feeding relationship between different organisms in an ecosystem. Food webs consists of a number of interlinked food chains.

If you look carefully at Figure 7.5, you will see other relationships between the organisms. As examples: dead plant leaves provide a food source for earthworms; fungi are decomposers and also obtain nutrients from dead leaves; worms and caterpillars are eaten by both birds and foxes. It is clear that in this diagram there are several food chains, and one organism may feed at more than one trophic level – foxes can be first-level or second-level carnivores, or even herbivores, as they are partial to fruit. There is a complex series of feeding relationships between organisms in an ecosystem. This set of relationships is referred to as a **food web**. Figure 7.6 shows a generalised food web based on Figure 7.5.

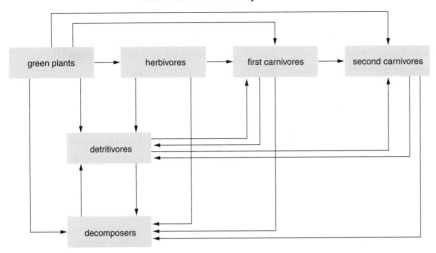

Figure 7.6 A generalised food web (the arrows show the direction of energy flow)

Constructing a food web involves detailed field and laboratory work. The main approaches include observation of predator–prey relationships, laboratory food preference experiments, analysis of gut contents and the use of radioactive isotopes such as ^{32}phosphorus (^{32}P). Plants can be labelled with ^{32}P and the passage of this isotope is then followed in nearby animal populations.

An example of a food web in a salt-marsh is illustrated in Figure 7.7, and shows the complex relationships between organisms. (Meiofauna are small invertebrate organisms which are adapted for living in the spaces between grains of sand and mud in marine deposits.)

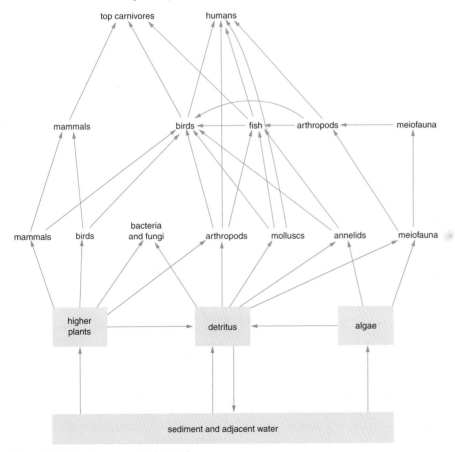

> **QUESTION**
>
> Identify the primary producers, herbivores, and first and second carnivores in the food web illustrated in Figure 7.7. How many trophic levels are present?

Figure 7.7 A food web on a salt-marsh

ECOSYSTEMS, ENERGY FLOW AND RECYCLING OF NUTRIENTS

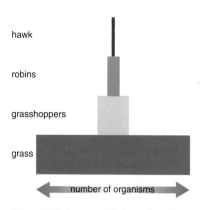

Figure 7.8 A pyramid of number is a diagrammatic way of representing an ecosystem, showing the numbers of organisms at successive trophic levels

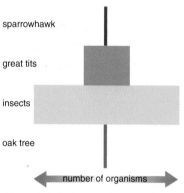

Figure 7.9 An inverted pyramid of number

Pyramids of number, biomass and energy

In an ecosystem, there are usually far more organisms at lower trophic levels than at higher trophic levels. Similarly, the biomass of primary producers present in an ecosystem is much greater than that of the herbivores, and successive trophic levels have a progressively smaller biomass.

We can represent these relationships as diagrams, known as **pyramids**. An example of a **pyramid of number** is shown in Figure 7.8. The width of each block is proportional to the numbers of organisms present at each trophic level.

One disadvantage of representing a food chain in this way is that it does not take into account the biomass of each trophic level. For example, one rose bush might support a very large population of aphids, so if this was represented diagrammatically, we would have an inverted pyramid of number (such as that illustrated in Figure 7.9).

A **pyramid of biomass** shows the mass of material at each trophic level. This usually results in an upright pyramid – the biomass of a rose bush would be much greater than the biomass of the aphids it supports. However, there are situations where an inverted pyramid of biomass can be obtained. Pyramids of biomass show the standing crop, that is, the biomass at one particular time, and do not take into account the fact that the biomass at each trophic level may vary over a period of time. For example, in January, the biomass of zooplankton in the Channel is greater than that of the phytoplankton (the primary producers). However, over the whole year, the total biomass of primary producers far exceeds that of the consumers in this ecosystem.

A **pyramid of energy** (Figure 7.10) gives a more accurate representation of the transfer of material from one trophic level to the next. Rather than plotting numbers, or biomass, of organisms at each trophic level, we plot the productivity for each level in the ecosystem. Productivity is a measure of the energy content of each level and can be obtained by converting the mass of new organic material produced per unit area per year into an equivalent energy value. This energy value for each trophic level is expressed in units of $kJ \ m^{-2} \ yr^{-1}$.

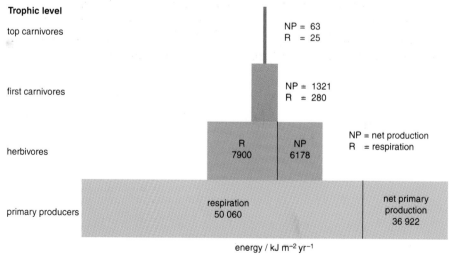

Figure 7.10 A pyramid of energy shows the energy content at each trophic level

Productivity and energy loss

We have already stated that successive members of a food chain incorporate into their biomass only about 10 per cent of the energy available in the food they eat. What happens to the remaining 90 per cent?

Let us consider the possible fates of the energy available in grass eaten by a herbivore, such as a sheep. Some of the grass will remain undigested and will be egested as faeces, so this represents one source of energy loss. The grass which is digested will be absorbed from the gut and assimilated by the herbivore. There are three possible fates of the energy contained in this assimilated grass:

1 It can be used in respiration and will be lost as heat
2 It can contribute to an increase in the biomass of the herbivore, termed **energy of production**
3 A small amount will be lost in urine.

These possible fates are illustrated in Figure 7.11.

We can write an equation which summarises the fate of all the energy consumed by the herbivore:

$$E_C = E_P + E_F + E_U + E_R$$

This equation accounts for all of the energy entering the herbivore. The energy of production, E_P, will be available as energy of consumption for a carnivore, and the sequence is repeated at the next trophic level. Only about 10 per cent of the energy entering one trophic level (the energy of consumption) is available for consumption by the next trophic level.

Recycling of nutrients

We have seen that a continuous supply of energy is essential for all living organisms. Organisms also require a range of chemical substances, including water, mineral ions and organic compounds. The original supply of energy is the sun, but there are only fixed amounts of chemical substances available on Earth. The chemicals needed to build the tissues of living organisms are used and re-used repeatedly. These substances move in cycles from the soil, water or the atmosphere, into plants and animals and back again. Cycles that operate in this way are known as **biogeochemical cycles** and include the carbon, sulphur and nitrogen cycles. The **hydrological cycle** is shown in Fig 7.12 and an outline of the **carbon cycle** is given in Chapter 9. The **nitrogen cycle** is described here in more detail.

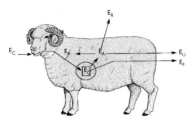

E_C = energy consumed
E_F = energy lost in faeces
E_U = energy lost in urine
E_A = energy assimilated
E_R = energy lost as heat in respiration
E_P = energy of production

Figure 7.11 Fates of energy in grass consumed by a herbivore

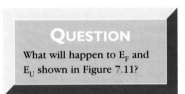

QUESTION

What will happen to E_F and E_U shown in Figure 7.11?

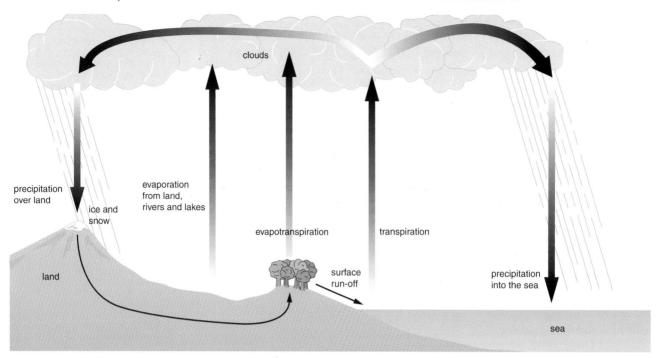

Figure 7.12 The hydrological cycle (or water cycle) consists of a series of natural processes by which water evaporates and forms clouds, falls as rain or snow, and eventually returns to oceans via streams and rivers

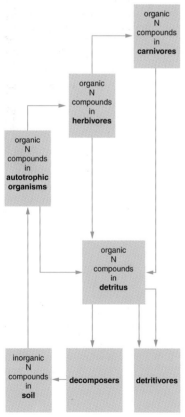

Figure 7.13 The biological part of the nitrogen cycle

The nitrogen cycle

Nitrogen is required by all living organisms, because it is a component of many substances, including nucleic acids and proteins. Plants and animals obtain their nitrogen in different ways. The source of nitrogen for green plants is in the form of inorganic ions, either nitrate (NO_3^-) or the ammonium ion (NH_4^+) present in soil or water. Heterotrophic organisms obtain their nitrogen only from organic substances.

In a typical green plant, nitrate ions taken up by the roots are reduced to ammonium ions in the cells and are then incorporated into organic compounds to form, for example, amino acids. These organic compounds then provide the source of nitrogen for detritivores, herbivores and, subsequently, carnivores.

Organic nitrogen-containing compounds in dead tissues, faeces and urine can be converted back into inorganic nitrate by the action of saprophytic bacteria and fungi, referred to as **decomposers**. We can illustrate the biological part of the nitrogen cycle in a simplified form, as in Figure 7.13.

Bacterial and fungal decomposers break down organic nitrogen compounds in detritus to release ammonium ions (NH_4^+). If no oxygen is available, or if the soil is waterlogged, cold or acidic, the process stops here and only ammonium ions are available to plants. In 'good' soil conditions, ammonium ions are oxidised by other soil bacteria (such as *Nitrosomonas*) into nitrites (NO_2^-). Another group of soil bacteria (such as *Nitrobacter*) further oxidise nitrite ions into nitrate ions (NO_3^-). The overall conversion of ammonium ions to nitrate ions is termed **nitrification**.

$$\underset{\text{ammonium}}{NH_4^+} \quad \overset{\textit{Nitrosomonas}}{\rightarrow} \quad \underset{\text{nitrite}}{NO_2^-} \quad \overset{\textit{Nitrobacter}}{\rightarrow} \quad \underset{\text{nitrate}}{NO_3^-}$$

Nitrate ions produced in this way are available for uptake by plant roots. However, nitrate ions are very soluble in water and, unlike other ions present in the soil, do not bind tightly to soil particles. As a consequence, nitrate ions are easily washed out of soil after heavy rain, in a process called **leaching**. Rainwater draining through soil carries nitrate ions into ponds, lakes, rivers and the sea. Leached nitrate (and phosphate) ions enrich bodies of water with minerals, a process called **eutrophication**. This can result in the excessive growth of algae in ponds and rivers. The environmental consequences of eutrophication are described in Chapter 9.

Another way in which nitrate ions can be lost from soil is through the process of **denitrification**. Under anaerobic conditions, such as when soils are waterlogged, denitrifying bacteria convert nitrate to nitrite and then to nitrogen gas, which escapes into the atmosphere. Denitrifying bacteria include *Pseudomonas denitrificans* and *Thiobacillus denitrificans*.

There are several ways in which nitrates can be added to the soil. They can be added as nitrogen-containing fertilisers in managed ecosystems. Small amounts of inorganic nitrogen compounds are also formed by the action of lightning in the atmosphere. This produces oxides of nitrogen which combine with rainwater to form nitrate ions.

Nitrogen-fixing organisms, known as diazotrophs, which live in soil, are able to reduce nitrogen gas to ammonia. This is a biological version of the Haber–Bosch process. Unlike this chemical nitrogen fixation, which requires temperatures of 300 to 500 °C, high pressures and an iron catalyst, biological nitrogen fixation is much more efficient, occurring at low temperatures and at atmospheric pressure. Biological nitrogen fixation is catalysed by nitrogenase, a complex enzyme containing iron and molybdenum.

$$\underset{\text{nitrogen}}{N_2} \quad + \quad \underset{\text{hydrogen}}{3H_2} \quad \overset{\text{nitrogenase}}{\rightarrow} \quad \underset{\text{ammonia}}{2NH_3}$$

Only certain bacteria and cyanobacteria can fix nitrogen gas in this way. Some of these organisms, such as *Azotobacter vinelandii*, are free-living in the soil. One genus of nitrogen-fixing bacteria, *Rhizobium*, forms a symbiotic relationship with legumes (plants such as peas, beans and clover). These plants develop swellings on their roots, called **root nodules**, containing *Rhizobium* (Figure 7.14). It is a symbiotic relationship because the bacteria receive carbohydrates and ATP from the plant, which obtains fixed nitrogen, in the form of ammonia, in return. Ammonia is then incorporated into organic compounds to synthesise amino acids.

One of the long-term aims of gene technology is to incorporate genes for nitrogen fixation into non-leguminous plants. This could have considerable

> ### DEFINITION
> The **Haber–Bosch** process is an industrial method for the production of ammonia, which can then be used to make nitrogen fertilisers. In this process, nitrogen and hydrogen react together at high pressure and high temperature to produce ammonia.

Figure 7.14 Nodules on the roots of the runner bean, Phaseolus multiflorus

ECOSYSTEMS, ENERGY FLOW AND RECYCLING OF NUTRIENTS

QUESTIONS

How do the following human activities affect the recycling of carbon or of nitrogen:
- burning fuels
- deforestation
- harvesting of agricultural crops
- intensive rearing of animals
- use of nitrogen fertilisers?

List any other human activities which are likely to disrupt the carbon and nitrogen cycles. [*You may find help with your answers in Chapters 8 and 9.*]

environmental and economic benefits, avoiding the need for expensive inorganic fertilisers, only about half of which are actually taken up by plants.

The complete nitrogen cycle, incorporating both biological and chemical elements, is illustrated in Figure 7.15.

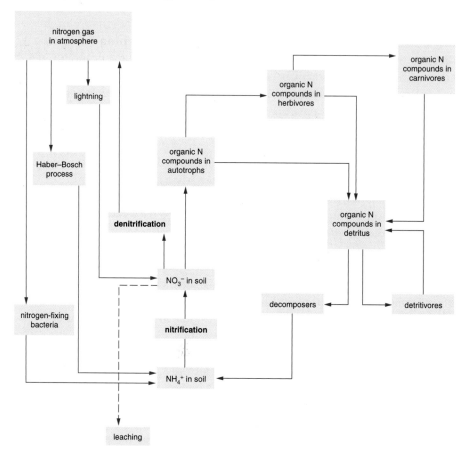

Figure 7.15 *The complete nitrogen cycle*

PRACTICAL   ## Estimation of pyramids of number and of biomass

Introduction

The purpose of this practical is to obtain data which can be used to construct pyramids of number or of fresh biomass. The ecological community chosen will, of course, depend on accessibility, but the exercise could be carried out on a rocky shore, in woodland or in open grassland.

Materials

- 1 m^2 or 0.5 m^2 quadrat
- Trowel
- Scissors
- Large white sorting tray
- Hand lens

- Beakers
- Forceps
- Pooter
- Identification key
- Balance

Method

1 Select an area and place your quadrat carefully. On a rocky shore you should ensure that the entire quadrat is occupied by only one type of community.
2 Collect the leaf litter, or cut plants at the base, and place in the white tray. If appropriate, record the number of individual plants.
3 Search carefully and remove all the animals present. Smaller animals may be removed with a pooter (Figure 7.16), larger animals should be handled with forceps, or fingers. Place in suitable containers, such as plastic beakers.
4 Weigh the plant material.
5 Sort the animals into two groups: primary consumers (herbivores) and secondary consumers (carnivores).
6 Weigh the groups of animals separately and record the total number of animals in each group.
7 Return the animals to their habitat.

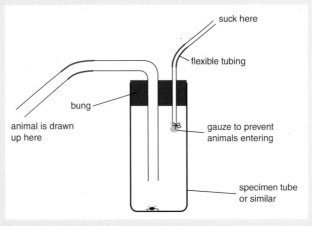

Figure 7.16 A pooter

Results and discussion

1 Construct pyramids of number and of biomass. A horizontal scale is chosen to represent either the numbers of organisms present per m^2 or the biomass per m^2. The lower block represents the producers (plants), the middle block the primary consumers (herbivores) and the upper block the secondary consumers (carnivores).

2 Consider the advantages and disadvantages of using pyramids of numbers and biomass to represent an ecosystem.

Further work

1 You could use this method to compare two communities, such as different areas of leaf litter. It is important that comparable samples are used in each case.

2 How could you adapt the method to construct a pyramid of number and of biomass in a pond?

Energy resources

Energy resources and sustainability

When early humans began to live in settled communities, they developed means of using external sources of energy as part of their way of life. Today, the main categories of energy use are essentially similar: to provide low temperature heat for human comfort and to cook food, to generate high temperature heat for light and to work materials in a way that has led to a vast range of industrial processes. We also harness energy to provide a force that allows movement and mechanical work to be done, which, of course, has expanded to include many different forms of transport. For centuries, traditional energy sources have included wood or dung mixed with straw for fuel, and animals, wind and water for power. A change in emphasis for fuel sources came with the greater requirements linked to the Industrial Revolution, and these demands have continued to increase up to the present day. Alongside this change in emphasis there has been heavy exploitation of fossil fuels, for generation of electricity as an almost universal source of energy (for heat, light and movement) and the use of oil for the internal combustion engine.

Over the past 30 or so years, there has been a growing concern over the consequences of using such high levels of energy in our societies on a global scale. Since the late 1960s, there has been increasing recognition of the **environmental impact** of energy use, particularly of fossils fuels. The harmful effects relate mainly to carbon dioxide output, the enhanced greenhouse effect and how far this affects global warming, and also to acid rain and to oil pollution of the seas. These effects are considered in detail in Chapter 9. The other major concern has been over the **sustainability** of our energy resources. There were worries, particularly in the 1970s, that reserves of fossil fuels would not last the lifetime of the younger generation at that time, if use continued at the same or a greater rate. It is very difficult to make realistic and reliable estimates, but the balance of opinion at the end of the 20th century is that more fossil fuel reserves do exist and are sufficient to sustain global energy requirements well into or through the 21st century. However, as we dig deeper (literally), the fossil fuels may be technically more difficult to exploit and hence more expensive. Ultimately, however, such reserves must be finite since the rate of formation lags far behind predicted rate of use in the 21st century.

Another factor which has caused concern is the way in which primary sources of energy or generators of energy, say in the form of electricity, have become centralised into a limited number of areas or companies. A possible consequence of this is that a major source of energy could become unavailable outside the region for political reasons, or that a generating plant becomes vulnerable to breakdown or deliberate damage.

These are some of the factors which have prompted a search for **renewable energy** sources that are economically viable and avoid, in particular, the worst effects of pollution. To complement this there is pressure also to develop and implement strategies for **energy conservation** and for more **efficient use of energy**, if society is to continue with its current life style into the 21st century.

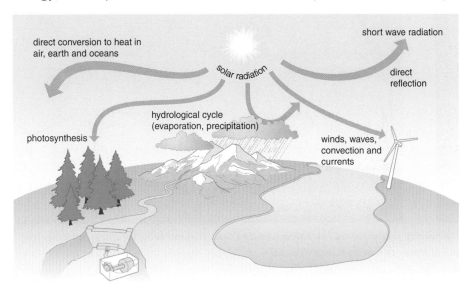

Figure 8.1 Solar radiation and how it is transformed into different forms of renewable energy

Renewable energy sources (Figure 8.1) can be defined simply as 'energy flows which are replenished at the same rate as they are used'. A more comprehensive definition has been offered by the UK Renewable Energy Advisory Group as '*energy flows that occur naturally and repeatedly in the environment and can be harnessed for human benefit. The ultimate sources of most of this energy are the sun, gravity and the earth's rotation*'. Theoretically, renewable energy sources are inexhaustible, though the practicality and technological expertise required to harness this energy on the scale required, as well as the economics of doing so, are areas that require furthur development and indeed are receiving active attention. Traditional uses of, say, wind power and to some extent fuel from biomass may have been adequate at the time, but there needs to be considerable expansion and development of renewable energy sources if they are to be appropriate for current and future global demands. An optimistic prediction suggests that, by the mid-21st century, about half the global energy requirements could be met from renewable energy sources.

Figure 8.2 A simple (homemade) solar collector for heating domestic water (in Suffolk, eastern England). Water is pumped through a series of copper pipes clipped onto aluminium plates which are sprayed black. With good insulation behind the plates and a single pane of glass on top, the family living in this house find that, in summer, they rarely need to use any other energy source for their hot water supply.

Some devices use **solar energy** directly, such as that in solar collectors for heating water (Figure 8.2), or by means of **photovoltaics**, in which solar energy is converted directly into electricity. Other technologies harness solar energy indirectly (Figure 8.3), and these include the effect of solar energy on the weather, hence the hydrological cycle leading to energy derived from flowing water as in **hydroelectric power**, **wind energy** and energy from **waves**. There is also potential for development of energy derived from **tides** and to utilise the **geothermal energy** within the Earth. In addition, there is the use of **biomass** as a renewable energy source and with this we can link the capture of energy from wastes, as much of this is itself derived from biomass.

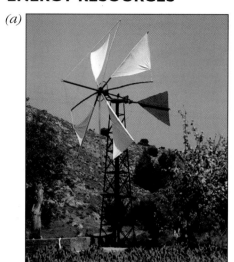

Figure 8.3 Harnessing wind as a renewable energy source: (a) traditional windmill in Crete (Greece) being used to pump water for irrigation of spring crops; (b) modern wind farm in Lanzarote (Canary Islands)

QUESTIONS

Explain why ecosystems in warm, damp environments usually have higher biomass values than those in cooler or drier environments. Which situation has a more rapid growth rate and in which situation is growth likely to be interrupted at certain seasons?

Biomass is defined as the total mass of living material in an area (see Chapter 7). Growing plants utilise solar energy in the process of photosynthesis. Solar energy is thus incorporated into biomass which then has the potential for use as a fuel by humans. The **biomass value** gives a measure of the available energy in an ecosystem. Biomass includes plants, animals and microorganisms, but in practice, biomass values usually refer to the plant mass above ground level. This chapter focuses on some ways in which biomass in its different forms, can be harvested and exploited as a renewable energy source.

Use of fossil fuels

Fossil fuels (coal, oil and natural gas) are derived from biomass that was living millions of years ago. Coal is formed from former vegetation which accumulated in peat beds in waterlogged, anaerobic conditions. Later it became buried under sediments, followed by slow processes of being compacted and compressed, which eventually turned it into hard rock (lithification). Oil (petroleum) also developed from anaerobic decomposition of former organic material. It is found as a liquid, trapped in reservoirs within sedimentary rocks, usually of marine origin. Natural gas probably arose in the same way and is found as a gas in underground reservoirs in rocks, often associated with oil deposits. The main constituent of natural gas is methane (about 85 per cent), and it also contains ethane, propane and small quantities of other hydrocarbons. On a global scale, these three fossil fuels together account for most of the energy used by humans, though compared with industrialised countries, less developed countries depend to a greater extent on recently harvested biomass. This is usually burnt as wood but is often converted to charcoal.

Reserves of fossil fuels are limited because the rate at which they are formed is very much slower than the rate at which they are being used. On a global scale, since 1950, production and use of these fossil fuels has more than doubled. In the case of natural gas it has increased ten-fold (Figure 8.4). Despite concerns that sources of fossil fuels will become depleted, known reserves of both coal, oil and natural gas should be sufficient to supply increasing energy requirements into the 21st century.

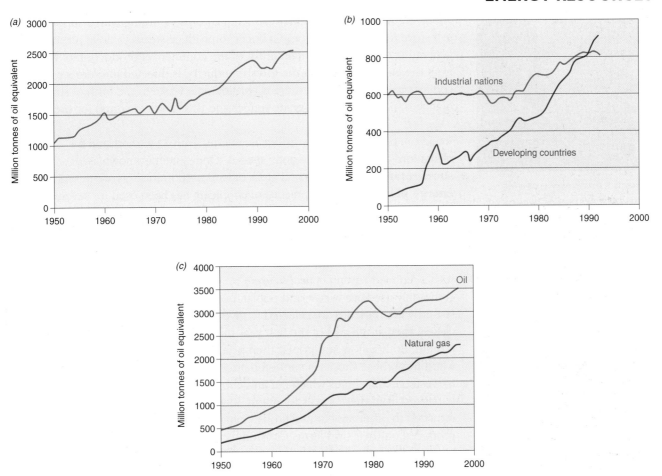

Figure 8.4 (a) World coal use, 1950–97; (b) use of coal in industrial nations compared with that in developing countries, 1950–93; (c) world oil and natural gas use, 1950–97

Fossil fuels are relatively cheap and easy to obtain, transport and store. The chief disadvantage of burning fossil fuels lies in their impact on the environment, because of the pollution caused by various emissions from industry and from motor vehicles. The effects of acid rain, and the build-up of carbon dioxide with possible long-term effects on global climate, are largely attributed to the use of fossil fuels (see Chapter 9). Coal is considered to be the dirtiest of the three, causing most environmental damage, whereas natural gas is the cleanest.

There is pressure for development of alternative energy sources, which are both renewable and minimise damage to the environment. In some countries, government legislation requires electricity generating companies to incorporate some non-fossil fuel sources in their generation of electricity. In England, this is called the non-fossil fuel obligation (NFFO) and has stimulated considerable research into development of viable renewable energy systems. The emphasis now is to explore their use economically, on a commercial scale, so that they become realistic alternatives to meet global energy demands.

Energy from renewable biomass

Energy crops

Traditionally, wood is the main form in which biomass has been used as an energy source, though other materials such as animal dung are also used. The

> **QUESTION**
>
> Why do you think use of fossil fuels has increased so much?

Figure 8.5 Traditional coppicing: these ash stools may be hundreds of years old

Figure 8.6 Short-rotation coppicing: a way of exploiting fast-growing woody species as a renewable energy source. This photograph shows young willows.

QUESTION

Summarise some of the benefits of growing short-rotation coppice.

energy in the biomass is usually extracted by direct burning with a supply of air, in a stove to provide heat, or in a boiler to produce steam to drive turbines for generating electricity. In Britain, most of the commercial production of wood from the growth of trees in the forestry industry, is directed into timber. When a conifer plantation is felled, there is considerable waste in the form of small branches, needles and low-grade timber and this can be diverted for use as fuel.

Wood can be exploited as a renewable energy source by using land for plantations of fast-growing woody species. One system is known as **short-rotation coppicing** and areas of land used in this way are described as **energy plantations**. The practice of coppicing has been used for several hundreds of years as a technique for management of woodland, particularly in Europe (Figure 8.5). A description of traditional coppicing is given in Chapter 9.

Short-rotation coppicing uses the same principle as traditional coppicing but with a reduced cutting cycle (Figure 8.6). In Britain, the species most commonly used are willow and poplar, because they are easy to propagate and fast-growing. Varieties are selected to give high yields. Cuttings are planted closely, then at the end of the first year they are cut off (coppiced) near the ground. Both willow and poplar then produce several side shoots. The crop of wood from these shoots is harvested after 2 to 5 years growth. The coppice is harvested by machines which cut and chop the material. Wood can probably be harvested from these stools for about 30 years, then the land would be returned to other agricultural crops. Some farmers use the wood chips produced on their own farms for running electricity generators; others sell the harvested crop to electricity generating companies as a fuel source.

The NFFO in Britain encourages the development of short-rotation coppice both on a large scale and in small plantations integrated within an existing farming system. Short-rotation coppicing is an attractive option to some farmers as an energy crop. It may be an appropriate way to exploit surplus land which, because of government controls, has been taken out of cultivation for food crops, such as cereals. Creation of coppiced areas with willow and poplar has benefits for wildlife, particularly in an arable farming area, because they provide an attractive habitat for birds and an increased diversity of plant species appears along the paths and within the coppice.

Other fast-growing species could be used as energy crops. One which shows potential as an energy crop is *Miscanthus*, a perennial bamboo-like grass. This grass grows in clumps and can reach a height of 2 to 3 metres in one season. In European conditions, *Miscanthus* can produce high yields – expectations are for 20 to 30 tonnes per hectare. The thick woody stems are cut down in the autumn, at the end of the growing season and, because of their low water content, can be used directly for burning. In the following spring, fresh shoots grow from underground rhizomes, so a crop can be harvested annually. It probably takes 3 or 4 years for the grass to give its maximum crop, and then can continue to yield for perhaps 15 to 20 years.

Straw left over after harvesting cereal crops is another material which has potential as a fuel source. In Britain, about 14 million tonnes of straw are produced annually (Figure 8.7). Some is used as bedding or for feeding livestock, but about half of the straw produced remained as an unwanted surplus. Until recently, surplus straw was usually burnt along with the stubble in the fields at the time of harvest, leaving the field clear for planting the next crop, but burning of stubble has been banned since 1992, so farmers have had to find other ways of disposing of the straw. Burners that can take straw bales have been developed and are used in some countries, notably Denmark and the USA, and a straw-fired electricity power station is planned in Britain. One estimate, for the year 2000, is that 800 000 tonnes of straw in the UK will be utilised in straw burning systems, a 4-fold increase on the 1996 figure. Compared with coal and oil, straw has very low levels of sulphur, but the main difficulties with utilising straw arise from the cost of collecting, storing and transporting a rather bulky material. Surplus wastes from tropical crops which are exploited to some extent for fuels, include bagasse (sugar cane fibre), rice husks and coconut fibres.

Biomass to gasohol

Fermentation of sugar by yeasts (*Saccharomyces* spp.), can convert the energy in biomass into ethanol which can be used as a fuel. An example is the fuel called **gasohol** which consists of 80 to 90 per cent of unleaded petroleum spirit with 10 to 20 per cent ethanol, and is used in motor vehicles. Most of the ethanol produced for gasohol uses sugar crops as its source material, though other plant species (such as maize and manioc), and waste materials (including wood and animal products), are also used.

Sugar is obtained from two different crops: sugar cane (*Saccharum officinum*) and sugar beet (*Beta vulgaris*). Sugar cane is grown in tropical and semi-tropical countries, whereas sugar beet is grown in more temperate regions. In the cane sugar industry, the cane is cut then processed. The initial milling yields two products: cane juice and bagasse (a residue of fibrous material). The juice can be further treated to the stage when sugar crystallises out, leaving a viscous sugary liquid known as molasses. Cane juice, bagasse and molasses can all be fermented to produce ethanol. Cane juice must be processed soon after harvest because it cannot be stored, whereas the molasses can be stored and fermented at a later date. Production of ethanol tends to be seasonal, linked to the time of harvest for the crop. Usually, small distilleries are set up at sites close to the crop. Bagasse is mainly cellulose, hemicellulose and lignin, and is often used to fuel the boilers used in the distillation process.

There is considerable potential for large-scale industrial production of ethanol for use as gasohol, but the decisions regarding its development are economic and political as well as environmental. Sugar cane and sugar beet are already grown in a wide range of climates and countries. Production of sugar crops could be expanded but at the risk of competing with other food crops. Ethanol has the advantage of being a relatively clean fuel, producing less pollution than the petrol it would replace if used as gasohol in motor vehicles. However, production of ethanol for gasohol is uneconomic compared with conventional petrol and would thus require both political and financial backing if it is to make a major contribution to the fuel used. Sugar cane growers may prefer to sell their crop to be refined as sugar rather than to be processed as ethanol. The most extensive gasohol programme is that in Brazil, initiated during the 1980s. Yields of biomass from sugar cane are high in Brazil, and because of lack of available funds at that

Figure 8.7 Bales of straw after harvest of cereal crops: surplus straw can be used as fuel

QUESTIONS

Why do you think burning of stubble has been banned? What is the main carbon compound in straw that gives off energy when burnt? What benefits to the soil would there be from burning the straw on the fields? In what other ways could surplus straw be used?

Figure 8.8 Other crops have potential as renewable energy sources: bright yellow oilseed rape (Brassica napus), grown for the harvest of oil from its seeds, can be used to produce a fuel known as biodiesel. The oils can also be used in industrial processes instead of oils derived from fossil fuels.

time there were difficulties in purchasing oil from overseas. However, a shift in oil prices or other political changes could alter the balance away from ethanol production and its development as a renewable fuel source.

Other biofuels

Certain vegetable oils, obtained by crushing seeds, can also be used as **biofuels**, without fermentation to ethanol. Their energy content is similar to that of diesel, and higher than that of ethanol. Such oils can be blended, for example, with diesel fuel to contribute up to 30 per cent, though some need further processing to prevent clogging of the engines. Rape-seed oil (Figure 8.8) has been used in this way in Britain and the fuel produced is known as **rape methyl ester** (**RME**). Other crops that yield suitable oils include coconut oil (used in the Philippines), palm and castor oil (in Brazil) and sunflower oil (in South Africa).

Biomass to biogas

Fermentation by bacteria can convert the energy in biomass into **biogas**, a gaseous fuel which consists mainly of methane. This process exploits the metabolic activities of different groups of bacteria which digest organic matter under anaerobic conditions. A typical fermentation would produce biogas with a composition of about 65 per cent methane, 35 per cent carbon dioxide and traces of ammonia, hydrogen sulphide and water vapour. The methane in biogas burns with a clear flame to produce carbon dioxide and water without any hazardous air pollutants. The process is used mainly with dung or slurries from animals so has the added benefit of turning waste material into a useful product. After digestion, the residue has value as a fertiliser. In Europe, the process is of particular value in the Netherlands and Denmark because there is a problem in finding enough land to spread waste pig slurry.

There are three stages to this rather complex digestion process. The material to be digested is likely to contain mainly carbohydrate with some protein and lipid. Initially, aerobic bacteria utilise these substrates and convert them by **hydrolysis** to simple sugars, amino acids and glycerol and fatty acids. As the available oxygen is used up, acetogenic bacteria convert the sugars and other substrates to short-chain fatty acids, mainly acetic acid, with some carbon dioxide and hydrogen. This stage is described as **acetogenesis**. The final stage is **methanogenesis**, which is carried out only in anaerobic conditions by methanogenic bacteria and involves conversion of the acids to methane. Methanogenic bacteria are **obligate anaerobes**, which means they are active only when there is no oxygen present. It is essential that conditions are anaerobic for the digestion to produce methane. For successful operation, temperatures are usually maintained between 30 and 40 °C. The methanogenic bacteria are sensitive to temperature changes and if fluctuations of more than 5 °C occur, the material goes sour due to build up of undigested volatile acids.

The digestion process is carried out in an enclosed tank, called a **digester**. The design of the digester may depend on locally available construction materials, but essential features are that it is strong enough to hold a large volume of the material to be digested and withstand the build-up of pressure inside. It must be gas-tight and allow the anaerobic conditions to be maintained. It should have an accessible inlet for loading the material, an outlet for the gas and a means of recovering the residue when digestion is completed. A plan of a simple but effective domed model, used widely in China, is shown in Figure 8.9. Sinking the digester in the ground helps to provide both support and insulation with respect to temperature. When digestion is completed, access to the digester pit is through the slurry reservoir. This allows the residue to be taken out and the reservoir cleaned. Often several digesters are used together to ensure continuous supplies of gas.

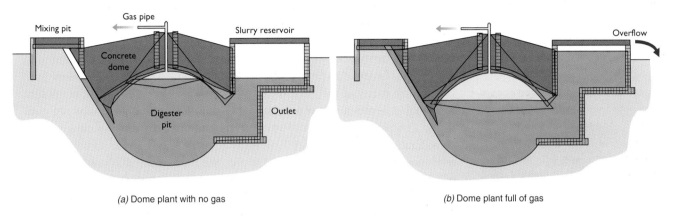

(a) Dome plant with no gas

(b) Dome plant full of gas

Figure 8.9 Fixed-dome biogas plant, commonly used in China. Gas given off collects in the dome and slurry is displaced into the eservoir. As the gas is used, the slurry flows back from the reservoir into the digester pit.

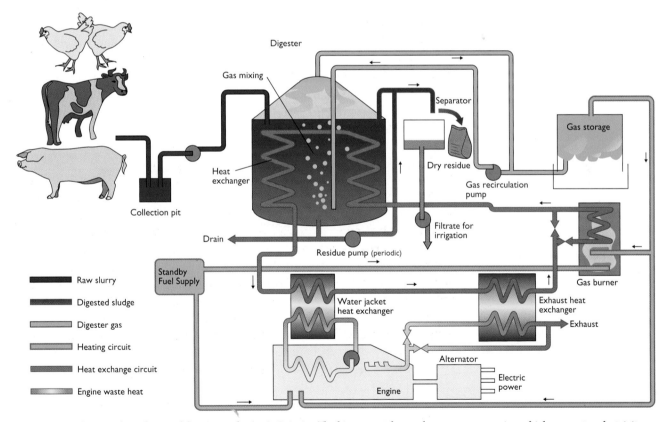

Figure 8.10 A biogas plant designed for use on farms in Britain. The biogas can be used to power an engine which generates electricity. In the digester, a suitable temperature is maintained by internal heating coils and heat exchangers, with biogas as the source of heat. Waste heat from the engine cooling system and exhaust can also be utilised, with a standby fuel supply for emergency. The contents of the digester are mixed by recirculation of the gas produced.

Figure 8.11 Using waste poultry litter to generate electricity – poultry litter in fuel hoppers at a power station in Suffolk

Figure 8.12 Mountains of domestic and industrial waste: most is dumped in landfill sites

QUESTIONS

In some areas in the UK, domestic households are requested to separate their rubbish into different bins (Figure 8.14). Materials that can be made into compost go into a separate bin from other waste.
What are the environmental benefits of separation? What can be recovered from the compostable materials and what about the rest?

QUESTIONS

List ways that biomass is used as a renewable energy source. As headings for your list, you could use:
1. agricultural wastes
2. energy from refuse
3. energy crops

In each case, indicate how far the source needs to be processed before the energy is transformed into a form that can be readily used.

Biogas has been produced on a small scale in China for more than 50 years. Other countries such as Nepal, India and developing countries in Africa and South America also find biogas useful for small-scale production of fuel, particularly in rural areas, where it also provides a way of disposing of animal wastes and human excreta. In Britain, biogas digesters (Figure 8.10) are being used increasingly as a means of disposing of the large quantities of animal wastes derived from intensive farming methods. Ideally, the digester is located close to the source of biomass (slurry from cattle or pigs, or chicken litter) to avoid transport costs.

Rubbish or energy?

Disposal of domestic and industrial waste has become a very large problem. In the UK, approximately 46 million tonnes of waste are produced each year, equivalent to 300 kg of domestic waste per person per year. These mountains of waste give rise to a number of environmental concerns. Dumping the waste occupies considerable areas of land and there is danger of leakage of toxic substances and other pollutants from the dumps. However, the waste material represents a source of energy which could be converted to fuel. In Britain, nearly 90 per cent of waste is disposed of in landfill sites (Figure 8.12). Biodegradable materials in the deposited waste (mainly paper, garden waste and foods) start to decay and soon use up available oxygen. Conditions thus become anaerobic which leads to the production of methane. This process has been described earlier in this chapter (see *Biomass to gasohol*). The gas is usually known as **landfill gas** when produced in the landfill site. The gas may seep out from the layers of compacted rubbish with the potential danger of igniting or causing explosions. A number of landfill sites are now being constructed so that landfill gas can be collected and the methane used as a fuel. A landfill site begins to produce gas about a year after landfill is completed and may be viable for up to 15 years (Figure 8.13). Sometimes rubbish is incinerated (burnt) and part of the energy from the biomass in the rubbish could be recovered as useful heat.

Figure 8.14 Separation of domestic waste: the brown bin is for biodegradable materials which can be converted into compost

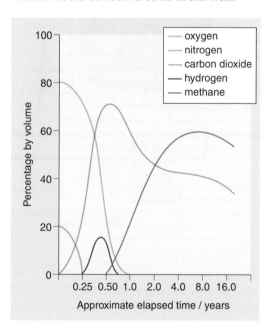

Figure 8.13 Production of gases in a landfill site and how the composition changes over time. Note the exponential time scale on the horizontal axis.

Human influences on the environment

Human activities and their impact on the environment

Early humans had relatively little impact on their surrounding environment. They gathered food plants, hunted animals, took small quantities of materials to build shelters and used wood as fuel to provide warmth and energy for cooking. As settled agriculture developed, their sphere of influence widened and humans began to change the environment in a more permanent way. Even so, as long as their activities remained on a small scale, disturbance of ecosystems was minimal and an equilibrium was more or less maintained.

By the end of the 20th century, the scale of activities has escalated to a stage where the influence of humans on their environment has become overwhelming. There is considerable concern that some of these activities will lead to irreversible changes to our planet Earth as we know it today. Pressures on the environment arise from increased population and the demands associated with an increasingly complex and technological way of life. The greatest changes have taken place during the last 150 years. This coincides with the period of the Industrial Revolution, particularly in Europe, and of colonial expansion by European nations. As we enter the 21st century, the human population continues to increase and industrialisation is still expanding in the developing nations (Figure 9.1).

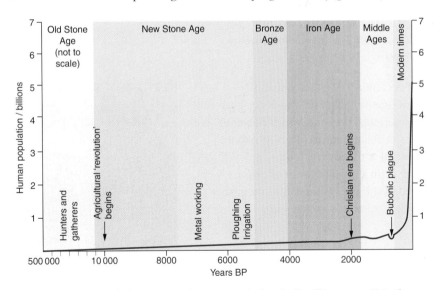

Figure 9.1 Increases in the human population over the last half million years. Note the very rapid rise up to the present day (BP = before present).

Over much of the globe, natural ecosystems have been converted to agricultural land, designated for producing food (Figure 9.2a). Agricultural land often approaches a monoculture and therefore has low species diversity. Further land is absorbed into living space as villages, towns and large sprawling cities (Figure 9.2b). There are industrial areas and a supporting infrastructure, including roads, railways, airports and seaports. Exploitation of natural resources, such as mining for minerals, has created further disturbance. Demands for energy have led to exploitation of wood for fuel, coal from mines and both oil and natural gas have been piped away from its source.

(a)

(b)

Figure 9.2 (a) Use of land for agriculture leads to loss of natural ecosystems – fields and hedges in England (left); terraced hillside in Nepal (right); (b) loss of natural ecosystems through urbanisation – buildings, roads and car parks

Pollution is a familiar word in our everyday vocabulary. We are repeatedly reminded of how a range of human (anthropogenic) activities produces harmful substances which contaminate the air, the water and the land which together make up the environment for living organisms. Pollutants are derived mainly from the waste materials produced by industrial activities (including agriculture) and from motor vehicles, with some coming from domestic sources (Figure 9.3). The consequences of pollution are observed in the effects on living organisms and, on a different scale, in the possible long-term effects on climate.

Changes in land use

Any change in land use is likely to alter the ecosystem that would naturally be present in the area. Here we look at **deforestation** and **desertification**, two specific examples of how natural ecosystems have been altered or destroyed through the activities of humans.

Figure 9.3 Atmospheric pollution from industrial activities: discharge from a sugar beet factory (in eastern England)

Deforestation

For thousands of years humans have invaded forests, cut down the trees and converted the area into agricultural land, to be used for growing crops or grazing animals. Often the debris has been burnt as part of the clearing process. In Britain, without human influence, much of the landscape would be dominated by woodland, whereas now only about 10 per cent of the land remains wooded. A similar situation is evident worldwide. Agricultural expansion during the second half of the 19th century led to large-scale deforestation in temperate regions, but towards the late 20th century there were particular concerns over the loss of tropical forest. Between 1960 and 1990, estimates suggest that about one fifth of all tropical forest was lost. The areas which suffered greatest losses were in Latin America, Asia and Africa (Table 9.1). This situation continued into the 1990s. Another way of putting it is that an area approaching 12 million hectares (about the size of England) has been disappearing from tropical forests each year. Amazonia, mainly in Brazil, remains the largest area of rainforest. On a global scale, it has been estimated that at least 200 million hectares of forest were lost between 1980 and 1995. As the rate of deforestation accelerates, recovery of *natural* forest may be impossible, and some of the changes may have long-term effects on global climate.

Table 9.1 *Population pressure and deforestation in areas with tropical moist forest – from a study made in 1989*

Country	Area / million km^2	Forest cover / 1000 km^2			Estimated population in millions		
		Original	1989	Primary forest in 1989	1950	1989	2020
Latin America							
Bolivia	1.1	90	70	45	3	7	15
Brazil	8.5	2860	2200	1800	53	147	234
Central America	0.5	500	90	55	9	28	54
Colombia	1.1	700	278	180	12	31	49
Ecuador	0.3	132	76	44	3	11	20
Guianas	0.5	500	410	370	1	2	3
Mexico	2.0	400	166	110	27	87	142
Peru	1.3	700	515	420	8	21	35
Venezuela	0.9	420	350	300	5	19	23
Asia							
Burma	0.7	500	245	80	18	41	69
India	3.3	1600	165	70	362	835	1374
Indonesia	1.9	1220	860	530	77	185	287
Malaysia	0.3	305	157	84	6	17	27
Papua New G.	0.5	425	360	180	2	4	8
Philippines	0.3	250	50	8	20	65	131
Thailand	0.5	435	74	22	20	56	82
Vietnam	0.3	260	60	14	24	67	121
Africa							
Cameroon	0.5	220	164	60	5	11	24
Congo	0.3	100	90	80	1	2	6
Côte d'Ivoire	0.3	160	16	4	3	12	35
Madagascar	0.6	62	24	10	5	12	30
Nigeria	0.9	72	28	10	41	115	274
Zaïre	2.3	1245	1000	700	14	35	89

On a small scale, loss of forest to traditional systems of shifting cultivation (often cleared by slash and burn methods) may be short-lived. After a few seasons the people who cleared the forest move on to a new area. Provided the human population is of low density, the forest regenerates, and in a few years is likely to recover. If the forest is managed successfully for its productivity (usually for timber), it remains reasonably stable. Controlled **reafforestation** replenishes the stock of trees, thereby maintaining the ecosystem.

Large-scale damage to forest ecosystems is occurring as a result of mechanisation, leading to massive clearance on an unprecedented scale (Figure 9.4). Pressures on forests, well illustrated by the Amazonian rainforest, arise from world-wide commercial demands as well as smaller but significant demands from indigenous people. The forests are exploited for their timber and fuelwood, mined for minerals (such as manganese, tin and iron), and used as a source for extraction of medicines (by large pharmaceutical companies as well as local people) and to provide food. Roads have been built to regions in the forest that were previously inaccessible except to the indigenous people. Rivers have been utilised to generate electricity through construction of hydroelectric schemes. In Central America, areas of forest have been destroyed to provide grassland for 'ranching' of cattle and overpopulation has encouraged semi-permanent settlements of smallholders to encroach upon forest land.

Figure 9.4 Deforestation in Sichuan province, western China (right); natural forest in Sichuan province in western China (left), one of the few remaining areas still inhabited by the giant panda. The natural habitat is being eroded because of deforestation, encroaching agriculture and spread of industrialisation.

An immediate effect of deforestation is on the soil. Trees and associated vegetation tend to act as a sponge, retaining water and releasing it slowly to the soil and streams, and as water vapour to the air. With removal of the forest this stops abruptly; the soil surface loses its roughness and surface run-off of water increases. Large quantities of soil particles and nutrients are washed into streams and rivers. In tropical rainforests, the soil itself is relatively poor in nutrients, though considerable quantities are locked away in the biomass of the forest plants. These become available to future plant life through natural recycling. Removal of forest products, such as timber, takes large quantities of nutrients away from the area. Disturbance to the soil and removal of surface organic litter upsets the microbial population and the natural nutrient cycling mechanisms. The remaining soil is thus relatively poor in quality for any future agricultural use. Sudden exposure of the soil means that the surface is heated up; it may become desiccated and is also subjected to the direct effects of rain and wind. The soil in the area is then more liable to suffer from **erosion**, which becomes particularly acute in sloping areas. Erosion can also affect more distant locations through deposition of sediment in rivers, which may lead to flooding.

The change from a forest ecosystem to agricultural crops or grassland for grazing may alter the utilisation of carbon dioxide in photosynthesis. If less carbon dioxide is used by the replacement crop, there will be a net increase in carbon dioxide in the atmosphere. The possible contribution to the greenhouse effect is discussed later in this chapter.

QUESTION

Global change is not new and some of the concerns today are echoed in this passage written by Plato, 2300 years ago.

There are mountains in Attica which can now keep nothing but bees, but which were clothed not very long ago, with fine trees producing timber suitable for roofing the largest buildings ... . There were also many lofty trees, while the country produced boundless pastures for cattle. The annual supply of rainfall was not lost as it is at present, through being allowed to flow over the denuded surface to the sea, but was received by the country ... where she stored it ... and so was able to discharge the drainage of the heights into the hollows in the form of springs and rivers with an abundant volume and a wide territorial distribution ...

How far are these words, written by Plato about Greece, still true today? What effects does deforestation also have on species diversity?

Probably the greatest resource of tropical forests lies in their biological diversity. Any attempt to estimate numbers of species is bound to be conservative, as many have never been recognised or described. Many of these unknown species are likely to be invertebrates, especially insects. A few examples from the Amazonian forest will give a hint as to their diversity. There are exotic birds, mammals and insects, often hunted for various trade outlets. Among the birds are toucans, parakeets and trogons; the monkeys include capuchins, howler and squirrel monkeys. There are anacondas, perhaps 10 m in length, boa constrictors and many other snakes, lizards, turtles, crocodiles, toads and frogs. The mammals include tapirs, anteaters, jaguars and capybara. A range of products from tropical forests have direct value to humans as food sources. Many vegetables and fruits eaten around the world originate in tropical forests. These include rice, maize and potatoes, pineapples, avocados and bananas, coffee and cocoa, palm oil and Brazil nuts. Plants with medicinal value are used by the indigenous people, and some have been used in modern medicine. Examples are quinine for malaria, and curare as a muscle relaxant in surgical operations. Curare is obtained from the bark of trees and for centuries was used by South American Indians as an arrow poison.

It is difficult to predict the long-term effects of the loss in biological diversity as forests are destroyed. Inevitably species are lost. Some species may adapt to life elsewhere, but others depend critically on factors in the forest ecosystem, say a food plant or the shelter provided. The giant panda exists in only a few locations in China, being largely dependent on bamboo for food, but its survival is seriously threatened by the destruction of forests in these crucial areas (Figure 9.4). Endangered species from other forests include apes, lemurs, elephants, leopards, tigers, some parrots and crocodiles.

The impact of humans is not a new problem. In prehistoric Britain there were large mammals: lions, leopards and hyenas, similar to species currently living in Africa, and more recently there were bears and wild swine. The demise of these large mammals was probably due to the combination of hunting and loss of the protective cover of native woodland as it was cut down. The last known aurochsen (ancestors of modern domesticated cattle) were observed in forests in Poland in 1627. Reduction of woodland to the point where surviving animals could be hunted and caught almost certainly contributed to their extinction.

The genetic reserves in both animal and plant species in the rich forest ecosystem are potentially highly valuable resources. The gene pools in commercial varieties of domesticated animals and crop plants used in agriculture have become dangerously narrow, with the risk that whole populations could be destroyed by disease or by pests. Wild populations may, therefore, provide sources of fresh genetic material, with the potential of introducing favourable characteristics, such as flavour and improved disease resistance, or allowing the crop plants to be grown in different climatic regions.

Forests, sustainability and biodiversity

Increasing awareness of both the short-term and the long-term effects of deforestation has led to the development of strategies designed to halt or reverse the level of global deforestation. Such strategies aim to encourage sustainable use of existing forest resources and also to promote deliberate planting of trees, in areas previously forested (**reforestation**) or those which had not recently been forest land (**afforestation**). These measures are often government backed, but they must be monitored and controlled at a local level (often in remote areas of a country) to ensure they are being implemented successfully.

In China, in the early 1980s, it was predicted that, if the rate of forest depletion continued at the then current rate, China would be virtually out of wood by the year 2000. In 1999, compared with only a few years earlier, personal observations showed that there was a noticeable reduction in logging traffic from the southwestern mountainous region of China. Roadside checks ensure that logging loads have valid permits, though some illegal felling certainly continues to occur. At the same time, there was widespread evidence of tree planting schemes, both in rural and urban locations. Indeed, many Chinese cities show the benefit of urban tree planting schemes. Some mountain areas which had been ravaged in earlier decades to produce fuel to boost industrial output are now supporting young forest cover. Such forests provide fuel for immediate local use as well as timber in the longer term. Some afforestation schemes are linked to stabilising of agricultural land by reducing soil erosion. One requirement of the 'Obligatory Tree Planting Programme' (adopted in 1981) is for all Chinese citizens over the age of 11 years to plant three to five trees each year or to make a contribution to afforestation work. With these and other plans, China should have created 66 million hectares of new forest by the year 2000, an increase of about 20 per cent in its forested areas. This would allow China to supply about two-thirds of its timber requirements in the year 2000. If successful, and if this rate continues, China could be self-sufficient in timber by the year 2040. This is a noticeable reverse of the position in the early 1980s. The positive signs in China are encouraging, both on a national and global scale.

Maintenance of forests for sustainability requires management if the forest is to allow harvest of its products and continue to be productive and also to support a diversity of both flora and fauna. This can be illustrated by management systems used in coppice woodlands, such as those found in Britain. Coppicing is a method of woodland management that has been practised for many hundreds of years. The wooded areas are usually laid out in blocks (or fells) and the coppicing or cutting of the woody species takes place in these blocks. The blocks are often separated by wide grassy tracks, with perhaps a shallow ditch each side. At intervals, certain tree species (such as alder, ash, birch, chestnut, hazel, hornbeam, maple, sallow, small leaved lime – or others, depending on the location) are cut down close to ground level. New side shoots then grow out from the stumps (known also as **stools**) and are allowed to grow for, say, 10 to 15 years, then are harvested as **poles** (Figure 9.5). Different blocks

Figure 9.5 Coppiced woodland as an example of sustainable management: Bradfield Woods (in Suffolk, eastern England) in late summer. The foreground shows 2 to 3 year growth from coppiced stools, interspersed with full height standards deeper into the woodland.

are coppiced in successive years, giving a crop of wood every year. Among the coppiced stools, a few trees (usually oak, but also species such as ash, silver birch, elm or willows) are allowed to grow to their full size as mature trees. These are known as **standards**. When felled, these trees supply timber, used in building houses. Trees regenerate naturally from seedlings. In Bradfield Woods

(Suffolk) some of the ash stools reach a diameter of up to 6 m, with an estimated age of at least 1000 years. They have probably yielded crops of wood continuously over this period. In the history of Bradfield Woods, the harvested wood has been used for the manufacture of various products, including wooden rakes, handles for scythes, thatching pegs, hazel for daub and wattle (used in local timber-frame buildings), fencing materials and hurdles as well as firewood. The series of coppiced areas, representing different cutting intervals within the 10 to 15 year cycle, show successive stages of regrowth of the shoots from the stools (Figure 9.6). This continual regeneration of trees from the coppiced stools maintains a supply of wood in a sustainable way.

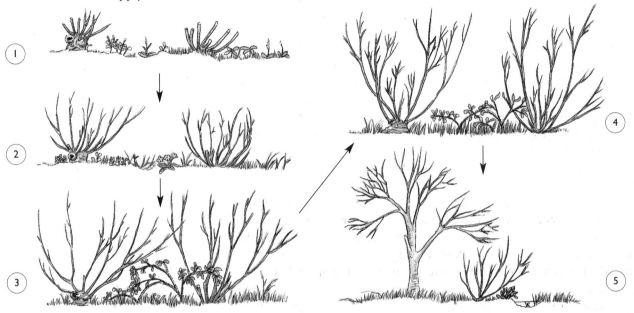

Figure 9.6 Management of woodland by coppicing helps to maintain biological diversity of species – some stages in the coppicing cycle in Bradfield Woods (Suffolk):

Stage 1: first year after coppicing. Ground species include dog's mercury and water avens. Herb Paris and early purple orchid may be seen, both indicators of ancient woodland.

Stage 2: second and third years after coppicing. Richest ground flora seen at this stage, in spring. Ground species include sweet violet, bugle, wood anemone, primrose, dog's mercury, patches of oxlip (now rare), bluebell and wood spurge.

Stage 3: fourth and fifth years after coppicing. More grasses, brambles and other species invade.

Stage 4: eight and nine years after coppicing. Ground flora more sparse, and has lost its colour and diversity (though the cycle starts again when the area is freshly coppiced).

Stage 5: climax woodland stage.

Coppicing also allows a diversity of plant and animal species to be supported within the woodland community. Comparison of the ground flora in different coppice areas reflects stages in a succession, from open ground through to areas with dense shading from the tree cover. Open rides offer sites for other flowers and along the edges of the rides there can be shrubs and taller vegetation, providing attractive habitats for insects, including butterflies. Ditches, if present, introduce yet another habitat for a different range of species. The different stages of the coppicing cycle create a range of habitats, hence a diversity of species. In Bradfield Woods, at least 42 native trees and shrubs have been described, about two-thirds of the total in Britain. Over 350 species of flowering plants are known from these woods, including a number of rarities. However, if left to grow without any management, the diversity of species within the wood would gradually diminish. Hazel is an example of a

QUESTIONS

The description of Bradfield Woods gives an example of how management of a woodland by coppicing allows harvest of its products.

- What evidence is there that this can be considered a *sustainable* management system? What evidence is there that *species diversity* is maintained or enhanced in Bradfield Woods, compared with the surrounding area?
- Think of another example, in your local area if possible, that illustrates a sustainable system. Look at how it is managed, what the products are and any evidence of good species diversity.
- Try to work out a concise definition for the term *sustainability*, that could be applied to forest management and to agricultural systems.
- How far is sustainability realistic for agricultural systems on a global scale?

woody species that does not compete well in dense, mature woodland. Similarly, in Bradfield Woods, as well as the abundant plant life, there are plenty of birds and the abundant birdsong includes that of willow warblers, blackcaps and nightingales. Other animal life includes adders, grass snakes, frogs and toads and a range of typical small woodland animals. All these are rare or absent in the surrounding farmland and would disappear if the woodland were to be destroyed.

Desertification

Natural deserts occur in both hot and cold regions. They are characterised by low and intermittent rainfall, usually less than 250 mm of precipitation per year. Sometimes total drought persists from one year to the next. Because of the low water availability, desert areas support only limited vegetative cover. The term **desertification** has been defined as 'land degradation in arid, semi-arid and dry sub-humid areas arising mainly from adverse human impact'. This definition recognises that *human activities* are the main cause of contemporary desertification and associates its progress with increased population and consequent pressure on the natural resources of the area. Concern arises about the loss of productivity from land which could be used for agriculture, leading to worsening poverty or even famine among the people the area has traditionally supported.

Pressures on the land come mainly from grazing flocks (often sheep, cattle or camels) and from gathering fuelwood. Some arid areas are just able to support the growing of crops, probably helped by irrigation, but the situation is usually already fragile. A dry season can be disastrous and result in crop failure. Any additional pressure, from increased human population or worsening of the drought conditions, means that grazing of animals and fuel gathering spreads over a yet wider area. Demands by the herds then exceed the carrying capacity of the land and the vegetation cannot support them, nor can it recover unless the pressure is removed (Figure 9.7).

Figure 9.7 Desert areas in Afghanistan: (a) sparse vegetation; (b) grazing pressure; (c) fuel gathering; (d) erosion in area denuded of vegetation

Lack of vegetation leads to a downward spiral in terms of deterioration of the land. The bare soils, exposed to direct sunlight, suffer further desiccation and, combined with exposure to winds, are more likely to suffer from **erosion**. Soil particles may be deposited elsewhere, perhaps over other marginal crops or grazing land, causing further loss of potential agricultural land. High rates of evaporation in the absence of plant cover are likely to alter the water–salt balance. Salts drawn up from the ground water are left behind in the surface layer of the soil. This leads to **salinisation** which contributes to the deterioration of the soil, which then becomes unsuitable for plant growth. Salinisation may also result from poorly designed irrigation systems, where the existing drainage is unable to handle an increased water supply. As the groundwater level rises, dissolved salts are brought to the surface, but the area effectively becomes waterlogged so the salts remain in the water. With high rates of evaporation, the salts then accumulate at the soil surface. The situation may be exacerbated if chemicals have been used on the land, either as fertilisers or for pest or weed control. Lack of vegetation alters the amount of moisture in the atmosphere, which may in turn affect the climate pattern in the area, particularly rainfall.

Two examples will emphasise how human pressures on the land have brought about desertification in areas where an equilibrium had previously existed. Disaster struck the Sahel region of Sudan in the early 1970s. This semi-arid zone had had a higher than average rainfall for about 20 years. This encouraged greater cultivation in the region, including cash-crops, such as peanuts. The pastoral people with their grazing herds were pushed further north into the fringe of the Sahara desert, crowded into land with already poor carrying capacity. When the drought returned, thousands of people and millions of animals died because they had no food, inadequate water and nowhere to go.

In the second example, in northern China, extensive areas of semi-arid grassland are undergoing desertification, seen as deterioration of the land with more sand blowouts and shifting dunes. Increased human population in the area is linked to political movements of people. Sedentary agriculture is replacing traditional practices which depended on seasonal movement of grazing animals. Since 1949, in an area of Inner Mongolia, the number of livestock has increased while the land available for grazing has decreased (see Table 9.2). Breeds of cattle, such as the European Friesian and Simmental, have been introduced. These have potentially higher productivity, but there has not been the necessary adjustment in herd size to take account of their higher food intake. Collection of fuelwood to support the increased population has worsened the situation.

Table 9.2 *Grazing pressures and desertification: Xilingole League, China (1949 to 1980)*

Year	Number of livestock	Grazing area / km^2	Density / number km^{-2}
1949	1 740 000	193 000	9.01
1958	4 750 000	193 000	24.63
1964	8 210 000	179 000	46.00
1970	5 780 000	123 000	47.04
1980	5 270 000	142 000	37.02

A variety of strategies is used when farming in arid areas to try to overcome the difficulties associated with minimal rainfall. Slopes are often terraced to prevent run-off and trees can be planted to create shade and wind shelter for crops. Leguminous tree species can be planted to increase soil fertility. Stones left on the ground trap moisture, reduce evaporation and create shade and shelter for seedlings. Stones can also be placed around the base of trees to help retain moisture. In sub-Sahara, research showed that survival of wild shrub seedlings depends on the proximity to stones – in the first summer 90 per cent survive if found within 0.5 cm of the edge of a stone, but rates are much lower if further away. In Australia, farmers are using new techniques to restore exposed, hard-baked areas suffering from degradation. Bulldozers are being used to cut a

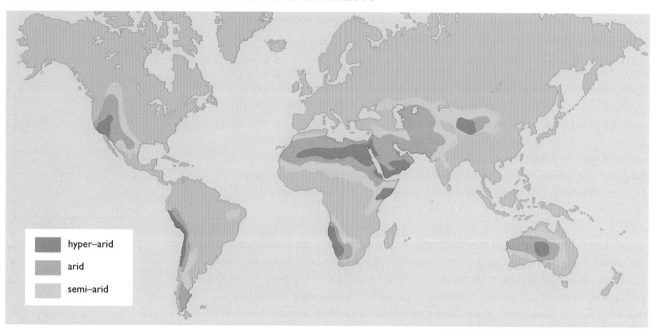

Figure 9.8 Areas of the world at risk of desertification. It is the arid and semi-arid lands that are at risk, whereas the hyper-arid zones are already natural deserts.

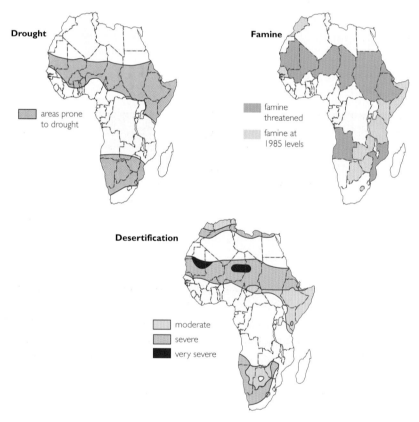

Figure 9.9 Areas in Africa prone to drought, subject to desertification and threatened with famine

series of shallow grooves and depressions in the ground. These artificial hollows act as traps for moisture and for wind-blown seeds. The small hollows then shelter the seedlings, enhancing rooting and increasing chance of survival. Iran, with over

5 million hectares of sand dunes, is adopting other strategies for prevention of desertification and spread of desert. In certain areas the dunes are being sprayed with oil which stabilises the sand surface. The coating of oil prevents seedlings from being blown away and retains moisture. After spraying, drought-resistant shrubs are planted in a series of narrow furrows, cut across the direction of the wind. One area of more than 60 km^2 was treated in this way, and, in 6 years was transformed from bare sand to a forest of trees more than 3 m high.

QUESTIONS

Desert regions suffer from low rainfall and often experience high winds. How would this affect plants growing in arid regions? List some examples of adaptations shown by plants growing naturally in arid regions (xerophytes) and explain how water loss is reduced. How far can these features found in xerophytes be taken into consideration when attempting to restore land subject to desertification so that it can be used for growing crops?

Fig 9.10 Crops being grown in a desert region in Chile

Atmospheric pollution

The term **atmospheric pollution** implies change in the constitution of the atmosphere brought about by human (anthropogenic) activities, causing harm to humans or to other living organisms in the environment. In the late 20th century, atmospheric pollution affects all nations of the world. The increase in pollution over the last 150 years is attributed to the increasing human population and the rapid growth of urban and industrial societies. However, the effects are not confined to urban or industrial areas, because the pollutants travel in air currents and spread across international boundaries.

Damage caused by atmospheric pollution affects people, their crops, buildings and wildlife as well as the global climate. There is considerable concern that some of the effects are irreversible because the atmosphere has limited ability for recovery. Increasing awareness of the effects of pollution has led to some changes in the relevant human activities, but a realistic reduction can only be brought about by efforts involving individual, local, national and international controls. The following sections look at the causes and consequences of two aspects of atmospheric pollution: increasing acid rain and the enhanced greenhouse effect.

Acid rain

Rain, snow and other forms of precipitation are naturally mildly acidic, with a pH of about 5.6. (Remember that pH 7 represents neutral pH and that change by one unit on the pH scale represents a 10-fold change in acidity.) The acidity is due to carbon dioxide in the air, which dissolves to form carbonic acid. We

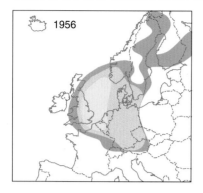

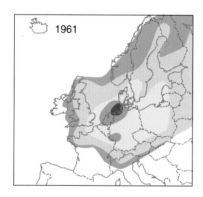

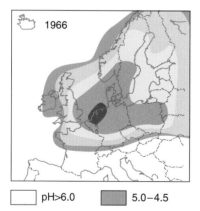

pH>6.0		5.0–4.5
6.0–5.5		4.5–4.0
5.5–5.0		<4.0

Figure 9.12 Increases in the acidity of precipitation in Europe between 1956 and 1966

use the term **acid rain** to describe precipitation of pH 5 or lower. This increased acidity is attributed mainly to the production of sulphur dioxide (SO_2) and oxides of nitrogen (NO_x) during the burning of fossil fuels.

Glaciers and ice sheets can be used to trace the history of the acidity of precipitation. For thousands of years up to the start of the Industrial Revolution, the pH was near to 6, or even higher, whereas by the middle of the 20th century, pH values of 4 to 4.5 have been commonly recorded in north America and Europe. Other evidence similarly shows a history of increasing acidity. As an example, diatoms have preferences for certain pH ranges, so the profile of diatoms deposited in sediments in certain lakes can give an indication of the history of the pH in the lake (Figure 9.11). Detailed monitoring of the acidity of rain in Europe over the 10-year period from 1956 to 1966 showed that the rain had become more acidic and that the area affected had expanded (Figure 9.12).

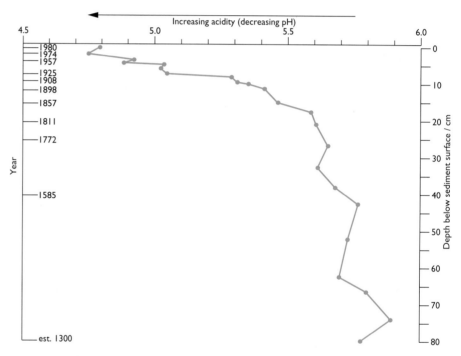

Figure 9.11 Fossil diatoms can give an indication of the history of the pH in a lake. These data show the analysis of diatoms from Round Loch, a lake in southwest Scotland. Despite its isolation, the lake shows sharp increases in acidity from about the time of the Industrial Revolution in the mid-19th century.

A complex series of reactions produces the acidity, mainly in the form of sulphuric and nitric acids with some hydrochloric acid (Figure 9.13). The proportions of the acids differ, depending on the origin of the pollutants. The deposition of the acid rain may be in areas that are considerable distances (even hundreds of kilometres) away from the source of pollutant, though it may be difficult to identify the exact source. Compared with lowland regions, mountainous areas are likely to receive a relatively high dose of acid rain, simply because of their higher rainfall. Scandinavia appears to have received a disproportionate deposition of acid rain. Some of this probably arises from industrial activities in Britain, but a substantial contribution is made by industries in Europe, including the eastern European countries. During the 1950s, the policy in Britain was for the introduction of tall chimneys for power stations. This was an attempt to reduce ground level pollution by lifting the emissions to a higher level so that they were dispersed away from the source. While at least partially successful on a local scale, this practice has undoubtedly contributed to acid rain deposition at more distant localities.

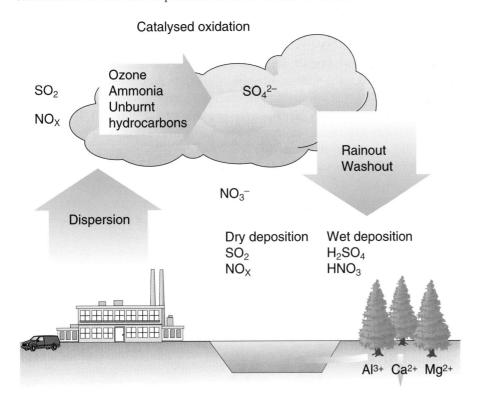

Figure 9.13 Formation and deposition of acid rain

The effects of acid rain on animal and plant life in both aquatic and terrestrial ecosystems, and also on buildings, are now well recognised. In freshwater ecosystems, particular attention has been paid to fish populations (or lack of them). In the late 1970s, a study made of 1679 lakes in Norway, showed a strong relationship between the pH of the lakes and the abundance of fish in them (Figure 9.14). Most of the lakes with a pH below 4.5 had no fish whereas virtually all those with a pH higher than 6.0 had good populations of fish. Similarly, there is evidence of loss of fish, because of the increased acidity, from rivers in Canada and the United States of America, and in lakes in Scotland and Wales.

Changes in pH affect fish in various ways. Below pH 4.5, trout do not produce the enzyme which breaks down the outer coating of eggs, so the larvae get trapped inside. This prevents successful reproduction. Acidity leads to reduced calcium concentration and some toxic metals are mobilised. One of these is aluminium, which appears to make the fish produce an excess of sticky mucus on their gills. This leads to reduced intake in salt through the gills which interferes with the osmoregulating process of the fish. Because of the mucus, the gills become clogged and gas exchange becomes difficult. Attempts to reverse the effects of acidity by adding lime to affected lakes may have some short-term benefit to the stock of fish in the lake.

HUMAN INFLUENCES ON THE ENVIRONMENT

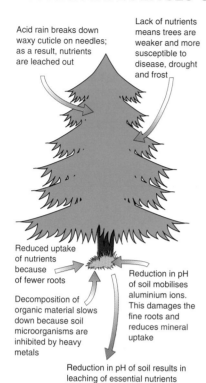

Acid rain breaks down waxy cuticle on needles; as a result, nutrients are leached out

Lack of nutrients means trees are weaker and more susceptible to disease, drought and frost

Reduced uptake of nutrients because of fewer roots

Decomposition of organic material slows down because soil microorganisms are inhibited by heavy metals

Reduction in pH of soil mobilises aluminium ions. This damages the fine roots and reduces mineral uptake

Reduction in pH of soil results in leaching of essential nutrients

Figure 9.15 The effects of acid rain on trees

Increased acidity in aquatic ecosystems is linked to a loss in phytoplankton. Water in acidified lakes is noticeably more transparent because there is less microscopic material in suspension. The effects spread through the food chains, some species becoming more abundant but others being lost. In some lakes where the pH is below 6, the moss *Sphagnum* shows vigorous growth, covering the bottom of the lake and pushing out other plant life.

In terrestrial ecosystems subjected to acid rain there is clear evidence of damage to plant life (Figure 9.15). In large areas of coniferous forest, the trees show poorer growth, lower productivity, discolouration of the needles, shallow roots and die-back of the crown. Many have been killed. In Europe, deterioration has been observed in some important tree species, notably Norway spruce (*Picea abies*), white fir (*Abies* sp.), Scots pine (*Pinus sylvestris*) and beech (*Fagus sylvatica*). Generally deciduous trees suffer less than conifers. Acid deposition affects other organisms in terrestrial ecosystems, and there is evidence that populations of animals have declined in areas affected by acid rain.

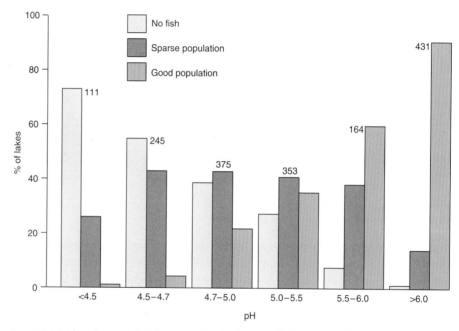

Figure 9.14 The relationship between pH in the water and abundance of fish. These data were obtained in the late 1970s from 1697 lakes in Norway and show how low pH (high acidity) appears to have a detrimental effect on fish. The numbers above each group of bars indicate the number of lakes observed within the particular pH range.

QUESTIONS

Suggest ways that acid rain can be reduced – on a local as well as on an international scale. How can *control* of acid rain be monitored? [*You may find some help at the end of this chapter.*]

Acid rain may also affect human health. A low pH in the soil releases ions of certain heavy metals, such as cadmium, lead and mercury, and these may contaminate drinking water supplies. Pregnant women are at risk from water originating from affected areas, because the fetus is particularly sensitive to mercury poisoning. Acidity may cause leaching of copper and lead from water systems. In Sweden, high levels of copper and lead have been detected in drinking water. Copper from this source may have caused outbreaks of diarrhoea in young children and account for green colouring to baths and even hair! Release of aluminium may be harmful because of the possible link between aluminium and Alzheimer's disease (pre-senile dementia) in humans.

The greenhouse effect

The greenhouse effect (Figure 9.16) is a natural phenomenon in our global atmosphere and plays an important part in maintaining life on Earth as we know it. Without a greenhouse effect, global temperatures would be some 30 °C lower. In Europe, for example, summers would be more like winter and the winter temperatures would approach those in the Arctic and Antarctic regions. There would be much less liquid water on the surface of the Earth, tropical rainforest would not exist and the crops that could be grown around the world would be severely limited.

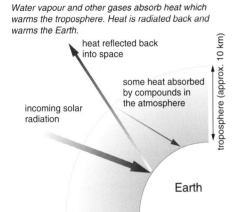

Water vapour and other gases absorb heat which warms the troposphere. Heat is radiated back and warms the Earth.

heat reflected back into space

some heat absorbed by compounds in the atmosphere

incoming solar radiation

troposphere (approx. 10 km)

Earth

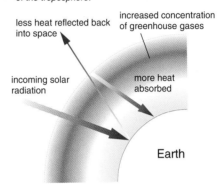

Greenhouse gases, such as carbon dioxide, methane and chlorofluorocarbons (CFCs) absorb more heat, so less is reflected back into space. This increases the temperature of the troposphere.

less heat reflected back into space

increased concentration of greenhouse gases

incoming solar radiation

more heat absorbed

Earth

Figure 9.16 The greenhouse effect

To understand the greenhouse effect, we need to trace the pathway of the energy received from the sun, through the atmosphere of gases around the Earth to the surface of the Earth. Radiation from the sun is emitted in a range of wavelengths. Those that are important to biological systems range from short-wave ultraviolet (less than 400 nm), through visible (400 to 700 nm), to infrared (more than 700 nm). Gases in the atmosphere are relatively transparent to this incoming radiation, although about 30 per cent is reflected back into space. Part of the ultraviolet is absorbed by the reactions between oxygen and ozone so the ultraviolet radiation is effectively filtered out in the stratosphere. Some of the remaining energy which passes through the atmosphere warms the surface of the Earth. Energy is then radiated back away from the Earth's surface as longer wavelength infrared (4000 to 100 000 nm). Part of this escapes through the atmosphere into space, but some energy is absorbed by gases in the troposphere because the gases are less transparent to this longer wavelength infrared. As a result of absorbing this energy, the troposphere warms up. This warm layer then re-radiates the heat energy it has gained. Some is radiated back to the Earth, again providing warmth. The effect of these gases in the atmosphere is to keep the surface of the Earth warmer than it would be without the gases. This way of trapping the heat is known as the **greenhouse effect**.

We can see a parallel (but not identical) situation in a greenhouse (glasshouse). The glass is transparent to incoming radiation, so both the ground and the air inside warm up. The panes of glass help retain the warmth, partly because they help prevent the warm air escaping by convection. The ground and air are thus kept warmer than they would be without the glass covering. The gases in the troposphere are equivalent to the panes of glass, though they retain the heat in a different way.

HUMAN INFLUENCES ON THE ENVIRONMENT

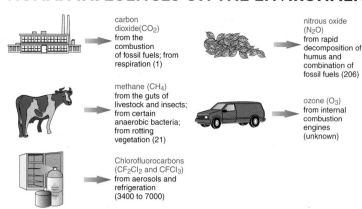

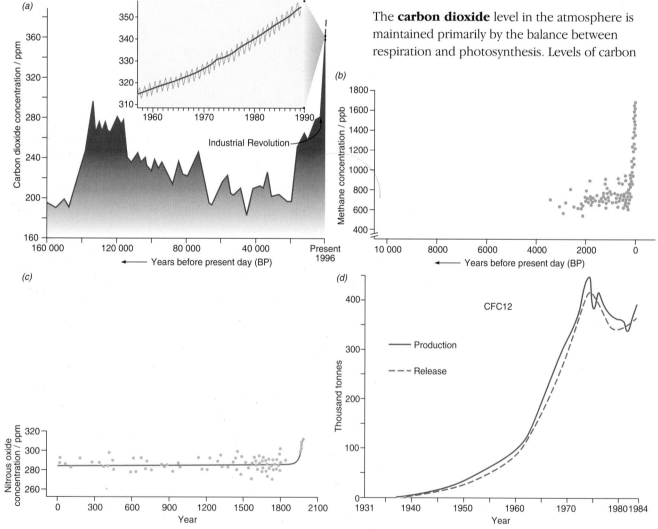

Figure 9.17 Sources of greenhouse gases. Numbers in brackets show the relative effectiveness as a greenhouse gas, per molecule of gas, compared with that of carbon dioxide

Several different gases absorb the long infrared radiation and these are known as **greenhouse gases**. The main greenhouse gases are listed in Figure 9.17, in order of their estimated contribution. With the exception of CFCs, all these greenhouse gases occur naturally, but all of them are also produced as a result of human activities. Increases in the levels of the greenhouse gases have become apparent over the last 150 years, alongside development of industrialisation. The rate of increase has accelerated in recent decades, as we move into the 21st century. The concern is that these anthropogenic sources of greenhouse gases are leading to an exaggerated or enhanced greenhouse effect and that the acceleration will continue unless positive steps are taken to limit the accumulation of greenhouse gases.

The **carbon dioxide** level in the atmosphere is maintained primarily by the balance between respiration and photosynthesis. Levels of carbon

Figure 9.18 Changes in concentrations of greenhouse gases in the atmosphere (note the different time scales): (a) carbon dioxide over 160 000 years, (inset) carbon dioxide detail from 1956 to 1990; (b) methane over 10 000 years; (c) nitrous oxide over 2000 years; (d) CFC12 over 50 years (from 1931 to 1984)

dioxide at different times have been estimated from carbon dioxide trapped as bubbles in ice in Antarctica and Greenland. These show a continuing and steady rise of carbon dioxide from pre-industrial level of about 280 ppm (parts per million) to about 315 ppm in 1958 and 353 ppm by 1990. These figures show how the increase has accelerated in the three decades from 1960 to 1990 (Figure 9.18a). The annual fluctuations reflect seasonal changes in the rate of photosynthesis, but the trend is clearly upwards.

Increases in carbon dioxide are attributed mainly to the burning of fossil fuels (coal, oil and natural gas). In the early 1990s, this was estimated to be in excess of 6 billion tonnes per year. The carbon in fossil fuels was fixed by photosynthesis millions of years ago when the vegetation was growing, so burning the fuels now releases carbon dioxide which had effectively been removed from circulation. Deforestation on a large scale may also upset the contemporary balance between respiration and photosynthesis. When forest trees are cut down and removed, the land is often converted to agricultural land which is then used for grazing or growing other crops. The amount of carbon dioxide used in photosynthesis is likely to be very much less than when trees were growing, resulting in a net increase of carbon dioxide in the atmosphere. Clearing the land during deforestation involves burning of residues in the forest and disturbance of the soil may release further carbon dioxide. The main events of the carbon cycle are summarised in Figure 9.19.

Chlorofluorocarbons are entirely anthropogenic. The two which make the most significant contribution to the greenhouse effect are CFC11 ($CFCl_3$), and CFC12 (CF_2Cl_2) (Figure 9.18a). Even though present at very low concentrations, CFCs are far more efficient than carbon dioxide in absorbing infrared radiation. (They are considered to be up to 7000 times more effective). CFCs persist in the atmosphere for 60 years or more, hence the concern over their potential long-term contribution to the greenhouse effect.

QUESTION

What measures can be taken to reduce the contribution of chlorofluorocarbons (CFCs) to global warming?

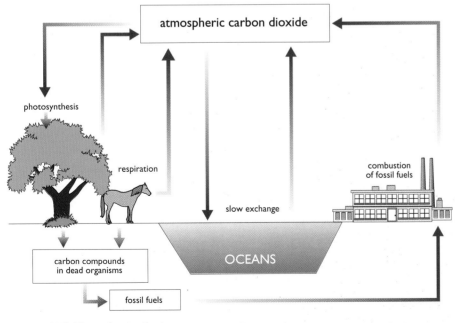

Figure 9.19 The carbon cycle

Methane is a hydrocarbon which is produced naturally by bacteria in wet, marshy, anaerobic conditions, hence its name 'marsh gas'. Considerable quantities of methane are produced from the activities of these bacteria in rice paddy fields. Another significant source of methane is from the guts of animals, particularly ruminants such as cattle, sheep and camels. A domestic cow can produce about 200 dm^3 of methane a day, but only 12 dm^3 of milk! Methane may also seep out from landfill sites, where it is produced from rotting vegetation, and some methane leaks from gas pipes and coal mines. With increasing demand for food, larger areas of rice paddy are cultivated and more cattle are reared. Numbers of cattle, for example, doubled between 1960 and 1980. These sources have certainly contributed to the doubling of methane levels over the last 150 years (Figure 9.18b). A global rise in temperature is likely to release further methane currently trapped in frozen northern tundra areas.

Nitrous oxide is produced naturally in the soil from nitrates by the activity of denitrifying bacteria. Increases in nitrous oxide, from a pre-industrial level of about 288 ppb (parts per billion) to a 1990 level of 310 ppb (Figure 9.18c), are attributed partly to the burning of fossil fuels and other forms of biomass, but also to the enormous increase in use of nitrogen fertilisers. Some nitrous oxide is produced from disturbance of soils and also from animal and human wastes.

The amount of **water vapour** in the atmosphere is affected by human activities, such as the burning of fuels and other industrial processes. Any rise in temperature would cause more water to evaporate from the sea, which would add yet more water vapour to the existing greenhouse gases in the atmosphere. The gas **ozone** also makes a contribution as a greenhouse gas (see Figure 9.17 on page 158).

It is well established that levels of greenhouse gases have increased over the last 150 years. It is also recognised that human activities produce greenhouse gases and that these activities have increased during the same period. This suggests that, as a result of these increases in greenhouse gases, there may be an enhanced greenhouse effect, leading to a rise in temperature on the surface of the Earth (Figure 9.20). This is described as **global warming**. Climatic patterns since the mid-19th century do show a rise in global temperature as a general trend. We cannot, however, say categorically that the temperature rises have been *caused* by human activities, even though we accept that there are strong links between the two. Events which determine climatic patterns are highly complex. Reconstruction of past climates shows that there have been considerable fluctuations in global temperatures at least over the past 20 000 years, dating back to the last glacial period. The recent rises in temperatures may be part of a general fluctuation, such as has occurred before. Extrapolation of present trends suggests, however, that during the early part of the 21st century, global temperatures are likely to rise to a level higher than at any time in recent history.

There is considerable concern about the implications of human activities and their possible effects on global climate but it is difficult to predict precisely what will happen in the immediate future. People may respond by reducing those anthropogenic activities which cause emission of greenhouse gases. This

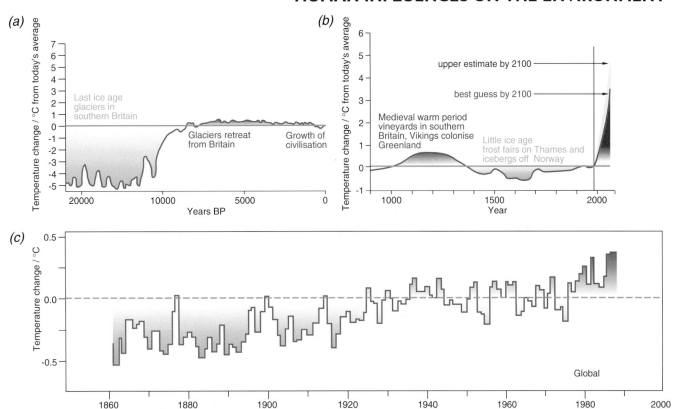

Figure 9.20 Generalised global temperatures: (a) estimated global temperatures during and just before the history of human civilisation, shown as a comparison with today's average temperatures; (b) detail of the last 1000 years, with prediction of global temperatures into the next century; (c) global temperatures from 1860 to 1988, compared with 1950 to 1979 (taken as the reference period)

could be supported by policies agreed on an international scale, though this cannot have an immediate effect because there has already been a build-up of certain persistent gases in the atmosphere.

If we assume that production of greenhouse gases continues at the present rate, a best estimate suggests that, by the year 2030, carbon dioxide concentrations will reach double the pre-industrial levels. Computer models predict that this doubling would lead to a global warming of between 1.5 and 4.5 °C. This may not seem a very large increase in temperature, but the effects could be far reaching. One certain result would be a rise in sea levels. This would be due partly to thermal expansion of the sea water in the oceans and partly to melting of glaciers and the ice sheets of Greenland and in Antarctica.

Climatic changes would also lead to changes in patterns of rainfall and temperature. There would probably be shifts in the distribution of both natural ecosystems and agricultural crops compared with their distribution today. Yields of crops might benefit from the higher temperatures and from higher carbon dioxide levels. The zones in which cultivation is successful may extend beyond their present limits. As an example, maize could probably be grown 200 km further north in Europe. However, weeds and crop pests would also benefit, and vectors of disease might alter their range, which in turn would affect crop losses. Perhaps with the warmer climate we would use less fuel to provide heating, but this could be offset by more air conditioning to help cope with the hot summers. We cannot predict the answers with certainty.

QUESTIONS

Why is it wrong to say that the greenhouse effect is *caused* by human activities? How far do you think that the increased human population has contributed to the enhanced greenhouse effect? Try to link specific human activities with the greenhouse gases they produce.

Water pollution

Water on the Earth continually circulates through the processes of evaporation, transpiration, condensation and precipitation. The main events of this **hydrological cycle** are summarised in Figure 7.12 (see page 130). Human activities can interfere with or pollute the water at any stage of the cycle (Figure 9.21). Pollutants may alter the physical conditions in the water, thus disturbing the balance of organisms living in aquatic habitats, or they may do direct harm to living organisms which would normally be present. There is increasing concern over contamination of human drinking water, which is extracted from groundwater and also from rivers. Some pollutants, such as nitrates, have reached unacceptably high levels in these water sources in certain areas. Pesticide residues in water may have harmful effects and polluted water may also encourage spread of disease.

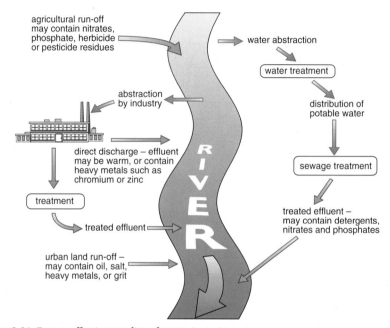

Figure 9.21 Events affecting quality of water in a river

An outline of the ecology of aquatic habitats

A brief consideration is given here of the physical factors of importance in an aquatic environment, with an indication of how these factors influence living organisms. This will help us understand the changes brought about by pollutants. We will focus on freshwater habitats, though similar principles apply to marine or brackish habitats. Even under so-called normal conditions, these factors fluctuate on a daily or seasonal basis. Further information on adaptions shown by organisms in aquatic habitats is given in Chapter 3.

In lakes and ponds the water is relatively static and mixing of water in different parts may be a relatively slow process. In rivers and streams, the water moves in one direction, though the flow rate may vary from very slow (as in canals or pool stretches of rivers) to extremely fast (in some mountain rivers). In a given stretch of a river, there is continual exchange of water, so that events at some distance upstream can affect the river much lower down. Movement of water sometimes creates turbulence, so mixing occurs more readily than in static waters. Often this movement considerably increases the oxygenation of the water.

The normal **nutrient status** depends closely on the bedrock, soil and vegetation of the surrounding catchment area. Water that is relatively poor in nutrients is described as **oligotrophic**, whereas intermediate nutrient levels are described as **mesotrophic** and water rich in nutrients is described as **eutrophic**. This classification of nutrient status refers mainly to levels of inorganic nitrogen and phosphorus, although other mineral elements are also important to aquatic organisms. Higher nutrient levels are likely to support high productivity in terms of biomass within the water environment (Table 9.3). **Organic compounds** found in water are derived mainly from decomposition of plant and animal material (detritus). They may include proteins, carbohydrates and fats as well as more complex particles of organic matter, which are sometimes suspended rather than dissolved in the water.

Table 9.3 *Comparison of nutrient levels (phosphorus and nitrogen) and productivity in oligotrophic, mesotrophic and eutrophic lakes (ppb = parts per billion)*

Nutrient level and biological productivity	Type of freshwater lake		
	Oligotrophic	Mesotrophic	Eutrophic
total phosphorus / ppb	<1–5	5–10	10–30
inorganic nitrogen / ppb	<1–200	200–400	300–650
net primary productivity / g dry mass m^{-2} yr^{-1}	15–50	50–150	150–500
phytoplankton biomass / mg dry mass m^{-3}	20–200	200–600	600–1000

Oxygen dissolves in water and its concentration is a critical factor in determining the types of living organisms (plants, animals and microorganisms) which are present in the aquatic environment (see Chapter 3). The solubility of oxygen decreases with increasing temperature (Table 9.4). Aeration is increased by turbulence, so shallow rivers flowing fast over a rocky substratum acquire more oxygen than stagnant pools. The oxygen level is also dependent upon the balance between photosynthesis and respiration. There is a diurnal fluctuation, with an increase in oxygen during daylight linked to its production by the photosynthetic activity of plants. Seasonal changes in temperature and light intensity influence oxygen availability through their effect on photosynthetic activity. Organisms use oxygen in respiration. The demand for oxygen varies considerably, depending on the number of organisms present and on their activity.

Table 9.4 *Solubility of oxygen decreases with increase in water temperature*

Temperature / °C	Oxygen solubility / mg dm^{-3}
0	14.6
10	11.3
20	9.2
30	7.6
40	6.6

The amount of oxygen being utilised by living organisms in the water is often expressed as the **biochemical oxygen demand** (**BOD**). The BOD of a sample of water is measured under standard conditions at 20 °C over a period of 5 days. Presence of polluting organic material in the water leads to increased activity from microorganisms involved in the decomposition of this material and this results in a high demand for oxygen. Measurement of BOD can, therefore, provide an indication of the level of pollution.

Carbon dioxide, like oxygen, dissolves in water and is more soluble in cool than in warmer water. Carbon dioxide forms carbonic acid, which is a weak acid, so even in non-polluted areas, the rain is likely to be mildly acidic. Carbonic acid dissociates into hydrogen ions (H$^+$) and hydrogencarbonate ions (HCO$_3^-$). The H$^+$ ions contribute to the acidity of the water, or make the pH lower. The hydrogencarbonate ions can dissociate further to produce hydroxide ions (OH^-) and carbonate ions (CO_3^{2-}). The hydroxide, hydrogencarbonate and carbonate ions contribute to the alkalinity of the water. Through these reactions, changes in levels of carbon dioxide lead to fluctuations in **pH**. Some organisms are sensitive to the pH of the water, particularly when acid (see *Acid rain*, page 153). Carbon dioxide is utilised by plants in photosynthesis. When photosynthetic activity is high, the pH rises because the carbon dioxide is used up, so there is less carbonic acid and the H^+ ion concentration falls (Figure 9.22).

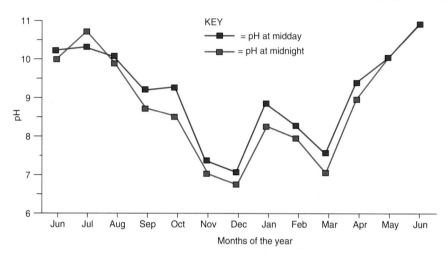

KEY
= pH at midday
= pH at midnight

Figure 9.22 Daily and seasonal variations in pH in a lake. The pH is higher during increased photosynthetic activity because carbon dioxide is used in photosynthesis. The pH is generally higher at midday than at night and higher during summer than winter.

QUESTION

Explain why the pH in a lake is likely to be higher during daylight than at night and higher when warm than when cool.

Temperature affects the density of water, which is greatest at about 4 °C. Sometimes, particularly in large lakes or relatively still water, there may be a sharp separation between layers of water of different density. The boundary between the layers can act as a physical barrier to small organisms, such as plankton, whereas larger organisms may move from one temperature layer to another where conditions may be more favourable. Compared with air and land, water takes longer to heat up and cool down. Water is thus a relatively stable habitat, though living organisms have their own tolerance limits in respect of extremes of temperatures as well as preferred optimum temperature ranges. The effect of temperature on dissolved gases, particularly oxygen, is described above.

Light intensity decreases with depth in the water and is also reduced by material suspended in the water. Such material may be inorganic, derived from bedrock or particles of soil washed into the water, or organic. The intensity of light at different depths within the water is a critical factor in determining the distribution of photosynthetic organisms.

Plant life in water ranges from microscopic organisms to larger plants (**macrophytes**). Most of the microscopic organisms (known as **phytoplankton**) are found in the surface layers, floating or swimming freely. The phytoplankton includes bacteria and blue-green bacteria as well as diatoms and other algae. Through the photosynthetic activity of its organisms, the phytoplankton plays an extremely important part in the primary productivity of aquatic ecosystems. Population numbers of these organisms can fluctuate dramatically in response to seasonal changes or availability of nutrients. Macrophytes include large visible algae, such as blanket weed (*Cladophora* spp.), as well as angiosperms, such as Canadian pondweed (*Elodea canadensis*) and water lilies (*Nymphaea alba*).

Animal life in water ranges from microscopic **zooplankton**, through invertebrates, to fish, amphibians, birds and mammals. The level of available oxygen is an important factor in determining the distribution of animal species. Certain invertebrate species can be used as indicators of pollution levels because some tolerate very polluted water with poor oxygenation whereas others are restricted to clean well-oxygenated water (see Chapter 3).

Sewage – inadequate treatment leading to pollution

Sewage from domestic sources consists mainly of human faeces and kitchen waste. The latter includes detergents and residues from food preparation. Sewage is also likely to carry some industrial waste, which may incorporate stronger liquids used in cleaning or in a variety of industrial processes. Other components may be present, including toxic substances. Examples here are chromium from leather tanneries or copper and zinc from metal-plating industries.

In Britain and many other countries, much of the sewage produced is treated in sewage treatment plants, which involves both physical and biological processes. The **effluent** (liquid) and **sludge** (solid) produced after treatment is

Table 9.5 *The main components of sewage and their effects in a river*

Component of sewage	Features	Consequences on environment
suspended solids	• size ranges from large and visible to colloidal and dispersed • usually organic, so are degradable and can be decomposed by microorganisms	▫ reduce penetration of light ▫ high demand for oxygen during breakdown of organic material by microorganisms
nitrogenous compounds → nitrates	• originate mainly from proteins and urea • often present in the form of ammonium compounds (NH_4^+) • oxidised in stages by nitrifying bacteria (see *Nitrogen* cycle) to nitrates: → nitrite (*Nitrosomonas*) → nitrate (*Nitrobacter*)	▫ NH_4^+ ions toxic to fish ▫ excess nitrate leads to **eutrophication** ▫ eutrophication leads to **algal blooms** ▫ respiration of algae during the night leads to an increased **biological oxygen demand (BOD)**, resulting in depletion of oxygen ▫ death of masses of algae results in an increase in BOD (while the algae are broken down) ▫ some toxins are produced during growth of algal bloom (from certain blue-green algae) ▫ high nitrate concentration is damaging to human health if the water is used as a source for drinking
phosphates	• present in faeces and modern detergents	▫ excess phosphate leads to eutrophication (described above for nitrates)
toxins	• heavy metals such as Cu, Pb, Zn, may accumulate persistent pesticides (from agricultural run-off rather than sewage)	▫ toxic effects on organisms in the water, or for humans if the water is used as a source for drinking water
microorganisms	• may include viruses, bacteria, protozoa, and fungi (some may be pathogenic)	▫ health risk for humans, particularly if the water is used for drinking without adequate treatment
detergents	• 'hard' detergents (used in the 1950s) create foam and are unsightly on the surface • 'soft' detergents (used since the 1960s) are biodegradable, but rich in phosphates	▫ foams on the surface interfere with aeration of the water ▫ high levels of phosphate may lead to eutrophication

completed can usually be used or dumped without harm to the environment. However, sometimes raw sewage is released into rivers or discharged into the sea without treatment, giving rise to pollution. In addition, occasional accidental leakage of sewage occurs, or treatment may be inadequate. Pollution may also result from leakage of animal slurries from farm wastes or from silage liquor.

Suppose some raw or inadequately treated sewage or slurry is discharged into a river. There will be instant changes in the physical factors of the aquatic environment and an impact on the organisms in the river. Table 9.5 shows the main components of sewage and summarises some of the effects of such pollution in a river. By looking at the graphs in Figure 9.23, we can follow this in more detail through various stages downstream.

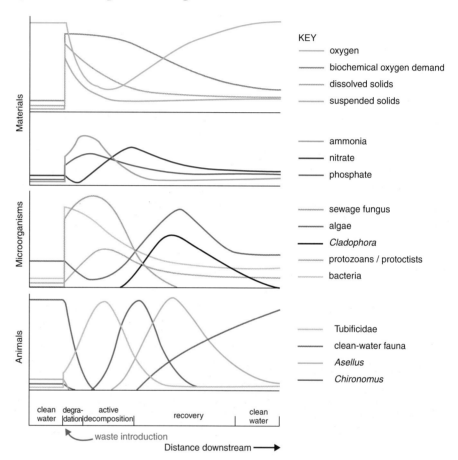

Figure 9.23 Typical changes in water quality and in plant and animal populations in a river after introduction of sewage (see text for discussion of events)

In the initial stage, just below the point at which sewage enters the river, there is immediate decomposition of the organic material, mainly through the activities of aerobic bacteria. These bacteria may have been present in the river water or associated with the sewage material. The demand for oxygen is high, resulting in a rapid decrease in the concentration of oxygen in the water. This 'oxygen sag' occurs when the rate of utilisation of oxygen in respiration by the microorganisms exceeds the rate at which oxygen is replenished. In extreme cases, the oxygen level may fall so low that conditions become anaerobic. In very polluted water, visible slime-like growths known as 'sewage fungus' are likely to appear. The term sewage fungus is misleading as the slime consists of filamentous bacteria, protozoa and algae as well as fungi. Sewage fungus is tolerant of high levels of ammonia and anaerobic conditions.

As the organic substrate is utilised, the numbers of aerobic bacteria decrease, but protozoans which feed on other organisms show an increase. An increase in the number of algae begins when the suspended solids begin to settle out or have been decomposed and the water becomes clearer. Improved light penetration allows algae and other plants to carry out photosynthesis and this helps to restore the oxygen level in the water. Inorganic ions are released from the decomposing material. Ammonia, though initially at high levels, is soon converted to nitrate by nitrification. The nitrate, phosphate and other ions released from the material are likely to be utilised by the increasing populations of algae.

The lowest graph in Figure 9.23 shows typical fluctuations of invertebrate populations in the different zones of the river downstream from the sewage discharge. The *Tubifex* worms and *Chironomus* (midge larvae) are tolerant of low oxygen levels, whereas *Asellus* (water louse), snails, leeches and fish require progressively cleaner water. These population numbers reflect changes in the clean quality of the water and demonstrate how the water can effectively go through stages of self-purification as a result of the activities of microorganisms in the water. In highly polluted waters, there is a danger that only very slow recovery from the initial drop in oxygen concentration will occur. The distance over which such purification takes place depends on many factors, including the temperature of the water, the severity of the initial pollution and the existing microbial population in the water. To some extent, the effect of the pollutant is diminished by dilution as it passes downstream.

Fertilisers, eutrophication and algal blooms

Use of chemical fertilisers on agricultural land has increased markedly with changing agricultural practices aimed at increasing yields of crops (Table 9.6). The main inorganic ions applied in fertilisers are nitrate (NO_3^-), phosphate (PO_4^{3-}) and potassium (K^+) (Figure 9.24). These ions dissolve in soil water and

> **QUESTION**
>
> Sometimes, as a result of a discharge of raw sewage, a sudden mass mortality of fish occurs, known as fish kill. High levels of ammonia are toxic to fish and there may be poisonous substances such as heavy metals in the water. What is likely to be the main reason for the sudden death of fish?

Country	Fertiliser production					Tonnes / km²
	1970	1975	1980	1985	1988	1988
Canada	100	184	301	403	371	2.6
USA	100	128	147	129	132	5.1
Japan	100	102	101	112	109	13.7
France	100	114	142	156	166	13.3
Germany	100	109	139	136	138	20.6
Italy	100	145	198	206	182	7.6
Netherlands	100	116	122	121	101	46.7
Spain	100	134	161	171	201	5.5
Sweden	100	115	111	111	103	7.6
UK	100	121	143	179	169	20.9
North America	100	130	152	138	140	4.6
World	100	136	185	212	242	5.4

Table 9.6 *Changes in fertiliser production in different countries between 1970 (taken as a score of 100) and 1988. The final column gives actual production in 1988. World-wide use of fertilisers has continued to increase during the 1990s, particularly in developing countries. The full potential of increasing crop yield through application of fertiliser has not yet been reached.*

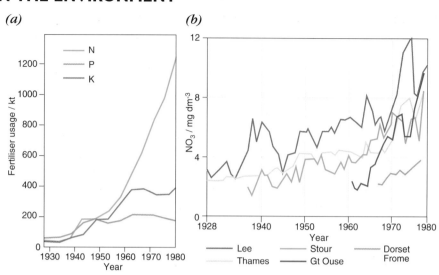

(a)   *(b)*

Figure 9.24 Increased use of fertilisers is linked with increases in the concentration of nitrate in rivers: (a) increases in use of fertilisers containing nitrogen (N), phosphorus (P) and potassium (K) between 1928 and 1980; (b) trend in nitrate concentration in five rivers over the same period. (Both graphs refer to the UK.)

are leached out by rain and water percolating through the soil. The water drains into lakes or rivers giving them an artificially enriched nutrient status. In some cases the body of water may initially have been oligotrophic, with a relatively low initial level of nutrient, whereas in other situations the nutrient status may naturally be higher (mesotrophic or eutrophic). We use the term **eutrophication** to indicate the artificial nutrient enrichment of an aquatic system, regardless of its initial status (Figure 9.25).

Excess or enrichment of nutrients in the water encourages rapid growth of algae and blue-green bacteria, resulting in a population explosion known as **algal bloom**. Such growths may also occur in natural situations stimulated, say, by a seasonal increase in temperature. The phase of rapid growth may be followed by sudden and massive mortality, perhaps because the supply of one of the nutrients has become limiting. Dead algae then rise to the surface of the water as an unsightly green scum.

Figure 9.25 Eutrophication is the artificial nutrient enrichment of an aquatic system. Here, excessive growth of water hyacinth fills channels leading into a lake in Kunming, southwest China.

The most serious consequences of algal blooms arise from the depletion of oxygen. While growing, the algae have a high demand at night for oxygen used in respiration, though during the day, the net output of oxygen from photosynthesis is likely to be greater than that used in respiration. When the algae die, the mass of organic material is broken down by microorganisms (mainly aerobic bacteria), making further demands on the supply of oxygen. If the level of oxygen falls too low, there may be sudden death of masses of fish, a situation known as **fish kill**. Waters that are severely eutrophic may become anoxic and under anaerobic conditions unpleasant odours become apparent, due to production of hydrogen sulphide. Under these conditions methane (marsh gas) may also be produced. Certain blue-green bacteria produce toxins which may also cause the death of fish. The bacterium *Clostridium botulinum* flourishes in anoxic conditions. The toxins it produces cause paralysis known as botulism, which can affect birds and mammals (including humans swimming in the water). Overall, there is usually a drop in species diversity as well as reduction in numbers. Some species, however, prefer or can tolerate the anoxic conditions.

Excessive growth of algae as a result of eutrophication restricts penetration of light into the water. Other water plants suffer from a reduced rate of photosynthesis and this further diminishes the supply of oxygen. So we can see how the events following eutrophication can lead to a rapid deterioration in the quality of water and changes in the populations of plants, animals and microorganisms. Recovery is generally associated with improvement in oxygenation as well as dilution of the original source of nutrient enrichment.

QUESTION

Why do you think the effects of pollution are probably less in a fast-flowing mountain stream than in a slow-flowing lowland river?

Oil pollution

Damage from oil pollution is associated mainly with marine environments, though freshwater lakes and rivers can also be affected. Coastal salt marshes, mangrove swamps and inlets are particularly vulnerable, especially when exchange of water or introduction of fresh water is slow or restricted. Large-scale disasters tend to hit the media headlines: most of us are familiar with the names of wrecked oil tankers and the reports are often accompanied by pictures of birds dragged from the sea or beaches, their feathers useless because of a coating of oil and tar (Figure 9.26 and Table 9.7).

The main source of pollution, however, is oil spills from oil tankers undertaking routine operations such as loading or discharging their cargo in ports, and seepage from oil installations, both on land and off-shore. Another source of oil spills comes from the emptying of ballast water, which is taken into the tanks to provide stability while returning to the loading terminal. Some oil remains in the tanks and is released with this water. Improvement in this area has been achieved by allowing the oil to rise to the surface in the tanks, then draining off the water but stopping before the oil layer is reached. Inadequate disposal of oil from motor vehicles also makes a contribution to seepage into the sea.

Oil consists of a variable mixture of substances, including long-chain hydrocarbons. After a spill, the oil initially spreads over the surface of the water but, as lighter fractions evaporate, the denser oils remain and sink. Chemical reactions produce tar, which forms into balls. Tar may persist in the water or on the shore, where it is particularly undesirable if the beaches are used by tourists. Over a period of time, weathering processes change the physical and chemical properties of the oil. A slick may be broken up into small droplets by wave action and gradually dispersed. Certain marine bacteria and microscopic

Table 9.7 *Examples of wrecked oil tankers*

Name	Date	Area affected	Oil lost (tonnes)
Torrey Canyon	1967	Scilly Isles, UK	119 000
Amoco Cadiz	1978	Brittany, France	227 000
Exxon Valdez	1989	Alaska	37 000
Braer	1993	Shetland Isles, UK	85 000
Sea Empress	1996	Pembrokeshire, UK	72 000

(a)

(b)

(c)

(d)

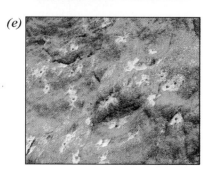
(e)

animals (such as copepods and small crustaceans in plankton) digest organic compounds in the oil and initiate the processes of **biodegradation**. In the presence of light, further chemical reactions break down the oil, eventually into carbon dioxide and water. The time for these processes to remove the oil successfully varies from just a few weeks to many years.

Pollution from oil affects living organisms in various ways. A layer of oil on the surface reduces the exchange of oxygen between the water and air. This affects organisms dependent on breathing at the surface of the water. Oil is also drawn into holes made by worms burrowing in the mud, so the layer of oil means organisms are denied access to oxygen. Plants also suffer, particularly in salt-marsh areas; their roots may become coated with oil, preventing normal ventilation. In salt-marshes close to a refinery near Southampton, the grass *Spartina anglica* has been killed over extensive areas.

Toxic substances from the oil may kill marine organisms, including plankton, shellfish (crustaceans and molluscs), fish and birds. There is evidence of reduced reproductive capacity in some bird species following oil spills. After the *Torrey Canyon* and *Amoco Cadiz* disasters, there was a marked decrease in breeding populations of puffins, guillemots and razorbills in the affected areas.

Oil trapped on feathers of marine birds causes considerable distress and the birds lose their ability to fly. Often seabirds are killed outright, but those that survive and attempt to preen their feathers suffer from ingestion of harmful substances in the oil. After the *Torrey Canyon* disaster an estimated 4500 seabirds died as a result of the oil pollution. Birds and mammals (such as sea otters) depend on the insulating properties of their feathers or fur to keep warm, but this is lost when the feathers or fur become clogged with oil. After the *Exxon Valdez* disaster, even though many sea otters were rescued and cleaned, they died from emphysema after breathing toxic oil fumes or from liver or kidney failure. Another problem is that oil taints the flesh of fish and shellfish. This leads to economic losses for the fishing industry until the pollution has been cleared, or until public confidence has been restored.

After a major oil spill, different methods have been used to clean up the pollution, particularly when it affects a popular beach area, valuable fishing ground (including fish farms) or numerous seabirds. Mechanical ways of

Figure 9.26 The Sea Empress *went aground and spilled an estimated 72 000 tonnes of oil on 15 February 1996, in Pembrokeshire, west Wales. Here we see the clean-up and some of the after effects: (a) clean-up operation at West Angle Bay, 17 February 1996 – Texaco operatives using 'squeegees', mini-barriers and septic-tank gulley-suckers to remove oil mechanically from the sandy beach; (b) oiling by 'chocolate mousse' (oil emulsified in sea water) on the Old Red Sandstone platform at Manorbier Bay, 23 February 1996; (c) guillemot oiled by almost neat North Sea crude oil prior to cleaning at Texaco refinery, 5 March 1996; (d) limpets (*Patella vulgata*) falling off the rocks in a narcotised state at West Angle Bay, 18 February 1996; (e) green phase – green alga (*Enteromorpha spp.*) covering rocks at West Angle Bay, July 1996 – clearings in the green seaweed are created as a result of grazing by limpets.*

removing the oil include pumping and using booms to skim the oil or the 'mousse' off the water. (Sometimes when it has become thoroughly mixed and emulsified with the water, the oil forms a 'mousse' on the surface.) Contaminated sand can be shovelled from beaches to remove offending lumps of oil and tar. Chemical dispersants and detergents can be used to break up an oil slick, but in some cases these chemicals themselves have caused damage to living organisms, perhaps more than the oil itself. Improved detergents with lower toxicity are now used when clearing an oil spillage from a restricted area.

Many naturally occurring microorganisms can break down the complex hydrocarbons in oil to simpler non-polluting compounds. Microbial action (biodegradation) is an important stage in recovery of an area from the effects of oil pollution. In the technique known as **bioremediation**, a polluted area can be seeded deliberately with suitable microorganisms. In 1991, there was a huge oil pollution problem on the shores of Kuwait and Saudi Arabia, arising from the Gulf War. The loss of oil was in the order of 1 million tonnes and the pollution spread along more than 700 km of the coastline. No immediate attempts were made to clean up the area physically, but some months later extensive blue-green mats had developed over some of the patches of oil on the beaches. These mats were made up mainly of blue-green bacteria, tolerant of the unusual conditions and capable of biodegrading the oil. It seems that the oil had killed off some of the other organisms which usually graze on the blue-green bacteria, allowing them to proliferate and, as it happens, carry out the useful task of degrading the oil. Given time, natural systems have considerable potential for 'self-cleaning' and recovery. In a similar way, population numbers of plankton, crustaceans, fish, seabirds and other organisms damaged by oil pollution, gradually rise as they re-invade the area.

Evidence for recovery after an oil spill can be illustrated by events at West Angle Bay, in Pembrokeshire, during the 3 years after the *Sea Empress* ran aground in February 1996. Over 72 000 tonnes of crude oil were spilled and the shores in West Angle Bay were among those most heavily affected. By chance, some 14 permanent quadrats (50 × 50 cm) had been established in this bay and these were already being monitored as part of a long-term survey of plant and animal life on this rocky shore. Three years later the monitoring was continuing and the records provide valuable insight into the overall effects of the oil spill, as well as some detailed changes. While mechanical clearing of oil deposited on the shore had been carried out at the time of the spill, the permanent quadrats were not subjected to any mechanical or chemical cleaning.

A noticeable immediate effect was a decline in numbers of limpets (*Patella* spp.). Instead of clinging with their usual tenacity, they were observed falling away from their 'home' position on the rocks. They had become narcotised by toxic substances in the oil. In this state, waves knock the limpets off the rocks or birds eat them and they were dying in large numbers. A month later, their density had fallen by about 70 per cent or more and their vertical range on the shore had also been reduced. Other gastropods showed less dramatic reduction in numbers, perhaps because they were able to migrate elsewhere on the shore. On the lower shore, certain red algae showed marked bleaching, though recovery from this damage occurred in a fairly short time. By May, about 3 months after the spill, the middle region of the shore was covered

HUMAN INFLUENCES ON THE ENVIRONMENT

QUESTION

Suggest why the time for complete recovery from pollution after an oil spill is likely to be much longer in sheltered areas than in those exposed to vigorous wave action.

QUESTIONS

"Pollution experts in bid to save coastline ... workers help nature in slow clean-up of blackened beach" (Headlines from the *Independent*, Sat 17 Feb 1996, in report on oil tanker *Sea Empress*, which ran aground off the coast of Pembrokeshire).
What damage to wildlife might be expected as a result of the oil spill? What do you think the "workers" would try to do? What would "nature" do? In the long term, how might this accident affect the environment?
Three years later, how much 'recovery' had occurred?

with bright green seaweeds, mainly *Enteromorpha* spp. This unusual flush could be attributed to reduced pressure of grazing by limpets. This was followed by a flush of a red seaweed (*Porphyra* sp.), and later a brown phase of the bladderless form of the bladder wrack, *Fucus vesiculosus* var. *linearis*. The latter had been rare on this shore before the oil spill.

A year later there were definite signs of recovery of the rocky shore communities, particularly from those species with planktonic larvae. These free swimming larvae invaded from distant shores and were able to recolonise the depleted rocky shore sites. Species showing this recovery included the limpets that had suffered so badly. By 1999, populations of limpets had even exceeded the pre-spill numbers. More precarious was the existence of the brooding cushion star (*Asterina phylactica*), a rarity found in West Angle Bay and only a few other sites. This species has no planktonic larva, but broods its young. After the spill, numbers had dwindled dangerously low – perhaps to a mere 10 individuals – but, with some careful nurturing (in a laboratory) of the very limited brood, healthy juveniles have now been returned to pools on the shore. There is optimism that colonies of this rarity will also build up and show recovery comparable to that of the limpets.

The monitoring work was carried out by Field Studies Council staff from Orielton Field Centre. Even the experts admit that they also have undergone a recovery: from extreme pessimism at the time of the spill to a welcome optimism some 3 years later. Perhaps the lessons are that, in the event of a spill, the bulk of the oil should be removed mechanically from sandy shores but that rocky shores should be left to the natural action of the waves to break up the oil deposits. On the shore, it is best to avoid the use of detergents, emulsifiers and high pressure hoses – areas 'cleaned' with high pressure hoses at West Angle Bay still (in 1999) lagged far behind in terms of recovery of its living communities. Perhaps the most reassuring lesson is to witness the remarkable recovery of the ecological communities of animals, seaweeds and lichens, despite the devastating damage recorded at the time of the spill.

Detergents

Detergents originate from both domestic and industrial effluents. Detergents used in the 1960s contained synthetic chemicals with multi-branched carbon chains which did not break down in water (hard chains). These reduced the effectiveness of processes in sewage treatment plants and gave a problem with foam that developed on the surface of water in rivers and elsewhere. These foams reduced access to oxygen by organisms in the water: a concentration of detergent of 0.1 ppm reduces the availability of oxygen in the water to about 50 per cent, and at about 1 ppm is likely to kill freshwater fish, such as trout. The foams were extremely unsightly and there was the danger that pathogenic organisms in the original effluent would be blown about in the foam and spread disease. Since the 1960s, 'softer' detergents have been used, in which the components are biodegradable, but the main problem comes from their high phosphate content, which can lead to eutrophication (Figure 9.27). Detergents also contain toxic substances which can harm or kill living organisms in the water.

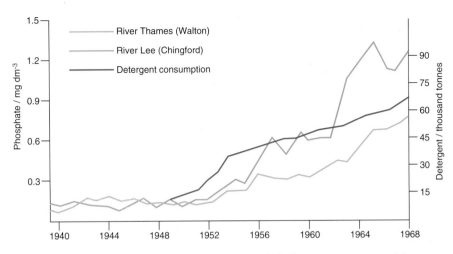

Figure 9.27 Increases in phosphate levels in rivers are linked to increases in use of detergents. The graph shows annual consumption of detergent between 1940 and 1968 and the phosphate level in two rivers over the same period.

Thermal pollution

The term **thermal pollution** is used to describe the unintentional raising of temperature above normal in a body of water as a result of human activities. The origin of the heat is usually effluents from industrial processes, particularly hot water discharged from the cooling towers of electricity power stations. Increases in temperature resulting from thermal pollution are usually in the order of 5 to 10 °C, but the persistence of the raised temperature and the overall effect depends on the rate of flow or size of the body of water affected. Temperature of the water in River Severn, for example, is affected by the Ironbridge power station. When the flow of water is low, the temperature may rise as much as 8 °C whereas, during floods, the temperature rise may be only 0.5 °C.

The effects of thermal pollution may be complex. In some cases the raised temperature may even be beneficial rather than harmful. Temperature changes affect the solubility of oxygen, which becomes less as the temperature increases (see Table 9.4 on page 163). Aquatic species have differing temperature tolerances: trout, for example, may be killed at temperatures above 25 °C. Temperature also affects development and growth rates of fish and influences behaviour patterns, such as migration and spawning. The time taken for fish eggs to hatch depends on temperature, expressed as day-degrees. Trout eggs, for example, require 300 day-degrees to hatch, so at 10 °C they take 30 days to hatch but if the temperature is raised to 15 °C, they require only 20 days. Some fish farms are deliberately located at sites close to effluents from power stations to exploit this enhanced temperature effect.

The communities of living organisms are likely to alter when exposed to thermal pollution. In response to a sudden temperature increase, some species are likely to be killed whereas others may grow more vigorously. The raised temperatures may encourage rapid growth of algae or, at higher temperatures, of blue-green bacteria, which may lead to the effects associated with algal blooms. If the raised temperature persists over a longer period, permanent changes in the species composition may result.

QUESTIONS

How might cutting down trees lead to thermal pollution? Why might a sudden discharge of hot water result in the death of fish?

Even after quite severe incidents of water pollution, recovery and rehabilitation of the habitat often occurs. Usually the most important stage is for oxygenation to be restored and then the plant and animal species need time to re-establish and build up their numbers, though the species composition may have changed. We can illustrate this by the effects of pollution in the River Thames over the last 200 years. The River Thames was once known as a notable salmon river, but by about 1830 these fish had disappeared because the level of pollution preventing them from reaching their spawning grounds upstream. Many other species disappeared during the hundred years or more leading up to the 1950s, but have gradually reappeared after massive clean-up operations from the mid-1960s. Some examples, illustrated in Figure 9.28 on page 176, indicate the success of the measures taken. The key factors in bringing about this improvement have been introduction of measures to control discharge of effluents into the river and the recognition of the importance of maintaining an adequate level of dissolved oxygen in the water.

Pollution, people and politics

In an ideal world, once a link has been established between the effects of pollution and its origins, people would modify their activities in ways that would reduce or minimise the harmful effects of pollution. However, as we move into the 21st century, it is clear that we live in a society that is dominated by the use of fossil fuels, with very widespread use of motor vehicles, and at the same time we live in a 'throw away' economy. Substantial changes are needed in personal lifestyle as well as in the industrial sector if we are to make a realistic impact, on a global scale, on controlling and reducing both the current levels of pollution and the demands on natural resources.

The prime targets for reduction are emissions of carbon and of sulphur, use of pesticides and artificial fertilisers, and the use of 'virgin' raw materials. The challenge to do this has been taken up on an international as well as a local scale and it is through legislation that the intended strategies are implemented. In the interests of political survival, no government can be too extreme in the measures it lays down, because individuals in society are rarely willing to accept a lowering of their standard of living. A balance needs to be found between those measures that are practical to enforce and those that are realistic in relation to the economic needs of the society. This balance must be acceptable on a local as well as a global scale. Some examples from past and recent legislation in the UK and the European Union (EU) are used here to illustrate legislation that has been drawn up with the aim of controlling levels of pollution in both air and water.

Even in 13th-century Britain, the adverse effects of smoke from burning coal were recognised and there were penalties, some severe, for using 'sea coal' in open furnaces. The mid-19th century really saw the beginning of modern pollution control measures. This was in response to pressure from the public over effects of smoke linked to bronchitis and damage to the countryside from the pollution near industrial plants. The Smoke Nuisance Abatement (Metropolis) Act of 1853 and the Alkali Act of 1863 were early attempts to curb the damaging effects of industrial smoke. A century later, the Clean Air Acts of 1956 and 1968 introduced smoke control areas which gave a measure of control over domestic and industrial use of fuels and encouraged greater use of smokeless fuels.

While there has been a noticeable decrease in smoke emission since the 1950s, in the 1970s there was concern over the continued high levels of sulphur dioxide and of other pollutant gases, such as carbon monoxide, oxides of nitrogen and ozone. During the 1970s, there were European Community (EC) Directives which attempted to lay down standards relating to air quality. These, for example, set out maximum permitted concentrations of smoke and of sulphur dioxide, and one aim of these directives was to protect health. Within the EC, there was a requirement for a network of air pollution monitoring stations to ensure compliance with the standards set. Other measures included controls over motor vehicle emissions and phasing out of leaded petrol. In the late 1990s, the EU defined and established objectives for air quality control, to 'avoid, prevent or reduce harmful effects on human health and on the environment as a whole'. Member states have responsibility for implementing the directive and for the accurate assessment of air quality.

In a similar way, water quality is carefully monitored and regulated under EU environmental legislation. EU water quality standards are laid down in a range of areas, including provision of drinking water, water for fish and shellfish, and for bathing beaches. Values are laid down which limit emission of nitrates, of urban waste water, sewage sludge and pesticides. The 'Blue Flag' scheme for beaches used by holidaymakers is an example of the application of these standards. Blue Flags may be awarded annually to bathing beaches, providing they comply with certain microbiological standards and satisfy a range of other criteria, including their amenities. In 1992, 17 beaches in the UK qualified for the award of a Blue Flag. Part of the requirement is that information relating to quality of water on such bathing beaches must be made available to the public.

Full details of the existing EU legislation relating to air and water quality cannot be given here, nor is there any reference to the methods used to implement the requirements. To be effective, controls (of pollutants) must be enforced and these must operate at the personal and industrial company levels as well as at national level. Enforcement is frequently through financial penalties for failures. There are signs, however, of increasing use of positive encouragement for good practice, through tax incentives and through education. The overall hope is that, through modification of personal behaviour and cooperation at an international level, there can be a noticeable reversal of the adverse effects on the environment of the pollution which is generated by anthropogenic activities.

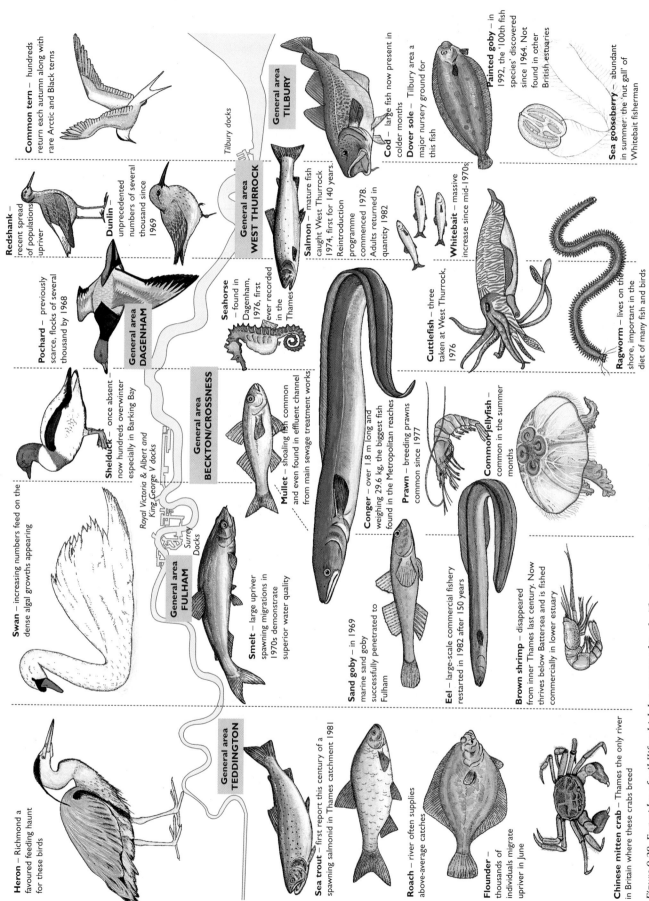

Common tern – hundreds return each autumn along with rare Arctic and Black terns

Redshank – recent spread of populations upriver

Dunlin – unprecedented numbers of several thousand since 1969

Pochard – previously scarce, flocks of several thousand by 1968

General area DAGENHAM

General area WEST THURROCK

General area TILBURY

Cod – large fish now present in colder months

Dover sole – Tilbury area a major nursery ground for this fish

Painted goby – in 1992, the '100th fish species' discovered since 1964. Not found in other British estuaries

Sea gooseberry – abundant in summer: the 'nut gall' of Whitebait fisherman

Tilbury docks

Salmon – mature fish caught West Thurrock 1974, first for 140 years. Reintroduction programme commenced 1978. Adults returned in quantity 1982

Whitebait – massive increase since mid-1970s

Cuttlefish – three taken at West Thurrock, 1976

Ragworm – lives on the shore, important in the diet of many fish and birds

Seahorse – found in Dagenham, 1976, first ever recorded in the Thames

Shelduck – once absent – now hundreds overwinter especially in Barking Bay

General area BECKTON/CROSSNESS

Mullet – shoaling fish common and even found in effluent channel from main sewage treatment works

Conger – over 1.8 m long and weighing 29.6 kg, the biggest fish found in the Metropolitan reaches

Prawn – breeding prawns common since 1977

Common jellyfish – common in the summer months

Swan – increasing numbers feed on the dense algal growths appearing

Royal Victoria & Albert and King George V docks

Surrey Docks

General area FULHAM

Smelt – large upriver spawning migrations in 1970s demonstrate superior water quality

Sand goby – in 1969 marine sand goby successfully penetrated to Fulham

Eel – large-scale commercial fishery restarted in 1982 after 150 years

Brown shrimp – disappeared from inner Thames last century. Now thrives below Battersea and is fished commercially in lower estuary

Heron – Richmond a favoured feeding haunt for these birds

General area TEDDINGTON

Sea trout – first report this century of a spawning salmonid in Thames catchment 1981

Roach – river often supplies above-average catches

Flounder – thousands of individuals migrate upriver in June

Chinese mitten crab – Thames the only river in Britain where these crabs breed

Figure 9.28 Examples of wildlife which has returned to the Thames since the big 'clean-up'

Assessment questions

Unit 2

The following questions have been chosen or designed to be similar in style and format to those that will be set for the AS assessment tests. They meet the requirements of the assessment objectives of the specification. The shorter structured questions test mainly knowledge and understanding of the topics, and the longer questions contain sections in which you may be required to interpret and evaluate data. In the Unit Test, one question will require you to write an answer in continuous prose.

The question styles are essentially similar to those which were used in examinations for the A level syllabuses that preceded the Curriculum 2000 qualifications, so you can find extra practice questions on past papers for those examinations, but you should check that they are relevant to the present specification. As many topics are interlinked, you may find that some questions require knowledge of more than one chapter.

Chapter 1

1 Read through the following account of the digestion of carbohydrates by humans, then write on the dotted lines the most appropriate word or words to complete the account.

One of the enzymes present in pancreatic juice is .... which hydrolyses starch to form .... Disaccharides are hydrolysed to their constituent monosaccharides by various enzymes secreted by cells in the .... These enzymes include sucrase, which hydrolyses sucrose into a mixture of .... and ....

(Total 5 marks)

(Edexcel GCE Biology (6042/B2), June 1999)

2 Gas exchange in insects involves pores in the cuticle which open into a network of tubes. These tubes have fine branches extending into all the tissues of the body.

(a) State **two** features of gas exchange surfaces. **[2]**

(b) In larger insects, such as locusts, the passage of air through the tubes is helped by pumping movements of the abdomen. A student carried out an experiment to investigate the effect of carbon dioxide on the rate of these pumping movements. She set up the apparatus as shown in the diagram below.

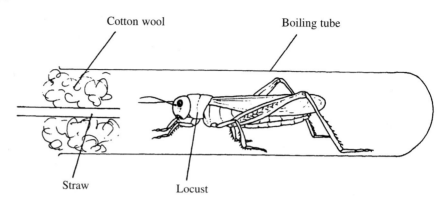

The locust was left in the boiling tube for five minutes. The number of abdominal pumping movements during one minute was counted. The student then breathed out once through the straw into the boiling tube and immediately counted the number of abdominal movements during one minute. She repeated this procedure varying the number of times she breathed out into the boiling tube. The results are shown in the table below.

Number of times student breathed into boiling tube	Number of abdominal pumping movements in one minute
0	16
1	59
2	61
3	58
4	60

(i) State why the student left the locust in the boiling tube for five minutes before she began the first count. **[1]**

(ii) Describe and explain the effect of breathing out into the boiling tube on the rate of abdominal pumping in the locust. **[4]**

(iii) During this experiment, the humidity of the air in the boiling tube may vary. Suggest how this experiment could be modified to control the humidity. **[2]**

(iv) Suggest **two** factors, other than a change in carbon dioxide concentration and humidity, which may have affected the rate of abdominal pumping. **[2]**

(Total 11 marks)

(Modified from Edexcel GCE Biology (6043/B3), June 1999)

Chapter 2

1   The graph on the next page shows oxygen dissociation curves for human haemoglobin at low and high partial pressures of carbon dioxide. The effect of high partial pressure of carbon dioxide on haemoglobin dissociation is known as the Bohr effect.

(a) Explain how the shape of the dissociation curve at a low partial pressure of carbon dioxide is related to the ability of haemoglobin to transport oxygen from the lungs to respiring tissues. **[3]**

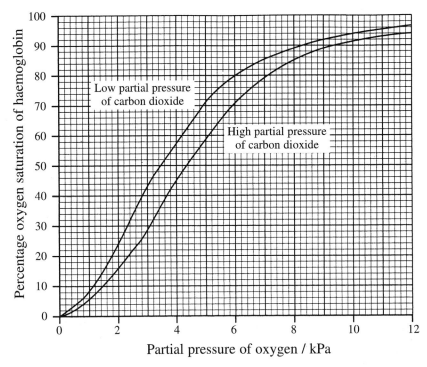

(b) (i) From the graph, calculate the difference in percentage oxygen saturation of haemoglobin at low and high partial pressures of carbon dioxide, at 4 kPa partial pressure of oxygen. Show your working. **[2]**

(ii) Suggest why the Bohr effect is of importance to tissues when they increase their activity. **[3]**

(c) The respiratory pigment myoglobin is found in muscle tissue. The dissociation curve for myoglobin lies to the left of the curves for haemoglobin and it is 97% saturated with oxygen at an oxygen partial pressure of 1 kPa. Explain the function of myoglobin in muscle. **[3]**

(Total 11 marks)

(Edexcel GCE Biology (6043/B3), June 1999)

2 The table refers to features of three types of cells present in mammalian blood. If a feature is correct place a tick (✓) in the appropriate box, and if the feature is not correct, place a cross (✗) in the appropriate box.

Feature	Erythrocyte	Lymphocyte	Neutrophil
Has a lobed nucleus			
Contains haemoglobin			
Produces antibodies			
Shows amoeboid movement			
Can destroy bacteria by phagocytosis			

(Total 5 marks)

(Edexcel GCE Biology and Human Biology (6043/B3) January 1999)

ASSESSMENT QUESTIONS

3 The graphs below show the changes in pressure in the aorta and in the left and right ventricles of the heart, during the cardiac cycle. Time 0 indicates the start of atrial contraction.

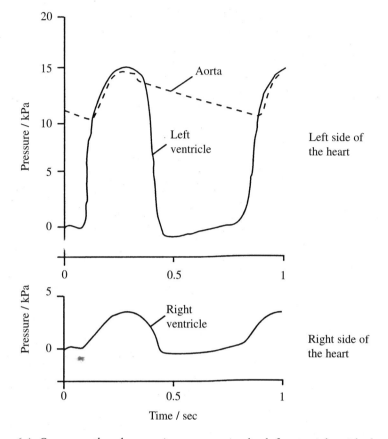

(a) Compare the changes in pressure in the left ventricle with those in the right ventricle, and give reasons for the differences. **[4]**

(b) Compare the changes in the pressure in the aorta with those in the left ventricle, and give reasons for the differences. **[3]**

(c) On the graph of changes in pressure in the aorta and left ventricle, show by means of an arrow when the aortic semilunar valve closes. **[1]**

(d) Cardiac muscle is described as myogenic. Explain how the cardiac cycle is coordinated within the heart. **[4]**

(Total 12 marks)

(Modified from Edexcel GCE Biology and Human Biology (B3), June 1998)

4 An experiment was carried out with cells of carrot tissue to determine the effect of temperature on the absorption of potassium ions.

Slices of carrot tissue were immersed in potassium chloride solution of known concentration. The changes in concentration of potassium ions in the solution were determined at intervals for 6 hours. From these measurements, the mass of potassium ions taken in by the carrot cells was found. The experiment was carried out at 2°C and 20°C. The solutions were aerated continuously.

The results are shown in the graph below. Absorption of potassium ions is given as micrograms of potassium per gram of fresh mass of carrot tissue ($\mu g\ g^{-1}$).

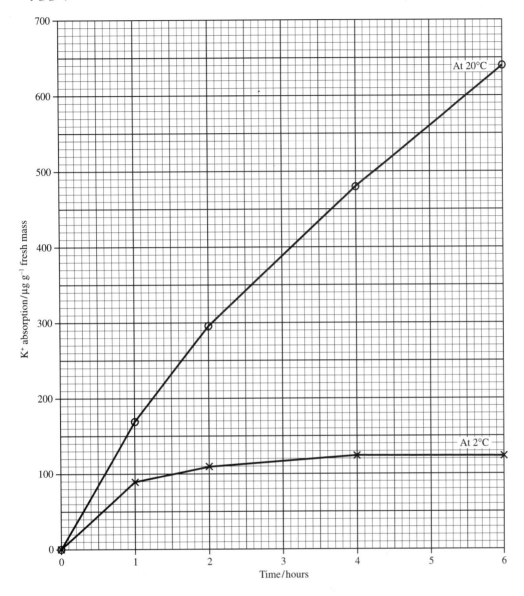

(a) During the first hour, some of the potassium ions enter the cells by diffusion. State **two** conditions which are necessary for a substance to enter a cell by diffusion. [2]

(b) Calculate the mean rate of absorption of potassium at 20 °C, between 2 and 6 hours. Show your working. [3]

(c) Compare the rates of absorption of potassium ions at 2 °C and 20 °C during this experiment. [3]

(d) Suggest an explanation for the differences in the rates of absorption of potassium ions at the two temperatures. [3]

(Total 11 marks)

(Edexcel GCE Biology and Human Biology (B/HB1), June 1998)

5 The diagram below shows a longitudinal section of two cells of phloem tissue in a plant stem.

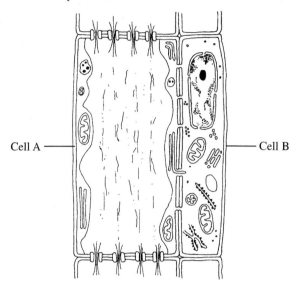

Cell A — — Cell B

(a) Name the cells labelled A and B in the diagram. **[2]**

(b) State the function of phloem in a plant. **[1]**

(Total 3 marks)

(Modified from Edexcel GCE Biology and Human Biology (B3), June 1998)

Human biology (2H) only

6 The rhythmic contraction of the heart muscle during the cardiac cycle is controlled by waves of depolarisation which spread from the sino-atrial node (SAN) across the heart. This electrical activity can be detected using electrodes placed on the surface of the body around the heart and displayed as an electrocardiogram (ECG). The diagram below shows an ECG for a healthy person.

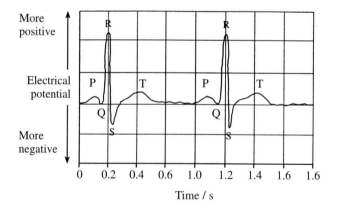

The part of the ECG labelled P represents the wave of depolarisation in the walls of the atria. The parts labelled Q, R and S represent the wave of depolarisation in the walls of the ventricles. The part labelled T represents the recovery of the ventricle walls.

(a) Explain what is meant by **depolarisation**. [2]

(b) On an ECG, the time interval between Q and T is called the **contraction time**. Suggest why it is given this name. [1]

(c) The interval between T of one cardiac cycle and Q of the following cycle is called the **filling time**. Suggest why it is given this name. [2]

(d) (i) Explain why there is a time delay between depolarisation in the walls of the atria (P) and the start of depolarisation in the walls of the ventricles (Q). [3]

(ii) Suggest how this time delay helps the heart to carry out its function efficiently. [2]

(e) From the ECG, calculate the rate of heart beats per minute. Show your working. [3]

(f) During exercise, the rate of heart beat increases but the contraction time normally remains almost unchanged. What must happen to the filling time during exercise? [1]

(Total 14 marks)

(Edexcel GCE Biology and Human Biology (6043/B3), January 1999)

Chapter 3

1 The photomicrograph below shows a transverse section through a leaf of *Erica*, a plant which shows xeromorphic adaptations.

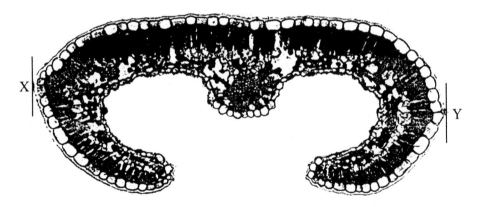

(a) Calculate the magnification of this photomicrograph, given that the actual width of the leaf between X and Y is 0.8 mm. Show your working. [2]

(b) State **two** xeromorphic features shown by xerophytes such as *Erica*, and, in each case, explain how the feature helps to reduce transpiration. [4]

(Total 6 marks)

(Edexcel GCE Biology (6042/B2), June 1999)

ASSESSMENT QUESTIONS

Human biology (2H) only

Chapter 4

1 In 1954, a team of ten mountaineers attempted to reach the summit of Makalu on the Nepal-Tibet border. They started at sea level, ascended to 4600 m in 20 days, and spent the next 62 days at this altitude before returning to sea level.

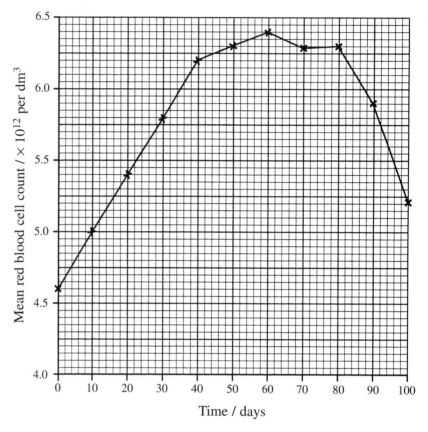

During the expedition, counts were made of the mountaineers' red blood cells. The mean red blood cell counts are shown in the graph.

(a) Describe the changes in the mean red blood cell counts in each of the following time periods and comment on these changes in relation to altitude.

    (i) 0 to 40 days **[2]**

    (ii) 40 to 80 days **[2]**

    (iii) 80 to 100 days **[2]**

(b) Explain why it is important for the numbers of red blood cells to increase at high altitude. **[2]**

(c) State **three** physiological changes, other than an increase in red blood cell count, which are likely to have occurred as these visiting mountaineers ascended to 4600m. **[3]**

(Total 11 marks)

(Edexcel GCE Human Biology (6049/HB2), June 1999)

Human biology (2H) only

Chapter 5

1　Give an account of implantation and the functions of the placenta.

(Total 10 marks)

(New question)

2　Explain each of the following.

　　(a) The significance of mitosis and meiosis in gametogenesis. **[3]**

　　(b) The roles of prolactin and oxytocin in lactation. **[3]**

(Total 6 marks)

(Edexcel GCE Biology and Human Biology (6050/HB3), January 1999)

3　Explain the significance of each of the following in the life cycle of flowering plants.

　　(a) Protandry and protogyny. **[3]**

　　(b) Mitosis and meiosis. **[3]**

(Total 6 marks)

(Edexcel GCE Biology and Human Biology (6043/B3), January 1999)

Unit 3

The following questions give you the opportunity to use your knowledge and understanding of Unit 3 content. Refer to the specimen questions provided by Edexcel or to Edexcel past papers for Curriculum 2000 to find other examples of the new style questions for Unit 3.

Chapter 7

1　The diagram below shows a pyramid of relative biomass for six trophic levels of a food chain in a pond ecosystem.

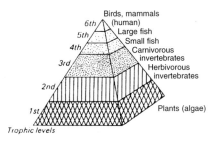

　　(a) Explain the meaning of the term **trophic level**. **[2]**

　　(b) What does a pyramid of biomass show? **[2]**

　　(c) State **one** advantage and **one** disadvantage of a pyramid of biomass rather than a pyramid of energy? **[2]**

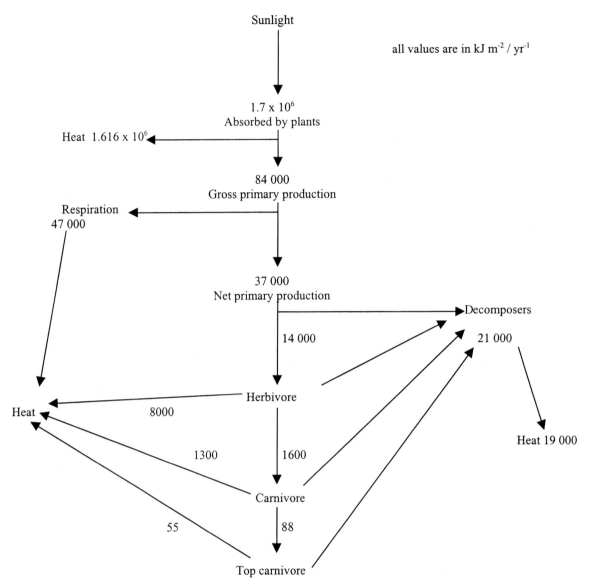

Refer to the diagram above, which shows how the energy flows through a food chain.

(d) The terms **gross primary production** and **net primary production** are used on this diagram. Explain the meaning of these two terms. **[3]**

(e) Using the values shown on the diagram, calculate the percentage of the gross primary production that becomes available as net primary production. Show your working. **[2]**

(f) As well as losses to decomposers and respiration, suggest **two** other ways by which energy can be lost between a producer and a herbivore. **[2]**

(g) The pyramid of biomass shows six trophic levels, while there are just four shown in the energy flow diagram. Suggest why the aquatic food chain has more trophic levels. **[3]**

(Total 16 marks)

(New question)

Chapter 9

1 In freshwater ecosystems, the number of different species present and the algal biomass can vary with changes in the nutrient content of the water.

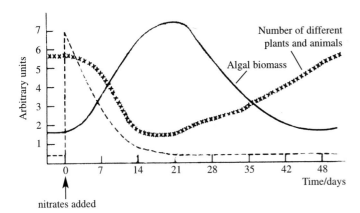

The graph above shows the effect of the addition of nitrates on the numbers of different plants and animals and the algal biomass in a freshwater pond. Observations were made as soon as the nitrates were added and for the next 7 weeks.

(a) State **two** possible sources of the nitrate. **[2]**

(b) Describe how the algal biomass could have been estimated. **[2]**

(c) Calculate the percentage increase in the algal biomass between days 7 and 21. **[2]**

(d) Describe the change in:

 (i) the nutrient concentration

 (ii) the algal biomass

 following the addition of the nitrates. **[3]**

(e) Explain the relationship between the changes in the nutrient concentration and the algal biomass over the 7 week period. **[3]**

(f) Suggest reasons why there were changes in the numbers of different species of plants and animals in the pond following the addition of nitrates. **[2]**

(g) Suggest what happens to the oxygen concentration of the water in the pond after day 21, giving an explanation for your answer. **[3]**

(Total 17 marks)

(New question)

Mark schemes

In the mark schemes the following symbols are used.
; indicates separate marking points
/ indicates alternate marking points
eq. means correct equivalent points are accepted

Unit 2

Chapter 1

1   amylase ; maltose ; villi / ileum / duodenum / crypts of Lieberkuhn ;
    glucose or fructose ; fructose or glucose ;

(Total 5 marks)

2   *(a)* large surface area ; thin ; moist ;   **[2]**

    (b)   (i)   acclimatisation / eq. ;   **[1]**

            (ii) one breath causes increase in the rate of abdominal pumping ;
                  further breaths have little effect on pimping rate / pumping rate
                  remains steady ; one breath filled the boiling tube (with exhaled
                  air) ; further breaths will not / will only have a small effect on the
                  level of concentration of CO_2 in the tube ; increase in rate due to
                  high(er) CO_2 concentration ; locust has reached maximum
                  ventilation / pumping rate ;   **[4]**

            (iii) (breathe onto locust) through drying agent or example ($CaCl_2$,
                  Si gel, anhydrous $CuSO_4$) ; situate drying agent in front of locust ;
                  soak cotton wool in water ; supply CO_2 from cylinder ;   **[2]**

            (iv) oxygen level ; temperature ; stress of locust ;   **[2]**

(Total 11 marks)

Chapter 2

1   *(a)* an S-shaped / sigmoid curve ; steepest part of the curve in the region of
          partial pressure of oxygen found in (respiring) tissues ; haemoglobin
          releases O_2 at low / lower pO_2 ; a small change in pO_2 causes a large
          change in % saturation / large % released / large % uptake of O_2 ; at
          high pO_2 / in lungs there is nearly always 100% saturation ;   **[3]**

    (b)   (i)   57 – 45 = 12 (%) (allow consequential error) ;   **[2]**

            (ii) more CO_2 released (as tissue) becomes more active ;
                  (dissociation) curve (of haemoglobin) moves to the right ; more
                  oxygen released / more oxyhaemoglobin dissociation / decreased
                  affinity for O_2 (accept converses of the above points) ; enables

188

more rapid respiration / metabolism / activity at same partial pressure of oxygen ; **[3]**

(c) oxygen store / reserve / deposit (not supply) ; only releases O_2 / dissociates at very low O_2 tensions / partial pressure of oxygen below one kPa ; enables aerobic respiration to continue / muscle to continue activity / continue to contract at (very) low (blood) oxygen levels (ignore myoglobin has a higher affinity for O_2 than haemoglobin, references to diffusion gradients) ; **[3]**

(Total 11 marks)

2

Feature	Erythrocyte	Lymphocyte	Neutrophil	
Has a lobed nucleus	✗	✗	✓	;
Contains haemoglobin	✓	✗	✗	;
Produces antibodies	✗	✓	✗	;
Shows amoeboid movement	✗	✗	✓	;
Can destroy bacteria by phagocytosis	✗	✗	✓	;

(Total 5 marks)

3 (a) Both rise and fall back to 0 kPa in 0.5 seconds / eq. ; greater change in pressure in left ventricle / smaller changes in right ventricle ; credit correct ref. to figures / range / difference / eq. ; left ventricle contracts more strongly / eq. / right ventricle contracts less strongly / eq. ; left ventricle has more cardiac muscle in wall / right ventricle has less ; to pump blood around the body / less distance to lungs / left ventricle pumps blood further ; so that pressure in the lungs is less ; **[4]**

(b) steep / rapid rise in both ; pressure in aorta rises later than in ventricle / starts higher in the aorta ; greater rise in left ventricle / converse / use of figures ; slight time delay in blood passing out of ventricle into aorta ; steeper fall in left ventricle / converse ; gradual fall between 0.4 and 0.8 / 0.9 sec / from 14 / 15 to 10 / 11 kPa in aorta ; caused by elastic recoil of aorta wall ; closure of semilunar / aortic valve ; **[3]**

(c) arrow placed top of left ventricle curve / crossover point of aorta curve and ventricle curve ; **[1]**

(d) initiated by sino-atrial node / eq. ; wave of electrical excitation / eq. spreads across atria ; stimulates contraction of (cardiac muscle of) atria ; passes to ventricles via atrio-ventricular node / AVN ; non-conductive tissue / eq. elsewhere between atria and ventricles ; some reference to time delay at AVN ; thus atrial systole occurs before ventricular systole ; excitation / eq. passes down Purkinje tissue / bundle of His ; ventricles contract from base / apex ; **[4]**

(Total 12 marks)

4 *(a)* Membrane must be permeable to substance ; must be a concentration gradient / higher outside cell than inside ; substance must be in solution / a gas / a liquid ; **[2]**

(b) $640 - 295$ or 345 ; $\div 4$; $= 86.25 \, \mu g \, g^{-1} \, hour^{-1}$; **[3]**

(c) fastest uptake occurs at start / both decrease ; rate of uptake at 20 °C is greater than at 2 °C / converse ; uptake at 20 °C continues, levels off at 2 °C ; credit manipulation of figures, e.g. final mass taken up at 20 °C is ×5 greater than at 2 °C / quoting two figures from graph ; **[3]**

(d) reference to increase in temperature increasing movement / kinetic energy / or converse ; (so) faster / eq. diffusion at higher temperature ; diffusion no longer occurs when there is no concentration gradient / eq. ; ions also taken up by active transport / ref. to ion pumps ; active transport increases at higher temperatures ; reference to increased respiration / increased ATP ; uses more K^+ at higher temperature ; **[3]**

(Total 11 marks)

5 *(a)* sieve tube element ; companion cell ; **[2]**

(b) transport / translocation of sucrose / amino acids / organic solutes / eq. ; **[1]**

(Total 3 marks)

6 *(a)* reversal / inside becomes more positive / less negative / outside less positive / more negative ; of membrane potential / resting potential ; **[2]**

(b) when ventricles contract / in systole ; **[1]**

(c) when blood fills / going into atria ; and then ventricles ; heart in diastole / ventricles relaxing / heart relaxed (when blood fills the heart / eq. 1 mark) **[2]**

(d) (i) layer spectrum of non-conducting tissue between atria and ventricles ; depolarisation / eq. begins in SA node / pacemaker in atrium ; depolarisation / eq. must pass through AV node ; AVN delays wave depolarisation ; wave of excitation / action potential passes down Purkinje tissue / bundle of His ; **[3]**

(ii) atria contract before ventricles / eq. so that blood in atria passes into ventricles before ventricular systole / contraction ; maintains one-way flow through the heart ; **[2]**

(e) time from T to T / for one heart beat = 0.8 sec ; 60 / 0.8 ; 75 (beats per minute) ; **[3]**

(f) decrease / reduce / get shorter ; **[1]**

(Total 14 marks)

Chapter 3
1 *(a)* (117 to 119) $\div$ 8 or 11.7 to 11.9 $\div$ 0.08 ; Answer: 146 to 149 or $\times$ 146 to $\times$ 159 ; **[2]**

(b) any two pairs ; feature & related explanation (second mark dependent on the first) ; thick waxy cuticle ; reduces evaporation / diffusion ; impermeable / waterproof / prevents water passing through / eq. ; (epidermal) hairs ; traps humid / moist air / references to diffusion gradient / reduces air flow near surface / eq. ; leaf rolled / curled / hinged (qualified) / coiled (not curved) ; reduces exposed surface area / traps humid / moist air / water vapour / ref. diffusion gradient / reduces air flow near surface / encloses stomata / eq. ; leaves small / as spines / deciduous / leaves lost ; reduces surface area for evaporation / diffusion ; few stomata ; less area for diffusion ; stomata in pits / sunken / eq. ; traps humid air / eq. ; stomata closed in day / in daylight (allow converse) ; less evaporation / diffusion / eq. ; cells have mucilage or more sucrose / solute / salts ; cells have lower (/ less evaporation / eq. ;   **[4]**

                                                                                                (Total 6 marks)

Chapter 4

1 *(a)* (i) constant / directly proportional linear increase with time / day / ref. to % increase or gradient / 0.04 day^{-1} / 35% ; no. of blood cells continues to increase after max altitude reached / eq. ;   **[2]**

   (ii) increase to 60 days, but then at lower rate / peak production 60 days / eq. / (then) decreases and levels off ; body acclimatised to altitude ;   **[2]**

   (iii) number of blood cells decreases as soon as / immediately altitude decreases / ref. day 80 ; constant / linear rate of decrease / inversely proportional ; decrease more rapid than the increase / steeper gradient ; number of red blood cells higher at the end than start / eq. ;   **[2]**

(b) lower pO_2 at high altitude / eq. ; more red blood cells to increase the carrying capacity of blood / carry more O_2 / more Hb to carry O_2 ; ref. O_2 for respiration ;   **[2]**

(c) headache / lack of concentration / mental alertness / eq. / dizziness / rapid heartbeat / palpitations ; nausea / vomiting ; muscle weakness / exhaustion (ignore tiredness refs.) ; fluid retention / swollen limbs / reduced urinary output / increased ADH production ; hyperventilation / increased frequency of breaths / eq. ;   **[3]**

                                                                                                (Total 11 marks)

Chapter 5

1 zygote divides to form a blastocyst ; blastocyst adheres to endometrium / lining of uterus ; blastocyst secretes human chorionic gonadotrophin (HCG) ; trophoblast cells multiply and form trophoblastic villi ; trophoblastic villi are for exchange of materials ; trophoblast will also form the chorion ; chorion (and allantois) will develop to form the placenta ; placenta allows exchange of substances between fetus and maternal circulation ; one example of a substance passed to fetus (e.g. oxygen /

named nutrient) ; one example of a substance passed from fetus (e.g. carbon dioxide / nitrogenous waste) ; placenta stores nutrients (e.g. carbohydrate / glycogen / protein / calcium / iron) ; placenta protects fetus against some microorganisms / harmful substances ; placenta allows passage of antibodies ; conferring passive immunity ; placenta has an endocrine function (secretes HCG / oestrogen / progesterone / human placental lactogen) ;

(Total 10 marks)

2 *(a)* mitosis involved in multiplication proliferation ; produces many primary spermatocytes / spermatagonia / oocytes / oogonia ; meiosis involved in the production of secondary spermatocytes / spermatids / 2° oocytes / ovum ; halves chromosome number in gametes / produces haploid cells / retains diploid on fertilisation ; ref. to genetic variation ; **[3]**

(b) prolactin stimulates milk production by mammary glands ; prolactin stimulates release / secretion / eq. of milk into ducts of mammary glands ; oxytocin stimulates milk release / ejection / eq. ; prolactin / oxytocin release stimulated by suckling / eq. ; oxytocin release inhibited by stress / eq. ; **[3]**

(Total 6 marks)

3 *(a)* in protandry anthers / pollen / stamens ripen / mature / eq. ; before stigma matures, and in protogyny stigma matures before anthers / eq. ; increases likelihood of cross-pollination / fertilisation ; reduces likelihood of self-pollination / fertilisation ; encourages outbreeding / reduces inbreeding ; increased likelihood of heterozygosity / heterosis ; ref. to hybrid vigour / variability ; **[3]**

(b) mitosis involved in (vegetative) growth / repair ; asexual reproduction / formation of genetically identical cells ; meiosis involved in gamete formation / sexual reproduction / genetic variation / eq. ; produces microspores / megaspores / haploid cells / eq. ; **[3]**

(Total 6 marks)

Unit 3

Chapter 7

1 *(a)* stage in a food chain ; it indicates an organism's feeding relationship with other organisms ; all organisms at the same feeding level are placed in the same trophic level ; **[2]**

(b) total mass of living organisms ; per unit volume/area at one point in time ; in each trophic level ; **[2]**

(c) advantage – biomass data more easily collected than energy values ; disadvantage – does not take into account how fast an organism grows / show productivity (amount of energy transferred from one trophic level to the next) / estimation of dry mass is usually impracticable and often undesirable ; **[2]**

(d) gross primary production – synthesis / storage of biomass by producers ; by photosynthesis ; light energy converted to chemical energy ; to make organic substances / glucose / starch etc ; net primary production – much of the gross primary production is used up in respiration / metabolism / growth / reproduction of the producer ; the remainder is available to primary consumers ; NPP = GPP – R ; **[3]**

(e) 37,000 / 84,000 × 100 ; = 44.0 % ; **[2]**

(f) not all of the producer is eaten / some parts inaccessible / underground ; indigestibility of food / production of faeces ; **[2]**

(g) productivity of aquatic plants / producers higher that terrestrial producers ; more NPP available to consumers ; terrestrial food chains have less efficient energy transfer / less than 10% is transferred ; less waste / lower respiratory losses in aquatic systems ; **[3]**

(Total 16 marks)

Chapter 9

1 *(a)* treated effluent from sewage treatment plant; raw sewage; fertiliser ; **[2]**

(b) the total mass of living algae ; in a given area ; at a particular time ; **[2]**

(c) (readings 3 and 7, difference 4) % increase = $\frac{4}{3}$ × 100 ; = 133.3% ; **[2]**

(d) (i) nutrient concentration decreased linearly for 14 days ; then it returned to the original level ;

    (ii) algal biomass steadily increased ; reached a peak at 21 days ; then steadily declined / returned to the original value ; **[3]**

(e) before addition of nutrients, nutrients levels were low ; this limited algal growth ; addition of extra nutrients, stimulated algal growth ; algae have short life cycle / reproduce quickly ; increase in number of algal cells depleted the nutrients, so nutrient concentration fell ; after 21 days the algae ran out of nutrients / nutrients became limiting again, so numbers fell ; **[3]**

(f) addition of nutrients favoured the growth of just a few species ; other species were out-competed / unable to survive in high nutrient concentrations ; the algae blocked out the light to other plants ; some invertebrates / pond animals lost their food source ; **[2]**

(g) oxygen levels fall ; algae die ; decomposition by bacteria / fungi ; bacteria / fungi respire, using up oxygen ; **[3]**

(Total 17 marks)

Index

Page references in *italics* refer to a table or an illustration.

INDEX

INDEX

INDEX